D1096177

Volume 28

INORGANIC CHEMISTRY

ZOOLOGY

ADDENDUM

INDEX

PRINTED IN THE UNITED STATES OF AMERICA

THE NEW how it works

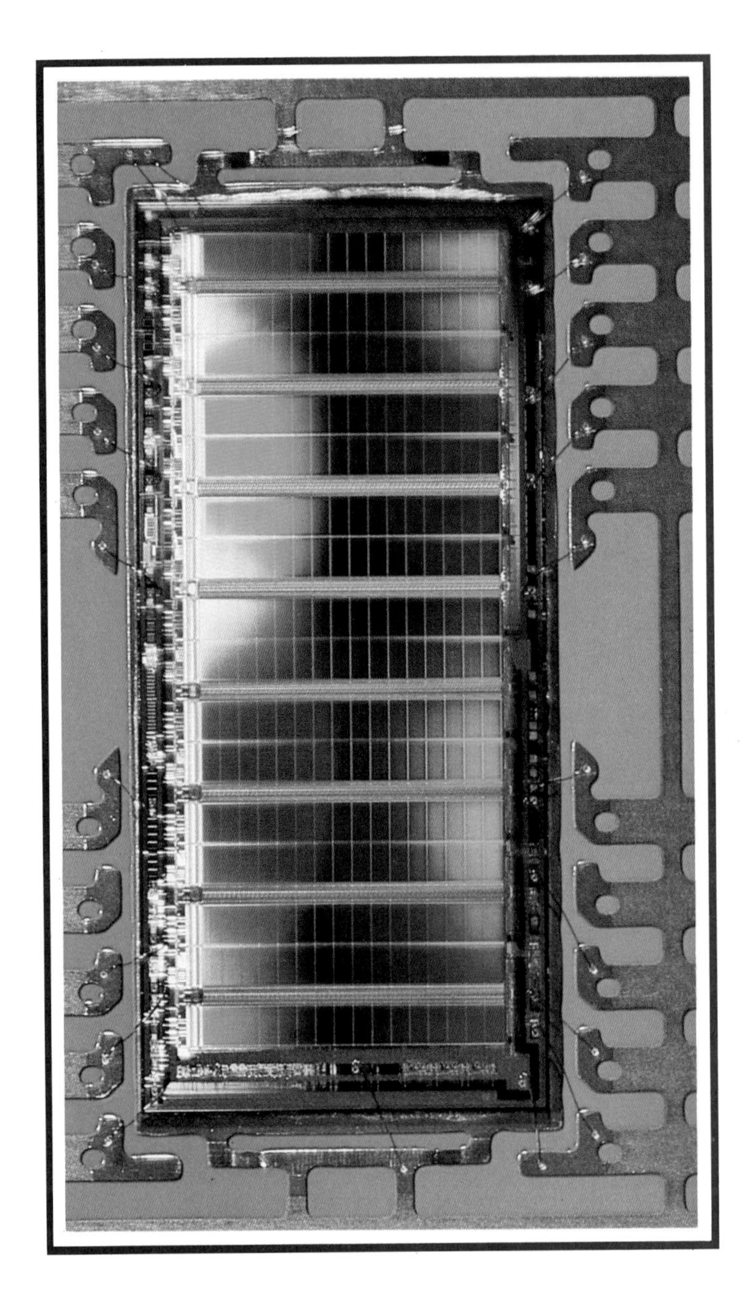

Technology has contributed to the development of faster computers as the capacity of DRAM chips has increased dramatically.

Photo: Peter Grumann
The Image Bank

THE *NEW* ILLUSTRATED Science and Invention ENCYCLOPEDIA

The Modern World

A COMPREHENSIVE REVIEW of the major sciences with particular emphasis on developing and evolving technologies as well as new discoveries about our natural world. The articles which are arranged alphabetically were specially written for this edition and are accompanied by dynamic, full-color photographs, drawings and diagrams that offer new insight into the modern world and all its wonders.

H. S. STUTTMAN INC. PUBLISHERS · WESTPORT, CONNECTICUT 06889

Contents

Volume 28

Published by H. S. STUTTMAN INC.
Westport, Connecticut 06889

Inorganic chemistry

Modern inorganic chemistry is a vast field. Many of the disciplines within it have become so specialized that any one chemist can no longer be "expert" on all aspects. The subject impinges on many other disciplines: some inorganic chemists study catalysts, others are experts in the solid state, and others seem to be more akin to physicists than chemists.

The modern periodic table is much bigger than that first proposed by the Russian chemist Mendeleev in the 19th century; many elements have been discovered since the advent of nuclear science and a number of elements have been synthesized by bombarding atoms of heavy elements with nuclear particles. Often these elements are produced in such small quantities that it is impossible to discover anything of their chemistry; that is, how they interact with other elements. Another important point is that some of the new atoms are too unstable to allow their chemistry to be studied. Nonetheless there are still over 100 elements which can be studied, and this has led to a huge knowledge base which is still expanding.

Many modern fields within inorganic chemistry are stimulated by a desire to know more of the fundamental properties of modern materials. The recent discovery of so-called high temperature superconductors (in fact here high temperature means about 150° C below room temperature) has led to the synthesis of many new compounds. The first high temperature superconductor contained oxygen, barium, lanthanum, and copper. It has been discovered that copper plays an essential role in the way in which the superconductors work. There has also been a spontaneous realization of the role of copper in the crystal chemistry of solid materials, leading to new research projects on "oxocuprates". Inorganic chemists have set out to discover how copper behaves in solids: an

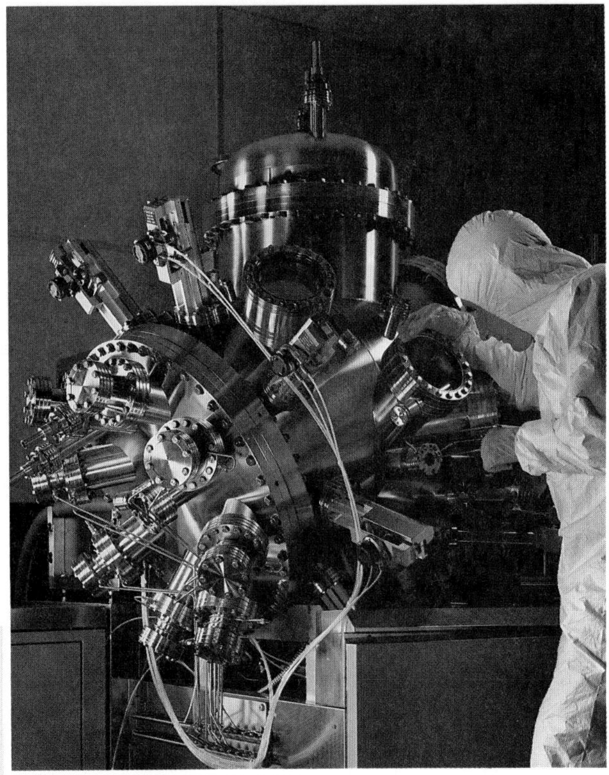

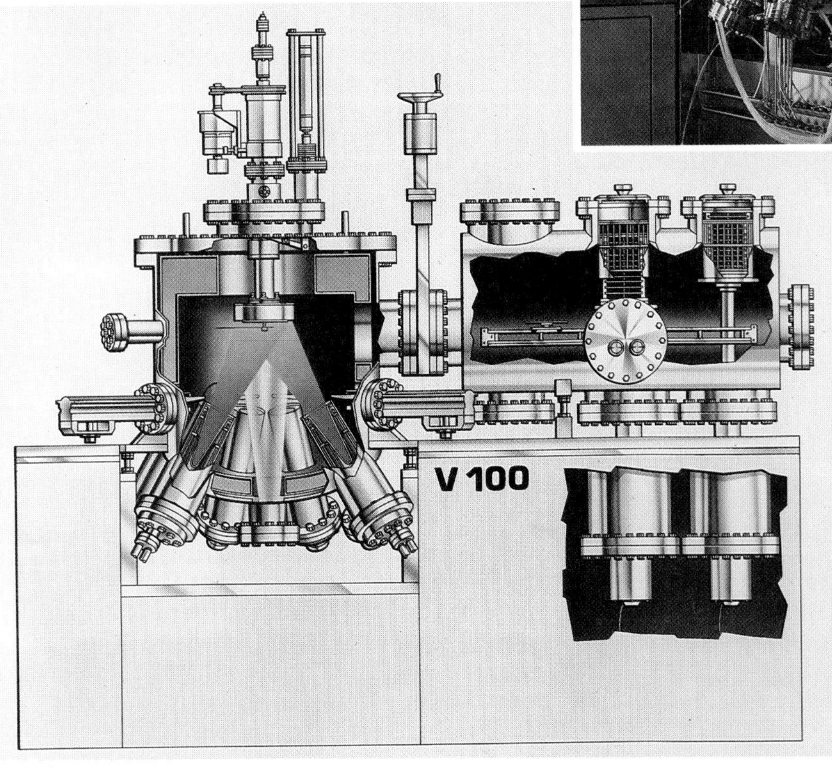

Above: A Molecular Beam Epitaxy machine, used to deposit molecular layers of materials to produce chips or detectors for the electronics industry. Left: Cutaway view of an MBE system. Beams of metal atoms are deposited on the substrate, kept at high vacuum by the apparatus at right.

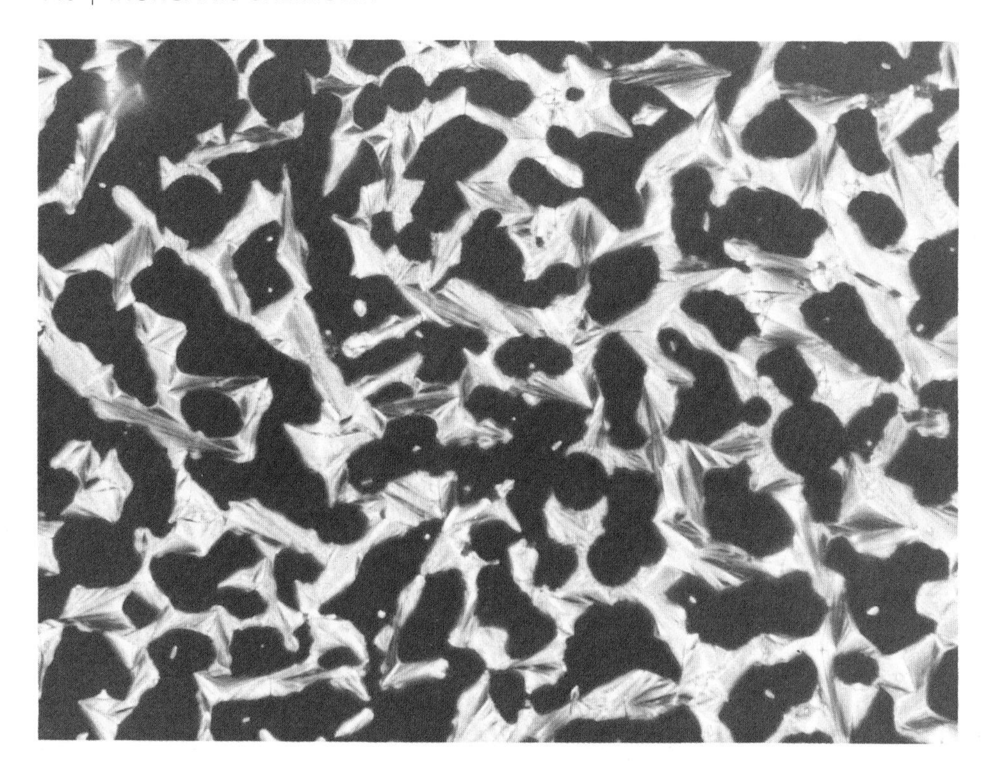

Left: Liquid crystal material, highly magnified and viewed by polarized light, in transition from its bright state to its dark state.

important tool in this investigation has been the recent advances in computer graphics. Many laboratories now have access to powerful computers which can display discoveries in 3D; these images are often very beautiful, being displayed in multicolors. Of course, the colors used are artificially chosen and merely serve to aid the scientist in visualizing the structural properties of the new solids.

By varying the exact composition of the copper oxometalates (by changing the elements involved and by varying their proportions), chemists can reach conclusions as to the role copper plays in the structures.

Many other aspects of solid state chemistry have been revolutionized by computers. Computers allow information to be collected more quickly and to be handled with greater ease. It has now become routine to establish the structure of a series of related solids and hence to discover the factors which influence their properties. Theoretical inorganic chemists can also use computers to make very long calculations using QUANTUM MECHANICS. They can now "design" solids to produce the properties they desire for specific uses in electronics.

Many inorganic chemists are involving in making molecules which may be used as precursors in the manufacture of the new solids. One of the problems faced in the real world (as opposed to the ideal computer world) is that scientists cannot make perfect solids. All materials are finite and contain many defects. Defects in a solid's structure change its properties. To make solids, high temperatures are often used (like potters use a hot kiln to fire their pots). The problem is that the higher the temperature the higher the number of defects. Inorganic chemists are hence faced with the problem of making materials at lower temperatures to reduce the number of defects. Another problem to be overcome is how to make very thin solids which are only a few atoms thick (the "so-called" two-dimensional solids).

A technique called *Metal Organic Vapor Phase Epitaxy* (MOVPE) solves both the problem of defects and of thin layer manufacture. What chemists have done is to make small molecules which are easily turned into gases. These gaseous molecules can then be mixed in the required proportions and passed into a machine which contains a heated sliver of pure silicon. When the gaseous molecules come into contact with the hot silicon they decompose and deposit thin layers of the required material. Although the silicon is heated the temperatures used are lower than in other manufacturing processes, therefore the number of defects produced is reduced.

As an example of the technology in action, consider a mixture of two volatile molecules which contain the transition metals scandium and titanium, respectively. The titanium molecule has five molecules of ethanol (alcohol) attached to it and when combined with the scandium-containing molecules a solid material containing scandium, titanium, and oxygen, in the proportions one to one to four, is produced. This technique has been exploited to produce many different materials and is now being applied to produce high temperature superconductors which contain four different types of atoms.

Another technique which also exploits small molecules is the Sol-Gel technique. Here the mixtures of small molecules containing metals and oxygen atoms are allowed to react slowly in solution and in the process to deposit solid materials.

Liquid crystals

Inorganic chemists have recently made advances in the field of liquid crystals. Liquid crystal displays are now widely used for calculators and electronic instruments, and are finding increasing applications in portable computers and color TVs. These devices incorporate liquid crystal mixtures formed from organic molecules, but recent research has resulted in the discovery of a wide variety of metal-containing liquid crystals formed from metal complexes with organic ligands. Although similar in many respects to their organic analogues, in the 1990s metal-containing liquid crystals are being developed to exploit the magnetic, optical, and electrical properties characteristic of the metal centers, which may lead in the future to new applications for liquid crystals.

Bioinorganic chemistry

Iron is used by all known forms of life. The "simple" biomolecules with iron-sulfur centers include the rubredoxins and the ferrodoxins. These molecules are known as iron-sulfur proteins. More complex metalloenzymes are also known; these contain additional groups which include nickel (such as the enzymes which are known as hydrogenases), molybdenum, and vanadium (nitrogenases).

The nitrogenases are found within bacteria which exist in nodules on the roots of leguminous plants and act to "fix" nitrogen, thus creating a natural fertilizer. This means that the enzymes take nitrogen from the air and chemically change it into ammonia. Ammonia can be used by plants to incorporate nitrogen into protein molecules. In order to do this the enzyme must add electrons and protons to the nitrogen molecules. Metals are able to bind to small molecules like nitrogen and to transfer electrons to it. The nitrogenase enzyme consequently contains a highly specialized molecule which can bind nitrogen to a molybdenum or vanadium atom and then transfer electrons to it from iron atoms.

Inorganic chemists are attempting to mimic the behavior of these enzymes in order to find new ways of fertilizing plants (thus avoiding the use of nitrates). To this end many studies have been carried out to characterize the metal centers in enzymes. Using the results from these studies molecules have been synthesized containing iron and sulfur atoms, as well as selenium and telluri-

Left: Root nodules on clover and other legumes fix atmospheric nitrogen, creating natural fetilizer. Chemists aim to mimic this process artificially.

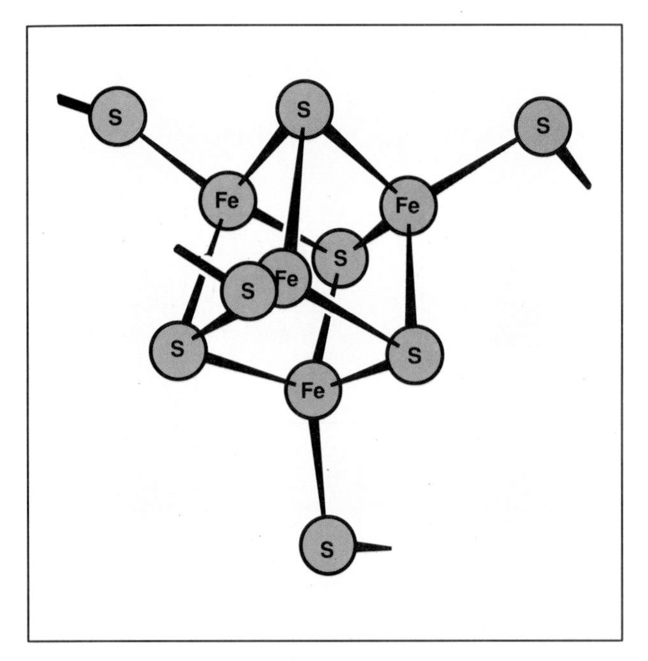

Left: Chemical structure of an iron-sulfur cluster of molecules, as found in some enzymes which have the ability to fix nitrogen.

um which are similar to sulfur. These molecules are often formed in clusters; that is, many iron and sulfur atoms are bonded together forming exotic shapes. These compounds frequently are able to accept and give up electrons like the enzymes they copy. Such molecules also mimic molecules which exist within animals and help to transfer the electrons required to drive many chemical reactions within ourselves.

Inorganic molecules as drugs

The biggest selling anticancer drug currently in use in the United States is cis-platin. This molecule contains the precious metal platinum and works by interacting with DNA. Thus the conventional view that drugs are purely organic molecules is false. Much effort has been expended on making molecules containing metals which might also interact with DNA, incorporating platinum and other metals. Another platinum-containing drug, carboplatin, is already on the market and has been shown to display fewer side effects than cis-platin.

Gold has since ancient times been recognized as having therapeutic qualities in the treatment of arthritis. The problem facing chemists is to make metal atoms soluble so that they can be absorbed by the body and hence be transported to the affected areas. To do this, they are synthesizing molecules containing gold and sulfur as well as organic fragments containing carbon. Chemists know that sulfur bonds strongly to gold, and that organic molecules often impart solubility. Therefore, the organic fragments are bonded to sulfur atoms and these sulfurs are subsequently attached to the gold atoms.

A similar solution can be used to solve another problem. Technetium is in the same group of the periodic table as manganese, but was only discovered after the atom bomb tests in Nevada. The reason for this is that technetium only exists in radioactive forms and so decomposes. However, technetium's radioactivity can be used for our benefit. Using similar methods to those used to bind gold, technetium can be injected into the body. Remarkably, for reasons still not fully understood, these soluble technetium atoms often accumulate in the heart or liver. Cameras sensitive to the radioactivity from the decomposing technetium can then take "real-time" pictures of the liver or heart. This technique is used to diagnose some heart and liver complaints. An additional property needed in these drugs is slow decomposition of the binding molecules which then allows the technetium to be passed from the body.

• FACT FILE •

- Chemists are attempting to use the energy in sunlight to produce chemical energy storage systems. Many metals absorb light but often they release its energy very quickly. Ruthenium, when bound to molecules called bipyridines, is able to store light for a relatively long time – though still only a millionth of a second. It has been discovered that by mixing the ruthenium molecules with other molecules the light energy can be converted into electrons. The aim is then to use these high energy electrons to split water into its constituent molecules, hydrogen and oxygen.

- This aim has been achieved, but unfortunately the process is not yet commercial since fuel, in the form of suitable molecules, is required to drive the process. Many chemists are working to modify the ruthenium molecules so that water can be split without consuming any fuel.

- In the meantime hydrogen engines have already been designed and built. Many other uses exist for hydrogen, which proves that when the process is economic, the energy produced can be used.

Lunar science

The detailed scientific study of the Moon virtually began and finished with the historic manned landings on the lunar surface between June 1969 and December 1972. Since then, the subject has been largely devoted to studying the 2196 samples of lunar rocks and dust which the astronauts brought back. In addition, three uninhabited spacecraft from the former Soviet Union, Luna 16, 20, and 24, also brought back soil samples.

As well as the lunar samples, apparatus left on the Moon has built up a picture of its interior. The Moon's core is metallic and may be 600 to 1000 miles (1000-1500 km) in diameter. Recordings of "moonquakes" have indicated that there is a region 600 to 750 miles (1000-1200 km) deep inside the Moon's interior where the rocks are hot enough to be molten. The crust on the far side of the Moon, which is always turned away from the Earth, may be thicker than that on the side nearest to the Earth. The loose surface layer, or regolith, is from 3 to 65 ft (1-20 m) deep and is firm enough to bear the weight of a spacecraft.

Analysis of the lunar samples shows that the Moon's materials are essentially the same as those we are familiar with on Earth. All the rocks are either igneous; that is, caused by volcanic processes, or breccias – shattered, crushed, or melted pieces of rock produced by impact processes. The youngest rocks are about 2900 million years old, and the oldest, 4400 million years. Rocks from the dark mare regions are dark basalts (volcanic rocks), but many of those from the highlands are anorthosites, light gray rocks containing the mineral feldspar. The highland rocks are older than the basalts. Although lava flows are still clearly visible on the Moon's surface, by Earth standards the rocks are ancient. The main period of lava flows ended about 3200 million years ago.

The Moon on Earth

There have been some interesting comparisons between the lunar rocks and meteorites found on Earth. Our main source of meteorites is now the

Left: This view of the Moon was taken in December 1990 by the Galileo spacecraft on its way to Jupiter. It was the first photograph of the far side of the Moon to be taken for almost two decades since the famous Apollo missions, and helped lunar scientists to fill in gaps in their knowledge of the Moon's surface features.

Right: The samples collected by scientist-astronaut Harrison Schmitt on the Apollo 17 mission in 1972 were invaluable in helping to explain the Moon's structure and origin. While terrestrial field trips can collect material regularly, Schmitt's work remains the only scientific on-site survey of the lunar geology.

Antarctic, where expeditions have located meteorites on ice fields which have been lying there undisturbed for a very long time. In 1979, a Japanese field party found an unusual meteorite in Antarctica that appears to have come from the Moon. Since that time a dozen of these "lunar" meteorites have been recovered from various parts of Antarctica. It has been suggested that these meteorites were blasted away from the Moon's surface by violent impacts, eventually finding their way down to the Earth.

This is given extra credence by the fact that the chemical compositions of these meteorites are remarkably similar to those of the samples brought back from the Moon. Another discovery – that of a "lunar meteorite" found at Calcalong Creek in Western Australia – seems to provide extra confirmation. It appears to be a lunar breccia, containing materials characteristic of both the lunar highlands and the mare regions. The abundance of potassium (chemical symbol K), rare-Earth elements, and phosphorus – KREEP for short – is remarkably similar to rocks collected at the Apollo 14 and 16 sites. Further studies of these "lunar" meteorites may also shed new light on the transfer of material from the Moon to the Earth.

Space pictures

Other investigations have been mainly carried out by space research methods. One satellite is called ROSAT: the Röntgen satellite, named in honor of Wilhelm Röntgen, the man who discovered X-rays. ROSAT has now obtained the first X-ray picture of the Moon, showing how the sunlit hemisphere is excited to fluorescence in the X-ray light from the Sun's outer atmosphere, known as the corona.

New lunar pictures were obtained from the Galileo spacecraft on its way to the planet Jupiter. Because of the lack of power of its launch vehicle, Galileo has been forced to travel to Jupiter by a rather circuitous route, making one pass of Venus and two passes of the Earth in order to pick up enough speed to send it out to its target; it should arrive at Jupiter in 1995. During its pass of the Earth-Moon system in December 1990, it took pictures of the Moon which covered some areas not well surveyed by earlier probes. Galileo provided the first clear image of the Aitken Basin, a large depression in the lunar surface about 5 miles (8 km) deep and 1250 miles (2000 km) across. We now have accurate maps of most of the lunar surface; in fact the Moon is better known than some of the more inaccessible regions of the Earth.

In January 1990, Japan made its first foray into practical lunar research with the launch of the Muses-A probe. It passed within 10,000 miles (16,000 km) of the Moon in mid-March 1990 and released a small satellite, "Hiten", into lunar orbit.

• FACT FILE •

- While no major lunar missions have been dispatched now for two decades, this situation should be changed before long. New expeditions should be dispatched, and a major lunar base established, which will almost certainly be international.

- Much may depend upon events in the former Soviet Union (now CIS), but the outlook is encouraging, and a lunar base will be of immense value in many fields of science and medicine. The far side of the Moon, which is permanently hidden from Earth, would be an ideal site for a large observatory for radio astronomy, for example, as it would be completely free from unwanted radio interference from the Earth.

- Provided that there are no delays due to political or financial constraints, the lunar base could well be established within the next two decades. Moreover, it must always be remembered that the Moon will be a real "testing ground" for future missions, including the first inhabited flights to Mars.

Above: The composition of this meteorite found at Calcalong Creek in Australia matches that of materials collected by Apollo astronauts. The deserts of Australia and the Antarctic ice sheet are particularly rich in meteorites.

Marine biology

The sea covers over two-thirds of the Earth's surface. In its vast realm there are more fundamentally different life forms than on land, including bacteria, plants, and animals, from the humble sponge to the blue whale. Any aspect of a marine organism, from its biochemistry, physiology, behavior, and systematics to its ecology, may be investigated by marine biologists.

Compared to what is known about life on land, our understanding of marine life is much less complete because of the difficulties of working in the sea. Only about 10 per cent of the sea has been sampled for living organisms.

Often, sampling methods rely on deploying nets, dredges, and other devices from ships. But recent investigations have used divers, manned submersibles, and high-resolution remote video cameras. Satellite imagery is being used to study ocean productivity. Whales tagged with small radio transmitters have been tracked from satellites to study their migrations.

Small computers have been attached to elephant seals to record diving time and depth. This work, published in 1992, has shown that the seals stay underwater longer than anyone had thought possible; now physiologists will have to figure out how they do it.

New and exotic species

The use of manned submersibles led to the discovery of completely new animal communities around hot water vents in the ocean floor (see OCEANOGRAPHY). The first hydrothermal vents were discovered in the late 1970s off Ecuador on the Galapagos Rift. Since then, expeditions have discovered life around vents in other areas of the Pacific and along the Mid-Atlantic Ridge. In the Marianas Trough hairy snails and barnacles predominate; in the Mid-Atlanic Ridge strange eyeless shrimp swarm over the vents; and in sites along the East Pacific Rise there is a wide range of tube worms, clams, mussels, and white encrusting polychaete worms, plus thick mats of bacteria.

Instead of depending on plants to harness solar energy to convert carbon dioxide into organic materi-

Below: Submersibles developed for deep-sea research below 6000 ft (2000 m) are self-contained. Electric propulsion is used, since this has no exhaust, but the range of the craft is limited to only short distances travelling at a few knots.

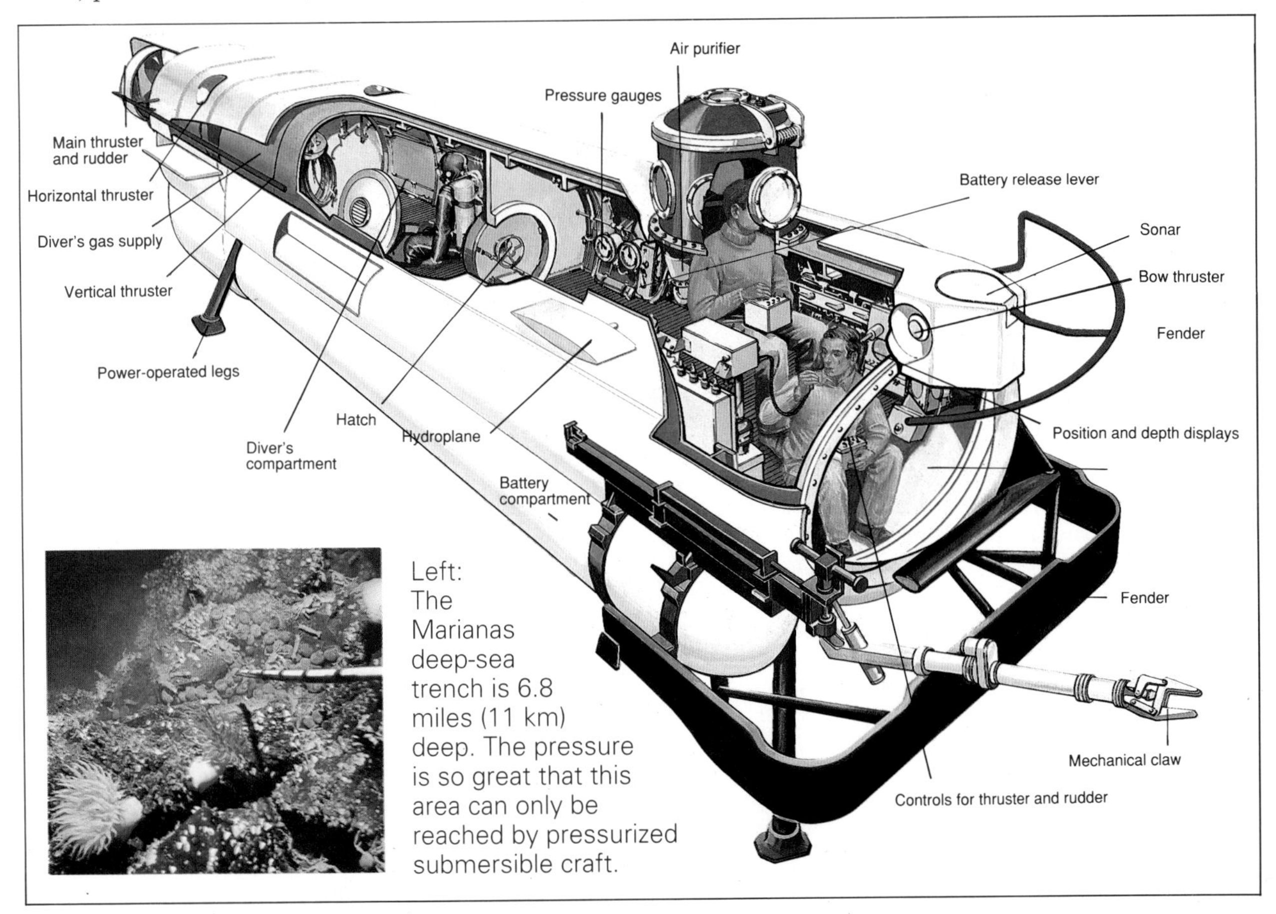

Left: The Marianas deep-sea trench is 6.8 miles (11 km) deep. The pressure is so great that this area can only be reached by pressurized submersible craft.

Right: The Galapagos vent was discovered in the late 1970s off Ecuador. Vent fields, or hydrothermal vents, such as this, are places where hot or warm water wells up from the molten interior of the Earth.

al, vent communities depend on bacteria which live on the energy of hot water and the sulfur compounds it contains. Some animals around the vents feed directly on the bacteria. Others actually have bacteria living inside their tissues. The giant tube worms from the Galapagos vents rely entirely on these symbiotic bacteria. The mussel Bathymodiolus from the Galapagos has bacteria living inside its tissue but also filters food from the water. There are also a few predators eating the animals that utilize the bacteria.

So far, over 200 different vent species have been discovered and most are found nowhere else in the ocean. Some appear to be survivors of ancient forms which became extinct in shallower waters. Some scientists even believe hydrothermal vents could be where life began.

Medical spin-offs

Studies of marine life often help us understand life on land. Workers at the Marine Biology Laboratory in Massachusetts have recently identified proteins that carry chemical messages through the axons of squid neurons, which are much larger than human neurons and therefore easier to study; these proteins may offer a clue to human nerve disorders like Alzheimer's disease. Similarly, studies of the sperm of the Spisula clam may lead to the development of a male contraceptive.

Like the Amazon rain forest, the sea may contain undiscovered drugs of great value. Certain corals, for example, have been found to produce substances that resemble steroid hormones like estrogen and cortisone.

Human interference confirmed

There is increasing evidence that human activity has altered the ecosystem of the oceans. Overfishing in the North Atlantic has sharply reduced the population of haddock, cod, pollock, and flatfish. Now the dominant species are dogfish, sharks, and rays, which are edible but not accepted in the American market. In the Antarctic, whales, seals, and penguins compete for the same food supply. Mechanized whaling has decimated whale populations, and seal and penguin populations have increased.

Even if human depredations cease, the formerly dominant species in the seas and oceans may not be able to compete now that their competition has multiplied. To restore populations of food fish or whales, marine biologists may have to meddle further to discourage the newcomers.

• FACT FILE •

- A multitude of microorganisms, ranging in size from a few to several hundreds of microns, live in the sea as part of the host of drifting life forms collectively known as plankton. New research tools have greatly improved marine biologists' ability to sample these planktonic microorganisms so that their role in marine food webs can be more fully understood.

- One technique borrowed from medical research, analytical flow cytometry, has been adapted for the rapid sorting and quantifying of planktonic protozoans. Protozoans in a sea water sample are passed through a laser beam, which causes each protozoan to produce scattered or fluorescent light. Different protozoans produce different light signals which can be stored on a computer for laboratory analysis.

- A further refinement is the use of fluorescently tagged nucleotide probes (based on short sequences of genes) which can target specific groups of microorganisms for identification. This technique allows population counts to be made every few hours or days, rather than every few weeks.

Materials science

Materials science spans a period of time from the Stone Age, when people learned to fire clay to make a durable material for containers, to the present Space Age. It has evolved to cover a wide variety of materials. In today's world, the traditionally separate subjects of METALLURGY, ceramics, plastics, and glass technology combine to form the subject of materials science.

Materials scientists need a wide background, including physics, chemistry, and engineering, since materials are used for structural, electrical, optical, and medical applications. They have to understand the microstructure and properties of materials in order to face the challenges of developing new materials and processes and of improving existing materials.

New materials lie at the heart of many modern advances, including the demand for lighter weight transportation to increase fuel efficiency and reduce exhaust emissions, the need for materials capable of withstanding the hostile environment of space, and the requirement for computers and communication systems that operate faster. Recent years have seen the introduction of totally new materials with exciting structures and properties. They can even be custom-designed to fit a specific need. Beginning in the late 1980s, this approach was extended one step further, with materials that can even respond to their environment. These are known as smart materials.

Smart materials

What makes a material "smart" is its ability to react to changing conditions. This new class of materials arose from research begun by the Pentagon to make aircraft and submarines vanish from enemy radar and sonar detectors. Smart materials display a range of abilities. At its most basic, the material simply responds to variations in its external environment, such as the photochromic lenses in eyeglasses. At its most sophisticated, the materials form part of a complex feedback loop in which the material senses changes in the environment and triggers a response. Developing, improving, and finding new applications for smart metals, ceramics, and polymers constitute one of the challenges facing materials scientists.

Smart metals – shape memory alloys

A class of metallic alloys, known as shape memory alloys, comprise one of the largest and most widely used smart actuator materials. When these alloys undergo plastic deformation – such as bending – at

Left: A honeycomb sandwich structure made from titanium aluminide, an intermetal. Metallic bonding holds the atoms together in a crystallike lattice. This panel has the strength of a solid metal panel but at a fraction of its weight.

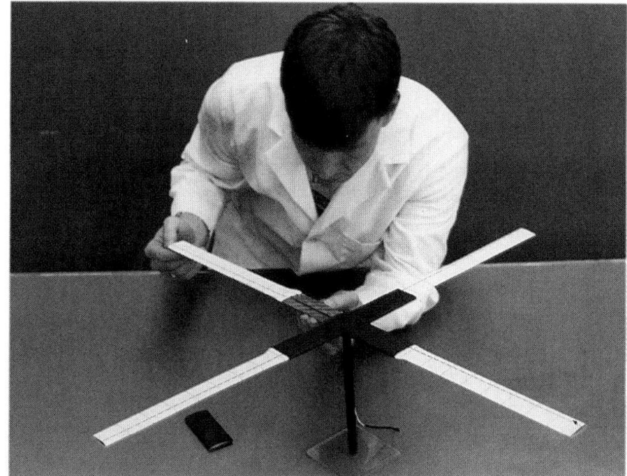

one temperature, they completely recover their original shape in a reversible transformation when raised to a higher temperature. If they are somehow restrained while recovering their shape, these alloys can also exert a force which varies with the temperature. These two characteristics enable shape memory alloys to be used in a variety of applications.

The shape memory effect arises from a change in crystal structure with temperature. For this effect to occur, the alloy must possess a crystal structure that can shift into a configuration known as martensite. The transformation occurs upon rapidly cooling the alloy to a critical temperature. When this temperature is reached, the parent crystal structure spontaneously transforms to martensite by a coordinated movement of large blocks of atoms. The temperature at which a deformed alloy recovers its memory relates directly to the temperature at which martensite formation begins, or to the higher temperature at which the alloy reverts back to the parent crystal structure. The martensite transformation temperature depends on the composition of the alloy and can be shifted by an applied stress. The materials scientist designs shape memory alloys with characteristics to fit specific needs, such as transformation temperatures ranging from 25° C for switches for automatic greenhouse ventilation systems to –120° C for satellite couplings.

The shape memory alloys available fall into two categories, ferrous (based on iron), and non-ferrous. Ferrous shape memory alloys under development include iron-platinum, iron-nickel-carbon, and iron-nickel-cobalt-titanium. Non-ferrous shape memory alloys such as nickel-titanium, copper-zinc-aluminum, and copper-nickel-aluminum are used commercially. The nickel-titanium system, known as Nitinol, has a transformation temperature range between –273° C and 100° C, produced by altering the nickel-titanium ratio or by

A series of experimental devices made at the University of Kansas to show the potential of a ceramic material that flexes when current is applied to it. Top left: A solid state aquatic vehicle which swims like a fish at up to 0.6 knots (1.1 km/h). Above: A smart rotor system for helicopters. When in production, rotors capable of tilting up to 9° will give a smoother, more efficient ride. Top right: A walker, compared in size with a quarter, capable of moving spiderlike at 10 feet/min (0.22 km/h). Right: A missile fin which warps to guide the missile as shown in the diagram, below. It has no mechanical linkages, yet will remain at full deflection in an airstream with a current consumption of a fraction of a watt.

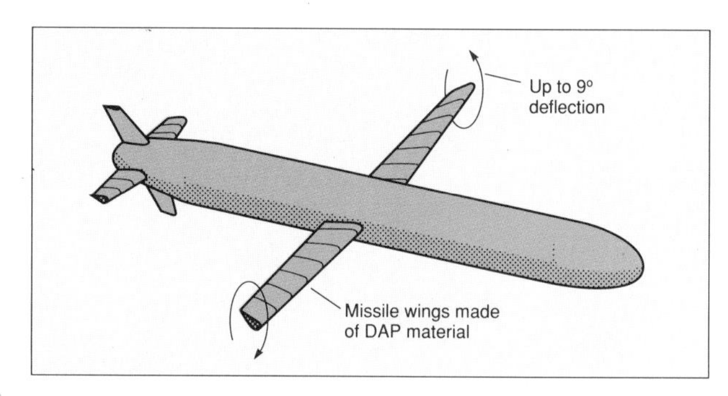

incorporating small additions of other elements.

Scientists at Goodyear Aerospace Corporation developed a Nitinol antenna for small spacecraft. The antenna begins as a ball with a diameter of 2 in (5 cm), crushed into shape at room temperature. As the temperature increases the ball slowly unfolds, and when the temperature reaches 77° C, the antenna resumes its original unfolded shape with a diameter of 10 in (25 cm).

The versatile characteristics of shape memory alloys such as Nitinol can also be exploited for medical applications. At present, cement forms the joint between artificial hip joints and bone. However, this causes problems of misalignment

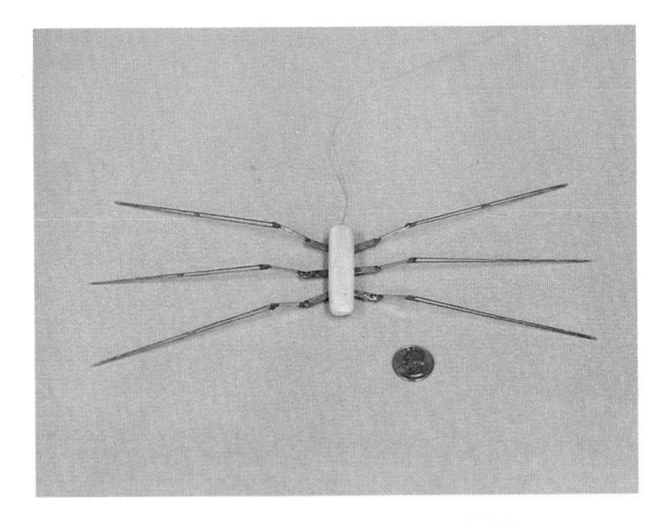

and loosening. As Nitinol is biocompatible, scientists are developing an alternative fastening method in which cooled Nitinol expandable clips inserted into the bone expand to form a tight lock upon reaching body temperature.

Smart ceramics — sensing ceramics

Materials scientists study ceramics as well as metallic alloys. Although ceramics never receive the same prominence as metals for structural applications, the "smartness" of ceramic materials rivals that of metals. Smart ceramics are mainly used in sensing and actuating systems. Some ceramics, such as zinc oxide, lose most of their electrical resistance when struck by lightning, and as a result, the current is grounded. This resistance change can be reversed so that it acts as a protection against current surges.

Lead zirconate titanate (PZT) is a piezoelectric material that has found a number of uses as a smart ceramic. Piezoelectric crystals are nothing new – many homes harbor them in crystal phonograph pickups or in mechanical gas lighters, in which pressure on a crystal makes it produce electric current. The explanation for this behavior is that a piezoelectric crystal has an asymmetrical distribution of positive and negative charges; that is, the centers of positive and negative charges do not coincide. In such a crystal, a mechanical stress alters the polarization of the crystal in the same way as an electric field would. Conversely, an electric field mechanically distorts the crystal.

One of the major implications of this behavior for smart ceramics involves the response of the material to an external electric field. Depending upon the direction of the field, the material either expands or contracts. The other important feature is the voltage change of the material in response to mechanical compression. These ceramics form major parts of sensing and actuating systems such as rain sensors for automobile windshield wipers that detect the amount of rain falling, and adjust the wipers to the optimum speed for the conditions.

Piezoelectric ceramics can also be used to control materials. Car shock absorber systems that improve the handling of the automobile and at the same time increase passenger comfort utilize smart ceramics. In such a system designed by Toyota, the road sensor consists of a five-layer piezoelectric ceramic mounted on the end of the shock absorber piston rod. When the car travels on a rough road, the sensor is mechanically compressed and the applied stress on the sensor creates a voltage. This voltage is then fed into a control unit which amplifies it and feeds it into another piezoelectric ceramic that serves as an actuator. This voltage causes the actuator to change shape and therefore to exert a force on the hydraulic oil in the shock absorber, altering the ride from firm to soft. The process also considers the vehicle speed and, in total, requires 20 milliseconds to make the whole adjustment.

Smart polymers — liquid crystals

Metallic alloys and ceramics are generally crystalline solids in which the atoms are arranged in a three dimensional periodic pattern repeated over long distances with a high degree of order. Like other materials, polymers are liquid above a certain temperature. Liquids normally have no internal structure – the atoms or molecules are randomly arranged. In a liquid crystal material, how-

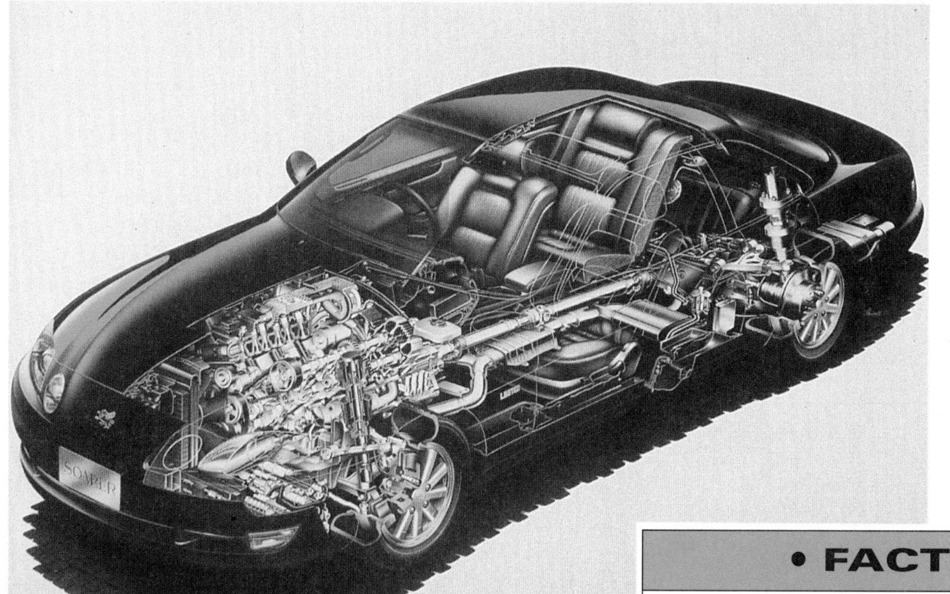

Left: The 1991Toyota Soarer introduced Active Chassis Control which uses piezoelectric ceramic road sensors and actuators to help control and improve the suspension characteristics.

ever, the molecules that make up the polymer are shaped like rods rather than spheres. If these rods were arranged as they would be in a totally crystalline state, they would sit in a particular position, known as positional order, with a specified alignment, known as orientational order. In a liquid crystal, the molecules exhibit orientational order, but not positional order. That is, all the rods are aligned nearly parallel to each other and in the same direction, but are distributed randomly in space. The orientation of the molecules does, however, mean that their reflectivity can be varied by passing an electric current through them. A familiar use of such smart polymers is in the display of an electronic watch.

Smart polymers developed by scientists at Pennsylvania State University have also found applications as coating materials that serve to make aircraft and submarines invisible to an enemy. These "active acoustic coatings" make submarines invisible by generating signals that act to neutralize reflections from sonar detectors.

A double layer of a smart polymer coats the surface of the submarine and senses sonar waves. This layer then instructs an electronic feedback controller below it. In turn, the controller measures the phase and direction of the incident sonar waves by detecting the small time lapse between the detection of the waves by each of the two polymer layers. Using this information, the controller activates a piezoelectric transducer to generate waves 180° out of phase with the incoming sonar, and the resulting destructive interference causes the submarine to vanish from the sonar detectors.

• FACT FILE •

- Smart composite materials are a way forward on the road to constructing "smart structures" such as buildings, bridges, and aircraft that respond to their environment and warn of possible failure.
- Composites are fiber-reinforced materials that ideally rival metals in their mechanical properties, but are often limited by their failure under certain conditions. By embedding stress and temperature sensors into the composite material during its manufacture, subsequent stages in the processing of the composite such as machining, assembly, and installation can be monitored, and the production control data obtained can be used to optimize the composite.
- Once in use, the presence of arrays of fiber optic sensors could detect the onset of failure within a structure. The array of fibers would produce a fixed light pattern, and any alterations in this pattern would indicate bending or fracture of fibers within the structure.
- Ultimately, the goal is to produce materials that will go beyond simple monitoring and have an active feedback and control system such as the smart composite skins under development by the U.S. Air Force. This research is driven by the limited space within fighter aircraft and the need to reduce the amount required by sophisticated avionic equipment.

Mechanical engineering

Mechanical engineering can be regarded as the "core" subject in engineering, as it finds a place in many related areas from CIVIL ENGINEERING to AEROSPACE ENGINEERING and even in electronics, in the manufacture and assembly of the parts. So mechanical engineering is found in all industries and affects the manufacture of almost every type of product or process, from the kitchen toaster to space vehicles.

Materials

Developments in MATERIALS SCIENCE have always been at the heart of engineering processes and the pace of change is speeding up. Among recent developments are shape memory alloys which have a mechanical memory built into them, triggered by a change in temperature. Based on nickel and titanium, the shape changes can be used to make permanent joints and fixings, taking the place of welding or other conventional means.

Superplastic forming has been known as a principle for many years, but its practical use has awaited the arrival of specially developed alloys. These alloys, when heated to 470-520° C (878-968° F), will stretch many times their original length under low pressure. Cheap one-sided molds with air pressure applied to the other side allow complex shapes to be made from thin alloy sheets. This is an ideal process for manufacturing aircraft panels.

Also being developed are "smart" materials that incorporate sensors through which instructions can be sent to "tell" the material to behave a certain way. Alternatively, sensors can feed information to a control station to relay back data about temperature, pressure, stress, or other parameters. The final stage will be to combine these two with a controller to produce "intelligent" materials which can respond to events as they occur.

Above: An industrial laser drilling a nozzle guide vane. The Nd:YAG (neodynium-yttrius-aluminum-garnet) laser can cut 200 holes a second and can cut through stainless steel up to 3 in. (75 mm) thick.

Metal cutting

Besides the many long-established methods of cutting metals such as turning, milling, grinding, sawing, and drilling, several new methods have been recently developed. Among these are plasma cutting, lasers, spark machining, and abrasive water jets.

Plasma arc cutting uses a gas stream which is heated in a tungsten arc to such a high temperature that it becomes ionized and can conduct electricity. It can cut almost any type of metal product.

Lasers produce a powerful concentrated source of energy which can be controlled and guided to cut materials used in engineering. They are becoming an everyday shop floor tool which can cut out parts faster and, more importantly, with better quality than conventional methods. They are also used to cut exotic materials which are dif-

Left: Orlando, Florida is the site of the first maglev train in the U.S. Due for completion in 1995, the train will whisk passengers 14 miles (22 km) from the airport to the tourist district at speeds up to 250 mph (400 km/h). It can accelerate to 185 mph (300 km/h) in only two minutes.

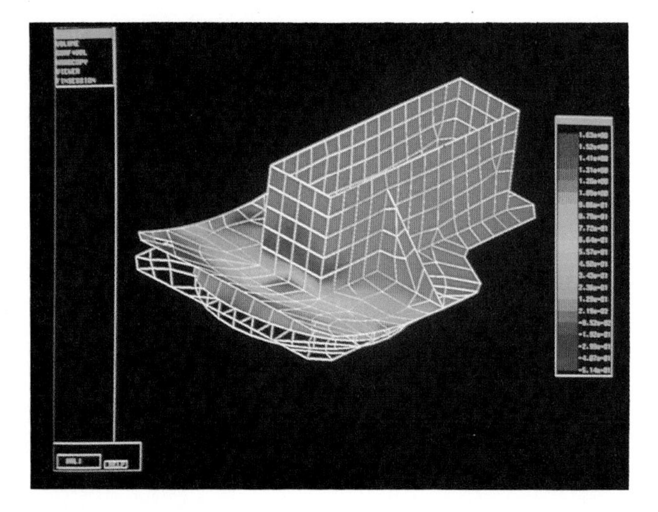

Left: A 3D image used in CAD. This drawing was produced using a finite element analysis program, which handles tasks too complex to be carried out using conventional design methods.

ficult to machine by other means, can weld without distorting the part, and can mark, engrave, heat treat, and even cut ceramics.

Spark machining, also called electro-discharge machining (EDM), uses the energy from a spark created between an electrode – the tool – and the workpiece by applying a voltage between them to erode or burn out the metal to the required shape. It is often employed in very precise work, usually computer controlled, such as making the die molds for intricate plastic parts.

Water jet cutting is more recent than the other methods, and incorporates a fine abrasive material in a high pressure jet of water directed at the part being cut. The jet is the carrier for the abrasive and provides the source of energy to give a clean cut through thick metal plates. Because of the cooling effect of the water there is no heat distortion; this process is also fume, dust, and noise-free.

Railroads

Rail transportation has remained fundamentally unchanged from the first steam-hauled locomotives: they still consist of railcars and wagons running with wheels on rails driven by an engine, be it steam, diesel, or electric motor. There have been attempts to build tracked vehicles on the principle of the hovercraft or air cushion vehicle, but no service based on this method is yet in operation.

Now a completely different principle, based on magnetic levitation, is under development in several parts of the world. This uses the fact that opposite poles of a magnet repel or force each other apart. Powerful electromagnets lift the cars about ⅜ in (9 mm) above the track. A linear electric motor propels the cars, giving a quiet vibration-free means of transportation as there is no direct contact between the vehicle and the track. The system is therefore virtually frictionless.

The world's first maglev system was installed in 1984 on a track about three-quarters of a mile (1 km) long running between the exhibition center and the airport at Birmingham, England. It is still running, though it is essentially a prototype slow-speed system. More recently, a major demonstration unit was built in Germany, and another in Japan where there is also a plan to combine superconductivity with magnetic levitation.

Electromagnetic technology has also been used in bearings to reduce friction. These are now in use with applications in machine tools, centrifuges, compressors, pumps, and mechanical handling envisaged. Transportation systems and bearings have always been limited by friction between their sliding and rolling surfaces. Frictionless systems have therefore always had a fascination for engineers.

Computers in engineering

The computer has invaded mechanical engineering as with most other aspects of science and technology. The advent of the computer has been the biggest change experienced by mechanical engineers in the last ten years.

Its influence begins at the design stage where the drawing board is being replaced by the keyboard and the screen. Drawings are made directly on screen, appearing in color and in three dimensions. The images can be expanded, contracted, altered, rotated, and parts analyzed for strength, behavior, and performance under load without ever printing a drawing or cutting metal.

Highly technical computer programs are avail-

Left: Traditionally, cars have been crushed for low grade scrap at the end of their lives. BMW is pioneering the recyclable car – all parts shown in green can be easily removed and recycled, while those colored blue are already recycled.

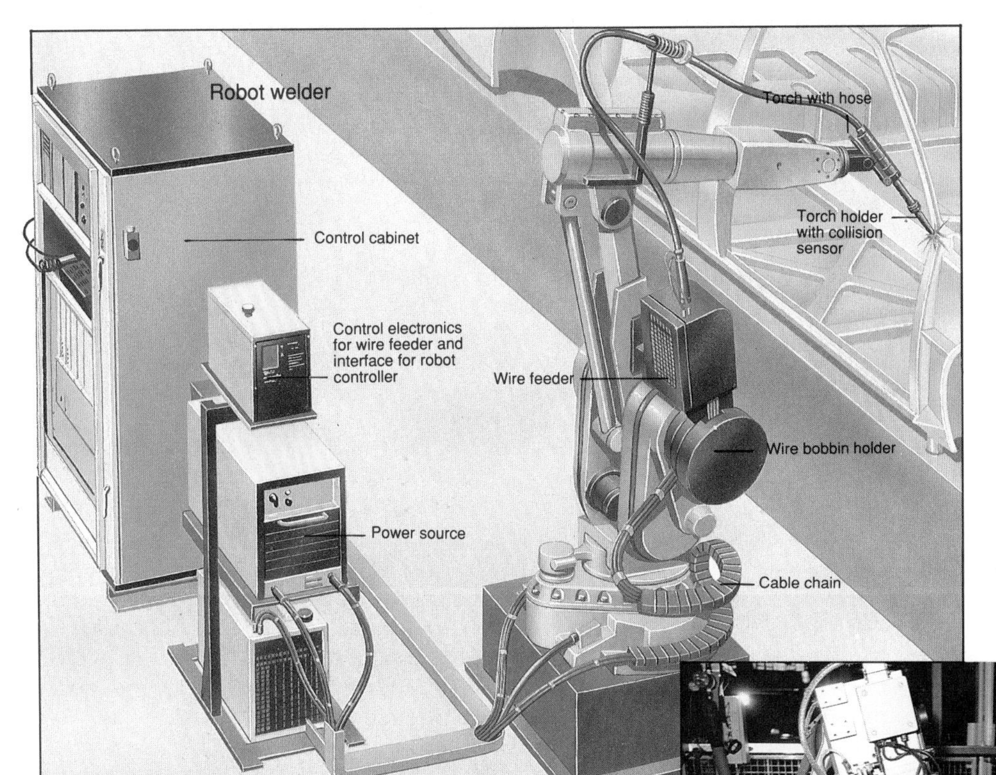

Left and below: A robot in a car factory lays glue beads on car hoods (below). A typical mechanism of a robot-based workstation is shown, left. The station includes the robot arm; software containing the robot's instructions; its tools – in this case, torches; and conveyor systems for workpieces such as wire and cable.

able to carry out finite element analysis, a technique for analyzing structures too complex to work out by conventional methods. Following the computer-aided design (CAD) stage, the design is transferred electronically to computer-aided manufacture (CAM) to be made in computer-controlled machines. Even the factory administration methods for ordering, scheduling, assembly, inspection, and test are controlled by the microchip.

There are few purely mechanical engineering products or processes left which do not have a computer or programmable logic controller (PLC) as part of the finished product. Many domestic products and most cars now have at least one computer built in. So far has this process gone that electronic engineers work together with mechanical engineers from the original concept stage to ensure that the most is made of the new technology. Now mechatronics, a new discipline fusing mechanical and electronic engineering, is springing up.

Marine engineering

Traditionally, marine engineering progress is relatively slow compared with that in aerospace and computers. Steam engines slowly gave way to turbines and then to diesel propulsion. Now there are electrically driven ships in which a large diesel engine or gas turbine drives a generator acting as a power station to provide all the power needs of the vessel electrically, including the ship's main propulsion. Large cruise liners are being constructed this way, driven by a cycloconverter-controlled AC system which needs no costly reducing gears.

Waterjet propulsion has been used for high-speed light craft for some time but large, fast, car/passenger ferries driven by 20,000 hp (15,000 kW) engines driving water jets are now coming into service. Water is drawn from beneath the vessel to an inboard pump and discharged astern to drive the ship forwards. Guide vanes at the rear can deflect the jet to aid steering. These ships have good fuel economy at speed, are maneuverable, have shallow draft and the impellers are protected from floating debris.

High-speed catamarans now offer high-speed comfort. One type, of nearly 20,900 tons driven by 15,000 hp (11,000 kW) engines, soon to be operat-

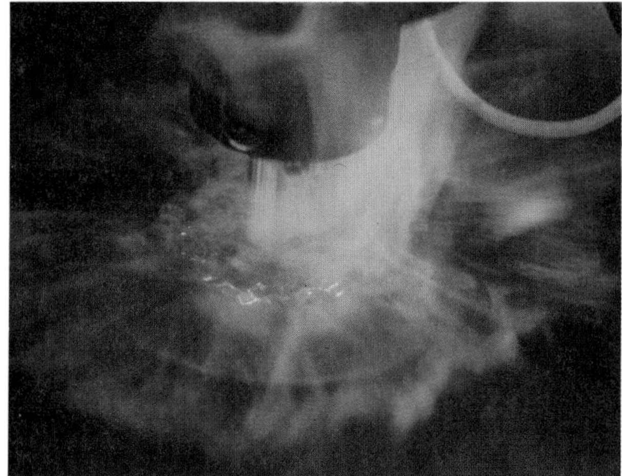

Left: During spark erosion metal cutting the workpiece is submerged in a dielectric fluid inside which the process takes place.

Right: A novel welding technique, announced in Britain in 1992, uses cheap, efficient microwave energy to produce a controllable plasma beam.

ing in the Caribbean, has two cylindrical hulls running just below the water surface. Another type, fast displacement catamarans, is designed to operate on trips up to 150 nautical miles (285 km), making them suitable for most ferry crossings worldwide. They are built with a central buoyancy hull below the cross deck in case the side hulls are punctured. In 1992 a craft of this type, Hoverspeed Great Britain, broke the transatlantic speed record, averaging almost 33 knots (61 km/h).

Robots

Once in the realm of science fiction, robots now perform many tasks previously done only by humans, from the simple repetitive to the highly complex which no person could achieve. They can cut, weld, screw, assemble, spray, inspect, and carry out many other duties. The largest use today is found in the automobile construction industry, but they are also used in space, in medicine for highly accurate work, and in nuclear power installations where it is unsafe for humans to go.

Recycling and the automobile

The automobile is a complex combination of a vast number of parts made from many different materials and combinations of materials. Although steel may comprise some 70 per cent of the materials of a car, this does not necessarily make it easy to recover because most of it is either painted or coated with some non-corrosive metal. Also, different types of steel are used in making a car for special purposes such as the fenders, frame, body, and engine.

Deliberate design for dismantling is already a reality; partly to gain a "green" image for their products several companies have embarked on schemes to recycle parts of their cars. One way is to make parts in simple, modular, snap-fit construction so that they can be easily stripped down for reuse. This economizes in labor which is the main cost of the recycling operation. BMW in Germany is already reprocessing many of the parts in its cars and a dismantling center is opening soon in Britain.

Plastics are obvious items for recycling as they are easy to shred, melt, and form into new parts, but they must be sorted into the correct grades, which means that the material must be easily identified. Often, plastic materials degrade somewhat in the process and must be reused for less demanding applications. The next stage in progress towards full recycling is to design parts so that they can be used again in a new vehicle.

Computer design

When a new part has been designed, either on a drawing board or a computer, the next stage is usually to make a sample, called a prototype, so that it can be visualized and tested with the other parts in the machine. With intricate components and difficult shapes this can be a very time consuming and expensive process. As a result, a part may have to be accepted as good enough because it would take too long to go through the process again with a changed design.

The technique of *rapid modeling* can help designers check their designs quickly and make changes if found necessary. One way is to connect the computer which contains the design to the machine tool directly and make the part without a skilled operator who needs to work from drawings.

Recently a new, faster technique, *stereolithography*, or three-dimensional modeling, has become available to designers. It involves ultraviolet-sensitive coatings used in the printing industry. The computer-aided design (CAD) model, which exists only inside the computer, breaks the design down into a large number of thin slices, which are then recreated by building up successive layers of light-sensitive liquid plastic to form the three-dimensional part. Each layer is rapidly solidified or cured before the next layer is laid on top.

Medicinal chemistry

Before the development of modern synthetic chemistry, plants and animals were the only known sources of biologically active molecules which could be used as medicines. Later, synthetic compounds came into use, but from whatever source, it was often necessary to use techniques of PHARMACOLOGY to "screen" a vast number of chemical compounds before an effective drug was found. Chemists now develop new drugs by synthesizing molecules with structures closely modeled on those of existing prototypes, or *lead compounds*, as they are often known. This process has been enhanced as improved knowledge of BIOCHEMISTRY shows exactly how the prototypes create their effects in the body.

Drug prototypes

About one fifth of all known drug prototypes are *alkaloids* extracted from plants by solvents and then purified. Some of these alkaloids are deadly poisons unless administered in very small doses, such as atropine used to dilate the pupil prior to examination of the eye, colchicine for gout, quinine for malaria, or the arrow poison tubocurarine to relax muscles during surgery. Plants create these poisons as protection against foraging predators.

Unmodified natural drugs are still sometimes prescribed, such as the plant-derived pain killers morphine and codeine which are obtained from opium, the dried latex secreted by poppy capsules. But many of the other 150 or so drug prototypes have serious side-effects. Fortunately, these have been avoided through the development of synthetic chemical analogues. For example, the local anaesthetic cocaine is a prototype extracted from coca leaf. It is so highly addictive that doctors rarely administer it to patients, preferring instead the non-addictive synthetic drug xylocaine which is just as effective.

Another important class of drug prototypes are the fermentation products produced by microorganisms. During World War II, the American pharmaceutical industry produced massive amounts of the newly discovered penicillin from fungi. Since then, synthetic penicillins and cephalosporin antibiotics and others modeled on natural antibiotics produced by fungi have saved millions of people from life-threatening bacterial infections. Doxorubicin, an antibiotic isolated from a streptomycete, is one of the most important drugs in cancer chemotherapy. It is active against leukemia and a wide range of tumors. (Streptomycetes are soil organisms that have much in common with both bacteria and fungi.)

Hormones constitute a major group of prototypes which have been widely exploited in recent years. These chemicals occur in minute amounts and relay signals throughout the human body to control its reaction to the environment. Hormones have been modified to provide medicines to treat asthma, high blood pressure, mental illness, rheumatism, and even cancer. Tamoxifen, a drug which resembles a female hormone, prevents cancer cells from using that hormone and thereby sometimes cures breast cancer. Clinical trials have begun in 1992 to see if it can also help to prevent the disease if taken by women at risk.

Above: Development of an organically-based chemotherapy agent – a chemist is measuring the volume of hydrogen absorbed during the hydrogenation of a nitro-compound, a stage in the synthesis aimed at overcoming resistance to chemotherapy by making the drug more selective. Developments in synthetic organic chemistry often proceed in steps, through the production of intermediate compounds

Design techniques

Medicinal chemists have concentrated their efforts on two principal approaches to drug design. The first is based on improving the fit of a drug to the tissue receptor into which it docks. Ranitidine, the world's best selling drug, blocks the action of histamine in the acid-producing cells of the stomach wall, which prevents release of gastric acid and allows ulcers to heal. Medicinal chemists are not always able to predict whether an enhanced fit will induce a better biological response or instead block access to the receptor by some important natural metabolite.

The other major approach towards drug design attempts to enhance the transportation and delivery of a drug to the receptors at which it will act. This will not only reduce the amount that needs to be administered, but can also help to reduce side effects on other parts of the body. Alternatively, a degree of drug targeting may be achieved by limiting the entry of the drug into parts of the body where it causes unwanted effects. For example, drowsiness can be caused by entry of antihistamine drugs into the brain. Modern antihistamines do not cross the blood-brain barrier.

The degree of fat solubility of any drug, relative to its water solubility, to a large extent determines the ease with which it crosses membrane barriers throughout the body. Medicinal chemists manipulate fat solubility by altering the chemical structure of compounds through changes in acidity, basicity, side-chain length, or electron distribution.

The fight against AIDS

Much attention is currently focused on the disease AIDS, which is caused by the human immunodeficiency virus or HIV. This robs its victim of the ability to fight diseases through the body's natural immune system, hence the full name of Acquired Immune Deficiency Syndrome. The first drug effective against HIV is zidovudine, originally known as AZT.

When DNA in the nucleus of a cell is activated, its genetic information is transcribed on to a strand of RNA which travels to another part of the cell as a messenger to direct the synthesis of a protein. The genetic material in HIV is RNA; the virus uses an enzyme called reverse transcriptase to create DNA corresponding to its own RNA. This DNA then takes over the machinery of the cell to make more viruses.

Zidovudine enters infected human cells, where it is converted to zidovudine triphosphate, which closely resembles thymidine, one of the natural building blocks for DNA. The reverse transcriptase utilizes the zidovudine triphosphate instead of thymidine and its action is blocked. No more viral RNA can then be transcribed into DNA, and HIV replication ceases as long as the patient continues to receive chemotherapy.

Zidovudine triphosphate, however, also has some effect on human DNA polymerase, a key enzyme required for normal DNA production. This results in severe toxicity and treatment with zidovudine is often abandoned.

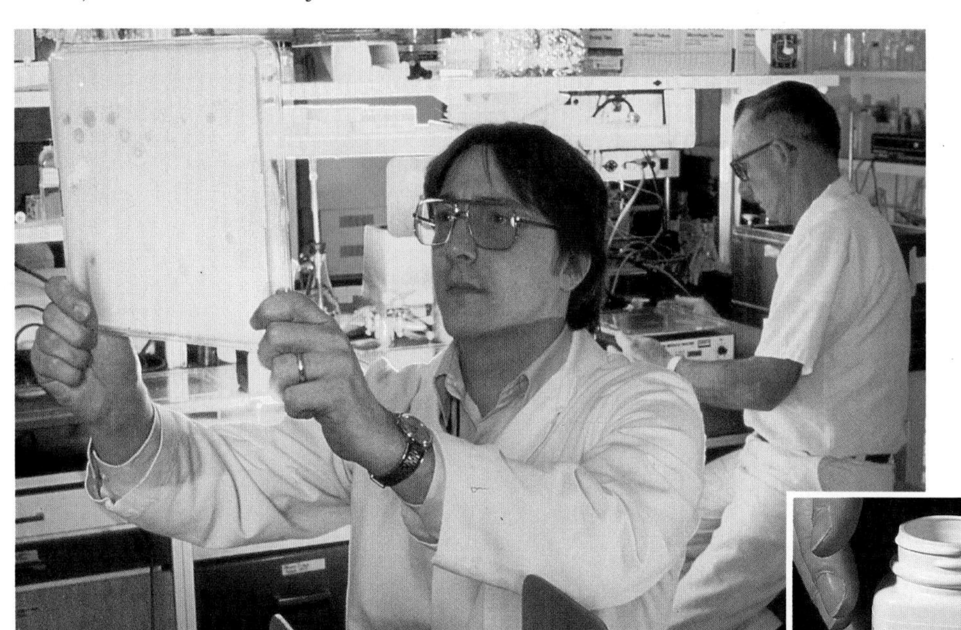

Left: Chemists working to develop novel anti-inflammatory drugs for Pfizer, USA, used to treat the symptoms of arthritis and rheumatic diseases.
Below: Packaging and capsules of Retrovir, or zidovudine, which has had some success in prolonging the lives of victims of AIDS.

Medicine

General medicine, as practiced by family practitioners, is undergoing its most profound change in many years, as is general hospital medicine. New drugs and diagnostic agents mean that diseases such as peptic ulcers and diabetes (see ENDOCRINOLOGY) can be treated by family physicians. And new technology allows family physicians to perform an increasing number of tests and procedures at office level. As a result, many community medical practices now have the facilities once found only in hospitals.

Peptic ulcers can occur in the stomach, duodenum, and gullet. Esophagitis – inflammation of the gullet – is also common and is usually caused by a hiatus hernia, when stomach acids flow back into the gullet causing the pain of "heartburn". Peptic ulcers and esophagitis often have the same treatment. Since the late 1970s there have been three new classes of drugs to treat both. The first to be synthesized was cimetidine, which inhibited the effects of histamine in the stomach. This was followed by ranitidine and famotidine, which are similar but have certain advantages. Then came misoprostol, which resembles a naturally occurring prostaglandin. The most recent drug is omeprazole, which inhibits the cell membrane pump involved in the formation of stomach acid.

Treatment of ulcers

A further discovery by Australian and British workers was that a bacterium, *Helicobacter pylori*, is found in the stomach and duodenum of ulcer patients but not in most non-patients. It was then shown to be the cause of the ulcers. Trials showed that there was an 80 per cent chance of eliminating it from the body with antibiotic therapy. The treatment requires two to three antibiotics taken simultaneously for several weeks and requires a highly motivated patient who will persist, despite side effects, because if the treatment is abandoned the bacterium becomes resistant to any further attempts at eradication.

Primary care physicians now recognize that many patients have physical symptoms caused by states of mind, including anxiety and phobias. Such symptoms are particularly common in people who drive themselves too hard (a common 20th century problem) and are unsympathetic to psychological symptoms. These physical symptoms include fatigue, irritability, palpitations, gut symptoms including irritable bowel, breathlessness, increased sensations of hot and cold, visual disturbances, and headache.

In the early 1980s a U.K. survey showed that 15 to 30 per cent of patients seen by hospital specialists have no physical cause for their symptoms. In the 1990s, this number has declined as family physicians have become more skilled at reassuring these patients that they have no organic disease and helping them develop strategies for coping with their symptoms.

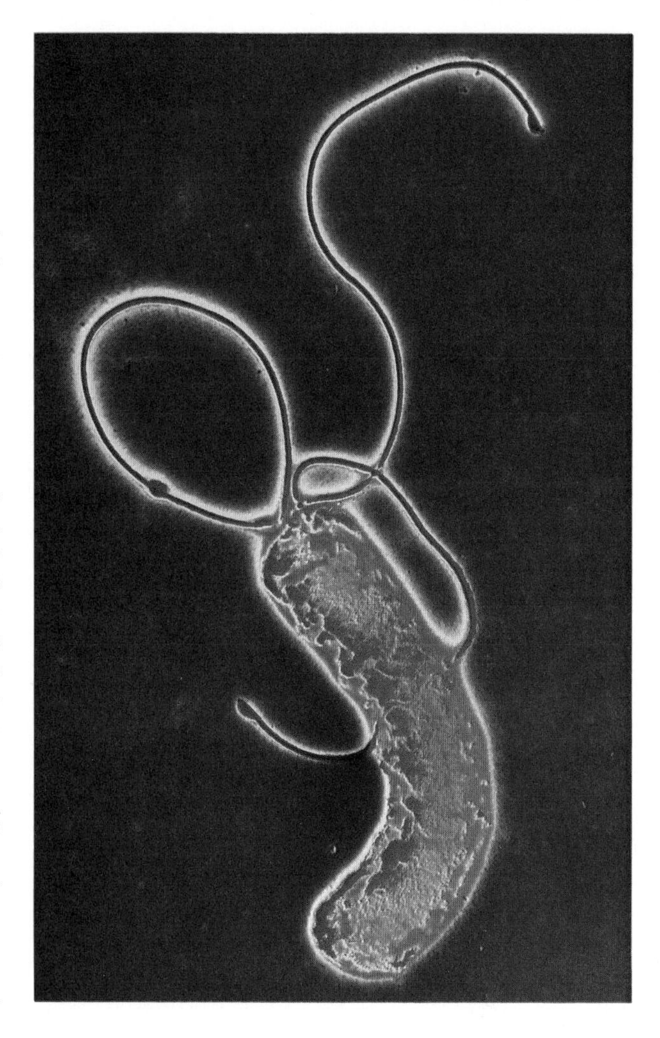

Above: An artificially-colored electron micrograph of the bacterium *Helicobacter pylori* which has been linked with the formation of stomach ulcers.

Fringe medicine

However, there are patients who are unwilling to accept that their symptoms could possibly arise from within themselves, and various branches of fringe medicine, calling themselves by names such as "nutritional medicine", "clinical ecology" or "environmental medicine" have sprung up as a result. Despite lack of recognition from the orthodox medical professionals and therefore insurance companies, they tend to have a cult following. They often diagnose diseases that have headline value, such as chronic Epstein-Barr syndrome, Candida hypersensitivity syndrome, multiple chemical sensitivities, total allergy syndrome, and myalgic encephalomyelitis.

The last decade or so has seen the development of new vaccines, of which the most important is for hepatitis B. The clinical trials of the hepatitis vaccine were done on volunteers from the gay community of New York, whose altruism deserves wide recognition. Hepatitis B is a serious disease in Western society, and chronic infection often leads to liver cancer. In the Third World it is the most common cause of liver cancer. This has led doctors to understand the importance of treating chronic hepatitis B infection, even in patients with few or no symptoms. They are now treated with a course of daily interferon injections, often lasting four or six months.

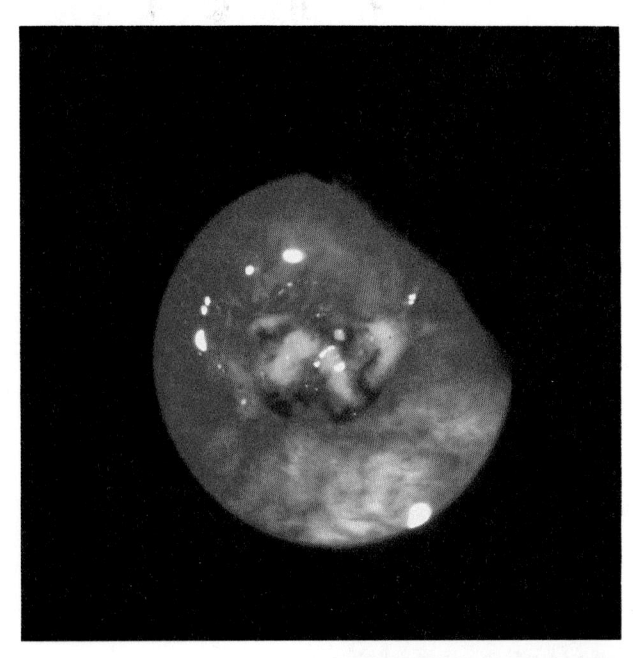

Arthritis remains a serious cause of ill health. Osteoarthritis, which should properly be called osteoarthrosis, is known from skeletons to have existed since ancient times. It remains difficult to treat, other than by the replacement of hips and knees by artificial joints in those who are severely affected. There are two forms of inflammatory arthritis: rheumatoid and ankylosing spondylitis. Both of these are autoimmune diseases, in which the body reacts against itself. Treatments using monoclonal antibodies are showing promise. Both these diseases have been known for only 200-300 years (this can be shown by examining ancient skeletons) and both seem to be declining in incidence for unknown reasons.

Suicide, which in the 1960s was the most common cause of death in young adults, has declined considerably and continues to do so. Part of this is because there are now widespread counseling services, including telephone helplines, and part because barbiturates are now rarely prescribed for insomnia. They have been replaced by benzodiazepines, which are not fatal in overdose, but these have caused addiction problems.

The arrival of AIDS

The end of the 20th century has seen a change in the types of disease known throughout most of his-

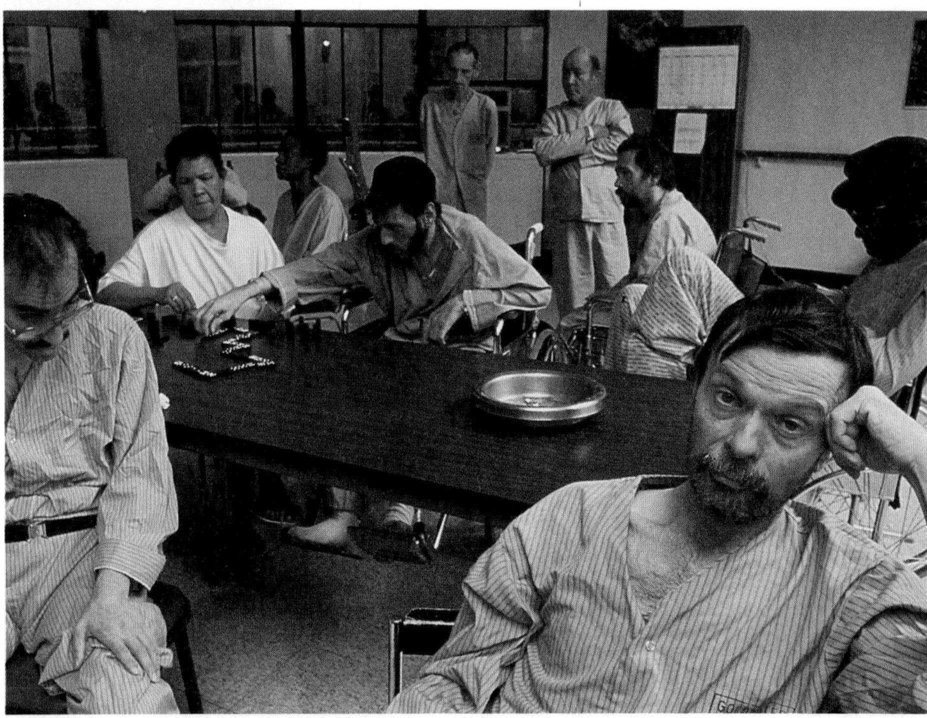

Above: An endoscope image of a stomach ulcer, a disruption of the lining of the stomach caused by digestion of the mucosa (lining membrane) by acid, pepsin, and bile. Fresh, red blood can be seen around the ulcer crater, the yellow base of which is obscured by black blood clots. Causes of gastric ulcers are related to diet, alcohol consumption, stress, and some drugs. Right: AIDS sufferers at the Goldwater Memorial Hospital, New York. The disease produces wasting, fatigue, and extreme sensitivity to infections.

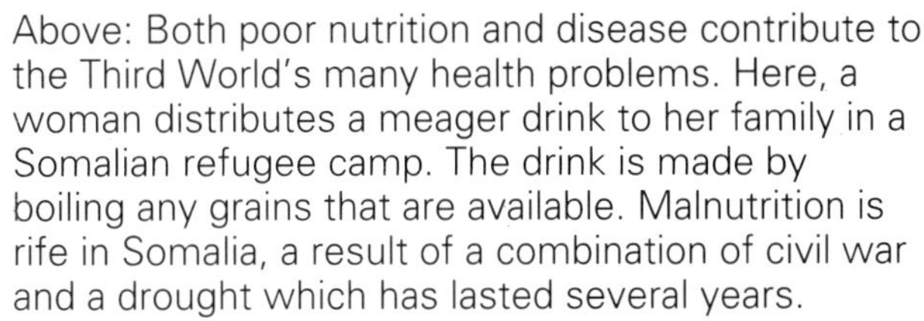

Above: Both poor nutrition and disease contribute to the Third World's many health problems. Here, a woman distributes a meager drink to her family in a Somalian refugee camp. The drink is made by boiling any grains that are available. Malnutrition is rife in Somalia, a result of a combination of civil war and a drought which has lasted several years.

Above: A community health worker (foreground) with a vaccination cold pack treats a family of Somalian nomads.

tory. Since the introduction of antibiotics in the 1940s, the Western world has been able to forget that acute infections can kill healthy children and adults. By 1950 the one common fatal infectious disease left was poliomyelitis. After that was conquered by vaccines invented in 1956, there were three decades when it was unusual for anyone in the West to die from an infection. Then AIDS arrived (see EPIDEMIOLOGY). It had been festering, relatively unnoticed, in Africa for some years, under the name of slim disease, so named because patients lost weight from it. It is caused by a slow virus that destroys the killer T-cells of the immune system. The only licensed treatment is zidovudine (AZT); massive research programs developing new drugs and vaccines are now under way.

In the late 1980s French and American workers separately showed that AIDS was caused by a virus, which the French called LAV (Lymphadenopathy virus) and the Americans called HLTV (human T-cell leukemia virus). In 1989 both agreed to call the virus HIV (human immunodeficiency virus), and a reliable test was developed. Meanwhile the only preventive measure is to ensure that the body fluids of infected people do not enter the bodies of uninfected people; in practical terms this means safe sex, antibody testing of blood donations, and sensible precautions when handling body fluids of patients. However, the virus is far less infectious than the hepatitis virus, which requires far more stringent precautions. History suggests that epidemics of sexually transmitted diseases will not be contained by frightening people into careful behavior, but by developing effective drugs and vaccines.

Syphilis is now a rare disease, but since the 1980s it has been recognized that the most common sexually transmitted disease is caused by a mycobacterium called Chlamydia. It causes what used to be called NSU – non-specific urethritis – in men, and diffuse symptoms in women.

Toxic shock syndrome

Toxic shock syndrome, an acute and sometimes life-threatening disease caused by staphylococcal infection, became common in the 1970s and 80s, and was traced to vaginal tampons, where the bacteria could multiply if tampons were not changed frequently. It has become rare owing to a change in the fibers used to make tampons. In the U.S., tampon packets contain a warning to women not to leave them in place for more than a few hours.

Western countries have two types of medical problems. There are the diseases of affluent societies, where people live to old age and develop heart disease, cancer, and failure of various organs. Western societies also have the mainly urban diseases and social problems of social breakdown and unemployment, including alcoholism, drug abuse, intolerance of mental handicap, and homelessness.

Third World health problems

Third World countries have all these and more.

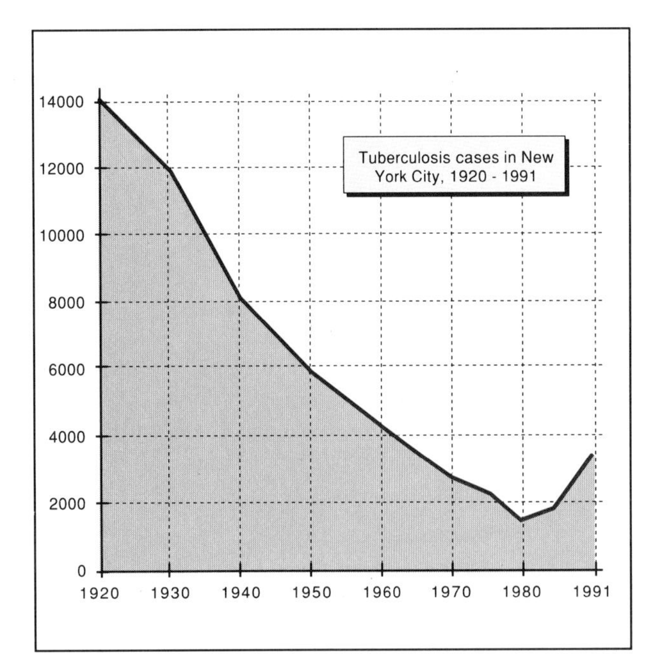

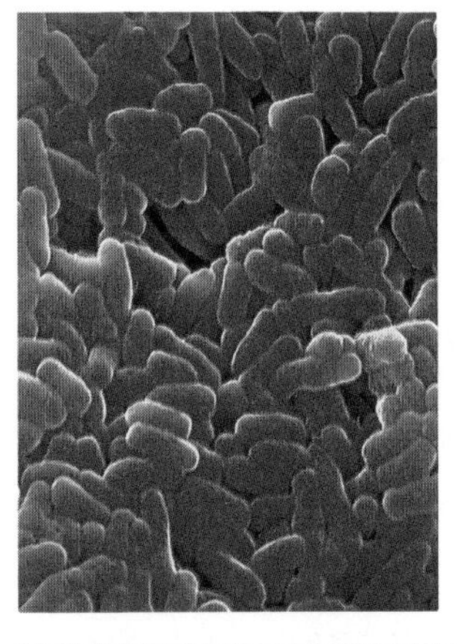

Left: Tuberculosis, once considered to be all but conquered, has made a dramatic comeback in the 1990s as shown by the graph. The bacterium (left) is spread by coughing or sneezing by carriers who may not even show any symptoms.

The city-dwelling middle classes have much the same health needs as their Western counterparts; the cities are also home to many unemployed, homeless, and vagrant people, and drink and drug problems abound there. In the rural areas there is also primary poverty, where people do not have enough to eat. Many countries, especially in Africa, produce sufficient food, but this is often unequally distributed and poorly stored so that it become unusable or harmful; repeated food poisoning is a common reason for malnutrition.

The idea that many Third World babies die as an indirect result of the promotion of baby formula is a fallacy. These products are used by the middle classes in towns, while most infant mortality is highest in rural areas where they are not used. Infant mortality in rural areas has been lowered by education about infant nutrition and weaning – for example, coconut milk looks like breast milk but is nutritionally poor – and by better treatment of acute diarrhea, a common condition in poverty-stricken areas.

There are also financial limitations to health care, even in the wealthiest societies. Moreover, increasing expectations lead to increasing – and usually justified – litigation, which adds to the overall costs and, arguably, makes doctors over-cautious about entering certain specialities such as obstetrics and gynecology.

AIDS has become the biggest cause of premature death in Africa and has spread over virtually the whole world. It is worth remembering that a century ago Western countries coped with thousands of people institutionalized with general paralysis of the insane, caused by syphilis. It disappeared overnight after antibiotics were discovered.

• FACT FILE •

- Despite enormous strides in medicine in recent years, many Third World health problems can be alleviated by low-tech remedies. For example, World Health Organization initiatives have taught people that a liter of water to which is added a spoonful of sugar and a pinch of salt is simple, cheap, and saves lives which might otherwise have been lost through dehydration.

- Increased vaccination has also reduced disease, and at comparatively little cost. However, many vaccines perish rapidly in warm temperatures and rely on the "cold chain" – transportation in insulated containers from one town's refrigerator to the next town's. Improvements here could save much wasted effort.

- Four-fifths of the world's children are now immunized against measles, tetanus, polio, diphtheria, whooping cough, and tuberculosis – compared with one-fifth in 1981. In many Western countries a typical childhood vaccine costs about $10, of which less than $1 is the basic cost; the rest covers litigation insurance. If litigation catches on in the Third World, vaccines would soon become too expensive, and governments could not afford to supply them – and many more people would die.

- The World Health Organization's aim of "clean water for all by the year 2000" is attainable; clean water will greatly reduce the incidence of many parasitic and infectious diseases.

Meteorology

Weather forecasting is only part, though a very important one, of meteorology, the science of weather. Meteorologists use some of the most powerful computers in existence. Employing complex mathematical models of the atmosphere, they can successfully predict the path and severity of hurricanes and other large scale weather events. They are beginning to understand many important processes, such as the buildup of electrical charges in thunderclouds, which leads to lightning. Yet predicting the weather several days or weeks ahead has proved much more difficult.

A new branch of mathematics, CHAOS THEORY, has shown the reasons for this. The theory proves that it is impossible to predict the exact state of the atmosphere at any particular place for more than a limited time into the future.

Even the slightest inaccuracy in our knowledge of all the billions of tiny factors that could affect the weather will very rapidly snowball and lead to huge inaccuracy in predictions. This is summed up (only partly in jest) as the "butterfly effect": if a butterfly flaps its wings in Brazil today, could it spawn a tornado over Texas next month? The atmosphere is extremely sensitive to small fluctuations in its initial conditions, which is one reason why the weather is never the same from year to year.

Studying current weather

One way in which meteorologists have tackled this fundamental limitation regarding the accuracy of their medium-term predictions is by improved "nowcasting" – determining exactly what is happening right now.

An example often seen on TV is the radar map of rainfall, which covers an area hundreds of miles across. Even more important are results from new Doppler radars, which operate just like the radar guns that police use to catch speeding drivers. These radars can map the distinctive echoes of air motions inside clouds, or in the early stages of tornados. They also detect "microbursts" – invisible intense downdrafts, which sometimes cause airplanes to crash.

Much of the weather is governed by conditions high in the atmosphere. Although instrumented balloons (radiosondes) are simultaneously released twice a day at a few hundred sites around the world, they provide insufficient data for really accurate modeling.

Right: Doppler radar is a valuable tool for weather forecasting and research. This dish antenna near Boulder, Colorado, both transmits and receives radar pulses. The returning signals reveal not only the location of clouds and precipitation but also their movement.

Left: The image of rainfall shown by Doppler radar on an advanced meteorological work station. The orange area at upper center shows where the heaviest rain, and possibly hail, is falling, while the band at the left edge is the Front Range of mountains in Colorado.

Above: A scientist working at computer terminals in the Meteorological Office at Reading, U.K. Staff here prepare weather forecasts for 18 European meteorological services.

Above: A NASA ER-2 high-altitude research plane being readied for a flight to study the ozone layer. Proposed plane designs will be unmanned and may stay aloft for as long as a year.

Satellites orbit well above the atmosphere, but satellite-borne instruments which can measure conditions between orbit and the surface are only just being developed.

These include "topside-sounding" radar and lidar (laser-ranging) sensors. Scattered over the American Midwest, the National Oceanic and Atmospheric Administration (NOAA) has about 30 experimental Doppler-radar vertical wind profilers. These continuously measure wind speeds and directions at heights between 2000 and 60,000 ft (about 0.6 and 18 km). This new information helps meteorologists to produce accurate models of local conditions, resulting in improved national weather forecasts.

Upper atmosphere studies

Vertical profilers are unable to determine humidity, and can rarely obtain temperature information. To discover these things, meteorologists need instruments at the altitude in question. Special lightweight GHOST balloons have been used in experiments. They maintain a constant height; some have made several circuits of the globe over the Southern Ocean. Researchers at the University of Colorado in Boulder are developing high-flying parafoil kites which can carry instruments at various heights on their tethers. They could be used at remote sites, well away from the danger of aircraft flight paths. In initial tests over Christmas Island in the Western Pacific, the kites reached a height of approximately 11,000 ft (3.4 km); maximum altitudes of about 12 miles (20 km) may be attainable.

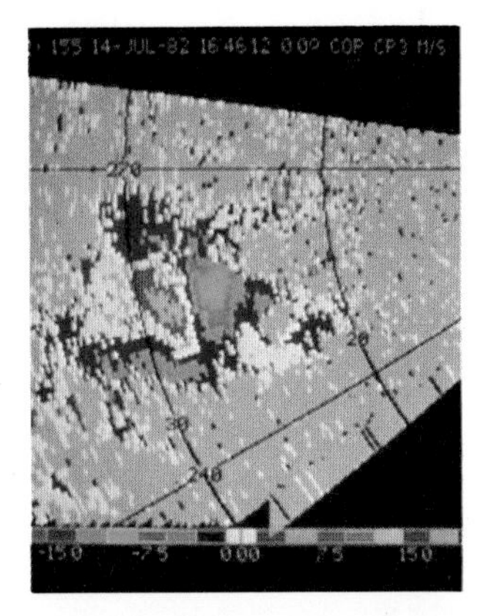

Left: Image of a microburst as captured on Doppler radar. Brown colors show winds moving away from the radar while green and blue indicate winds moving toward the radar. This occurs where the downburst hits the ground and spreads outward.

Accurate forecasting

Many experts believe the most accurate predictions of the weather are made by the European Centre for Medium Range Weather Forecasts in Reading, U.K. The meteorologists there use a Cray Y-MP C90 supercomputer, which was installed in 1992 and is capable of carrying out 16 billion calculations per second.

The forecasters use what is called the Monte Carlo method, introducing random variations into the simulation. The computer produces 40 different forecasts a day with these slightly altered starting points. When several forecasts agree, they indicate that the modeling is stable to small fluctuations, and that the actual weather will probably match the forecast.

A typical global model incorporates about one million data points – measurements of pressure, temperature, wind speed, humidity, and so on, made at sea level and at various levels in the atmosphere. Using this information, the computer is able to calculate the weather for several days in advance.

Microbiology

Microbiology as a science was born with the work of Louis Pasteur in France in the 1860s. For centuries scientists had speculated that disease resulted from "spontaneous generation", but Pasteur demonstrated that food spoilage was caused by microscopic organisms present in the environment and could be prevented by applying heat to kill them (as in the "pasteurization" of milk). Following up on Pasteur's work, Robert Koch in Germany and others discovered some of the actual microbes that caused disease.

Modern microbiology seeks a better understanding of how microorganisms – bacteria, fungi, viruses, and simple protozoa (see PARASITOLOGY) – behave. This understanding leads to improvements in clinical treatment, the exploitation of microorganisms in food production, industrial processes and research, and an appreciation of the important environmental role played by microorganisms.

Bacteria

Bacteria range in shape from common rod-shaped *bacilli* and spherical *cocci* to comma-shaped *vibrios* and unusual forms such as the coiled *spirochaetes*. Bacteria have a rigid outer cell wall which maintains their shape; below this lies the outer cell membrane. Nutrients and waste products diffuse across the membrane, which may be folded to enclose cellular compartments with specialized functions, including photosynthetic activity. Bacteria belong to a class of organisms called prokaryotes, meaning they have no nucleus but carry their DNA in the cellular fluid, which is known as the cytoplasm. The cytoplasm contains subunits called ribosomes for protein synthesis and may often also contain particles called inclusion bodies carrying such material as stored fat.

Bacterial growth is rapid: under ideal conditions, the human gut bacterium *Escherichia coli*, for example, will replicate every 20 minutes. The rapid growth and relatively simple culture requirements of bacteria make them attractive for research and industrial applications. Specially tai-

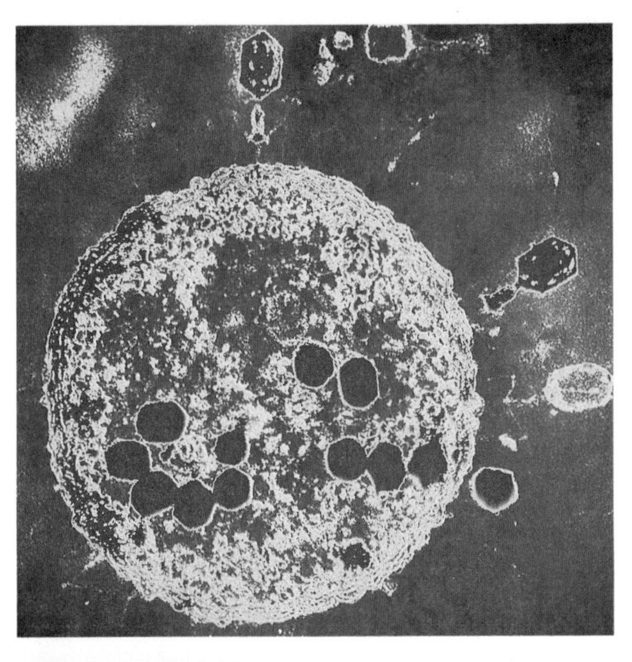

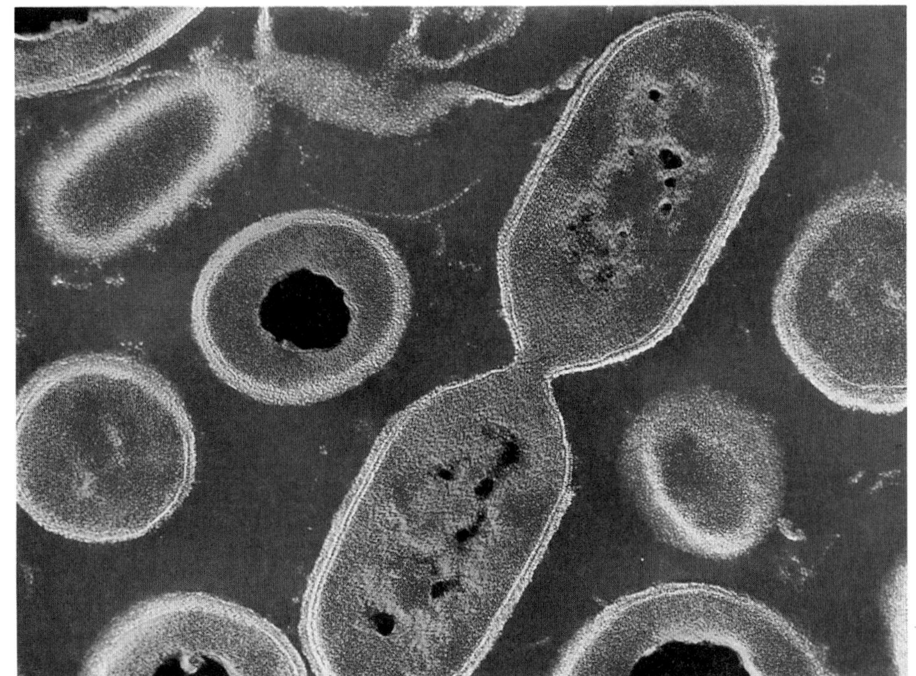

Above: A bacterium of *E.Coli* (circular cell) infected by red T2 bacteriophages. Bacteriophages are viruses which infect only bacteria, some being specific to a single species. Having no reproductive machinery, they commandeer the bacterium's to ensure self replication. The colors on this electron micrograph are false.
Left: False-color image of a colony of *Listeria* bacteria, magnified 30,000 times. The bacterium at center is dividing into two (binary fission).

lored strains of *E. coli* are used in molecular biology and genetic engineering. Genes from other organisms have been inserted into *E. coli* to allow large scale commercial preparation of products such as human growth hormone and insulin in a process called fermentation (see BIOTECHNOLOGY).

Growth conditions can be optimized in sealed, controlled culture vessels or *fermenters*. Nutrients, oxygen, acidity, and other factors can all be monitored and maintained at ideal levels to obtain the best yields. Commercial-scale fermenters allow huge volumes of cells – perhaps up to 25,000 gallons (100,000 liters) at a time – to be cultured, harvested, and their products collected.

Fermentation technology is applicable to other bacterial species, and to fungi. One class of bacteria, the filamentous actinomycetes, are of particular interest because they secrete antibiotics. Examples include *Streptomyces griseus* and *Strep. aureofaciens*, from which Streptomycin™ and Tetracycline™, respectively, are produced.

Fungi

Fungi are more complex than bacteria, having a greater degree of cytoplasmic organization. Many fungal species also secrete antibiotics – penicillin, from *Penicillium*, being the classic and best known example. Common fungi (molds) are shaped like filaments and grow from the tip. When you see mold on bread you are looking at colonies of fungi. Under a microscope you would see new growth occurring around each colony's outer edge.

Among fungal microorganisms, the yeasts have had some of the most widespread commercial use. Yeasts are single-celled organisms, again showing a higher degree of organization inside the cell than bacteria. The brewer's yeast *Saccharomyces cerevisiae*, for example, has its DNA packaged into 17 chromosomes, held together in a discrete nucleus. As eukaryotes (organisms with a nucleus), yeasts have a cell biology more in common with higher organisms than bacteria. Expression of cloned genes from higher eukaryotes is therefore often easier in yeasts; researchers are currently investigating the genetics of these organisms as an alternative to bacterial species for biomanufacturing. *S. cerevisiae* and another yeast, *Schizosaccharomyces pombe*, are also being intensively investigated as simpler model systems in which to study processes such as cell division in higher eukaryotes.

Viruses

Both eukaryotic and bacterial cells may be infected by a third class of microorganism, the viruses. Viruses are much smaller than bacteria, and are made up simply of DNA or RNA surrounded by a protein coat known as a capsid. Sometimes viruses that infect animal cells will be found surrounded also by pieces of membrane from previously infected cells. The DNA or RNA encodes the genetic information for making more copies of the virus, but the virus lacks the machinery for doing so; to replicate, the virus must enter a cell and "hijack"

Below: Although bacteria, sometimes known as microbes, are popularly considered to be harmful, they have a wide range of uses. Those shown here cause diseases, but others are beneficial. Many antibiotics, including penicillin, are made naturally by bacteria and fungi found in the soil.

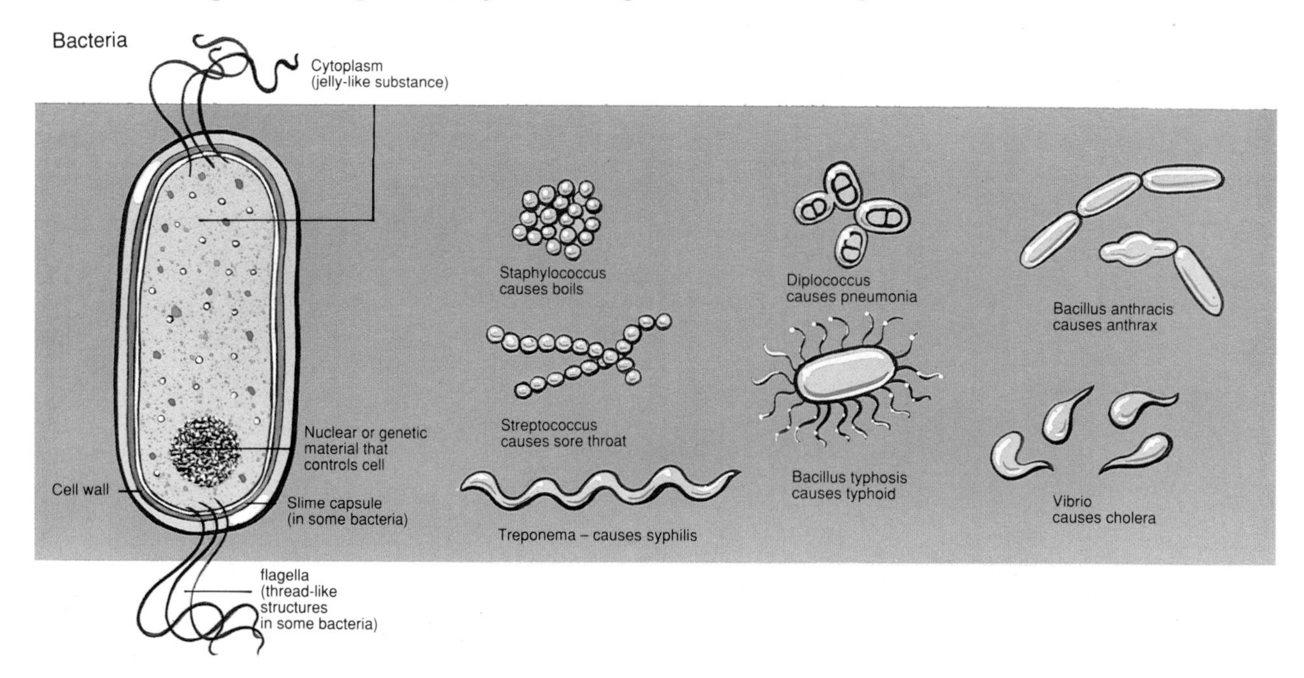

Above: Microbiological research is carried out by growing colonies on dishes of agar nutrient. The effects of drugs can be tested by placing them on the dishes to see if they inhibit the growth of the bacteria.

its systems for protein and nucleic acid synthesis.

E. coli is infected by a number of viruses called bacteriophages, of which perhaps the best-studied is known as lambda; modified versions of lambda are used in molecular biology and genetic engineering as *vectors* to insert genes into bacteria. Lambda consists of a molecule of DNA 50,000 bases long, encased in a protein capsid. The tail of the capsid recognizes, and will attach to, the outer surface of *E. coli*, after which the DNA is injected into the cell. Lambda can then follow one of two pathways. The DNA can integrate into the chromosome of the host, replicating in a benign fashion in tandem with its host, or it may initiate a process called the lytic cycle.

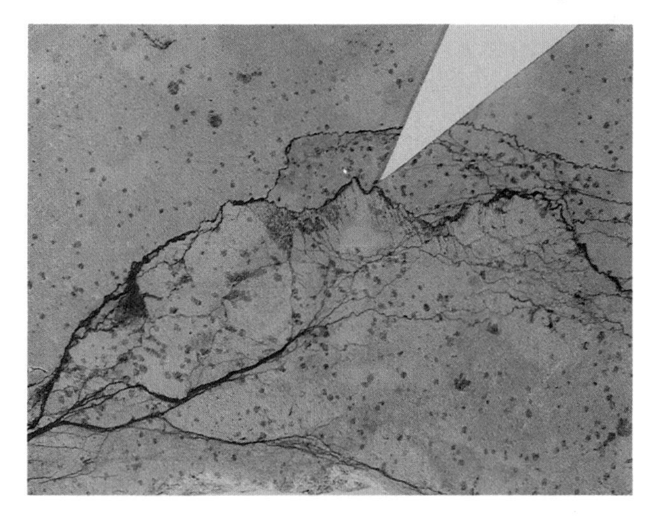

Above: No more than 10 per cent of the world's bacteria are known to science. Apparently unimpressive algae, such as these organic laminae, can have their uses, and form a gene pool that scientists are currently investigating.

In the lytic cycle, bacteriophage genes are expressed to produce many copies of the bacteriophage DNA and of the proteins which make up the capsid. The DNA and proteins assemble into more copies of the virus, and after a time the *coup de grace* is delivered: the infected cell is burst open or *lysed* by an enzyme also encoded by the bacteriophage DNA, releasing about 100 virus progeny which may then go on to infect more cells. Regions where lysis has occurred can be seen in bacterial growth on agar plates as clearings called *plaques*. Each plaque represents virus infection spreading from a single infective center.

The viruses which infect eukaryotic cells have more complicated growth patterns and grow more slowly than bacteriophages. For obvious reasons, great effort is expended in the field of virology in attempting to understand the workings of viruses which infect and cause disease in humans. In particular, the human immunodeficiency virus (HIV, the causative agent of AIDS) is the target of intense research.

Exploiting organisms

While they are often portrayed as being harmful, it is important to be aware that bacteria and fungi had been exploited by humanity in a number of valuable roles, long before their nature was known. Yeasts, for example, are of great use in baking and brewing. *Lactobacilli* are used in the production of processed dairy goods such as yogurt, while several species of fungi are exploited in cheese manufacture.

Compost production involves fungi which produce enzymes called ligninases which reduce woody material to its components. Researchers are seeking to isolate improved ligninases to speed waste processing and disposal.

Bacteria against pollution

The ability of several microbial species to survive under hostile conditions and live on unusual nutrients is the key to their future exploitation in areas such as waste management. Some *Pseudomonas* bacteria can break down complex organic compounds found in toxic wastes. Specially tailored bacteria and fungi should help to control environmental pollution.

Microbiological breakdown of organic material has been exploited for a long time. Composting involves the concerted action of a succession of bacteria and fungi to decompose dead organic matter. Important to this process are fungi which pro-

Above: Bacteria are the most tenacious forms of life on Earth: they can exist around hydrothermal vents such as this one on the floor of the Pacific, where hot, often sulfur-laden, gas escapes from the Earth's interior. Discoveries such at this suggest that bacteria may have been the first life forms.

duce enzymes called ligninases which break down the woody material in plants. Researchers are seeking to isolate improved ligninases for future application in waste processing and disposal.

Bacteria can be used in energy production. Species like *Methylobacterium* or *Methanococcus* generate methane, the principal component of natural gas, from decomposing waste.

As world oil resources decline it has been proposed that bacteria which secrete large amounts of thick, syrupy carbohydrates could be used to increase petroleum yields. The sticky, viscous substance that the bacteria would produce while growing on unusable hydrocarbon fractions would surround droplets of otherwise inaccessible oil in wells and could then be flushed out with water. This process may also be used to clean up oil that has spilled into soil.

Unappetizing as the idea may initially seem to most of us, bacteria may also serve as a useful food source in the future. Again exploiting otherwise unusable material derived from petroleum, researchers are currently investigating the possibility of culturing bacteria on refinery waste to produce protein. The successful use of such material as cattle feed offers hope of a partial solution to the world's growing food demands.

Clues to the origins of life

Many bacterial species are remarkable in their tolerance of harsh conditions, including heat, cold, high salt concentrations, and desiccation. The ability to survive inhospitable conditions has been taken by evolutionary biologists to indicate that bacteria probably played an important part in the early development of life on Earth.

The best available current scientific theories of the origin of life suggest that the first organisms to appear, sometime within a billion years after the Earth's formation, were simple bacteria, scavenging nutrients from their environment. It is sobering to reflect that, for the more than two billion years which followed, microorganisms remained the Earth's sole tenants. Development of photosynthesis by one class of bacteria, the blue-green algae, led to important chemical changes in the Earth's atmosphere: oxygen began to accumulate, paving the way for more complex life forms.

Archaebacteria, presumed to bear a close resemblance to early primitive bacteria, can still be found today, often in hostile oxygen-free environments which may resemble those in which cellular life first arose. One example is the hot-spring pools in Yellowstone National Park. Other recent surprising discoveries have included the presence of bacterial growth in the sulfur-rich hot environments around vents ("smokers") on the deep ocean floor, in regions such as the Mid-Atlantic Ridge where lava emerges from below the Earth's crust. More startling still was the discovery, announced in 1992, of bacteria in drilled samples from great depths into the Earth's crust.

Eukaryotic cells contain several small internal structures called organelles, each with some special function: ribosomes, for example, manufacture proteins, mitochondria process energy and, in plants, chloroplasts carry out photosynthesis. Several characteristics of mitochondria and chloroplasts suggest that they might once have been free-living bacterial organisms which became incorporated, perhaps via a symbiotic lifestyle, into the cytoplasm of more complex cells. Thus microbiological research not only has important implications for understanding how modern bacteria function, but may also yield important clues to how life itself arose and developed in the first place.

Microelectronics

Microelectronics is the technology of fabricating electronic components in ultra-miniaturized form within microelectronic devices, technically known as integrated circuits, but more commonly known as 'silicon chips' or just plain 'chips'.

Today microelectronic technology has become so advanced that individual electronic components such as transistors can be miniaturized to the point where 50 of them in a line measure just one-thousandth of an inch (0.025 mm) end to end, allowing up to 50 million of them to be fabricated into a single chip the size of a postage stamp. By the end of the 1990s further advances will make even this ultra-miniaturization look crude, with designs incorporating over a billion transistors on each chip.

Microelectronic miniaturization is big business. From its early days as a small, specialized industry in California's Silicon Valley in 1960, the worldwide microelectronics industry has grown to achieve sales of over $50 billion a year.

Although silicon chips are found in a wide range of products, there is one single type of chip that has come to dominate the whole technology and business of microelectronics – the dynamic random-access memory chip or DRAM.

Today, DRAM chips are manufactured by the million, fulfilling what seems to be an insatiable demand for electronic memories in practically every type of electronics equipment. Regularly, as microelectronic technology advances, new generations of DRAM chips come into production, providing four times the memory capacity per chip as the preceding generation and so stimulating demand even further. This regular generation-by-generation evolution of DRAM technology has now become an established pattern maintained over more than a quarter-century, with a new generation coming into production every three years.

The latest generation of DRAM chips has a memory capacity of sixteen million bits (16 Mbit) per chip, or in computer terms two megabytes (2 Mbyte, 1 byte = 8 bits) per chip. To put this into perspective, in 1970 only a few of the largest supercomputers could boast 1 Mbyte of memory, and a 1 Mbyte memory unit cost almost a million dollars and filled a whole room of an air-conditioned computer suite. Using the new 16 Mbit DRAMs, a single chip costing just a few dollars

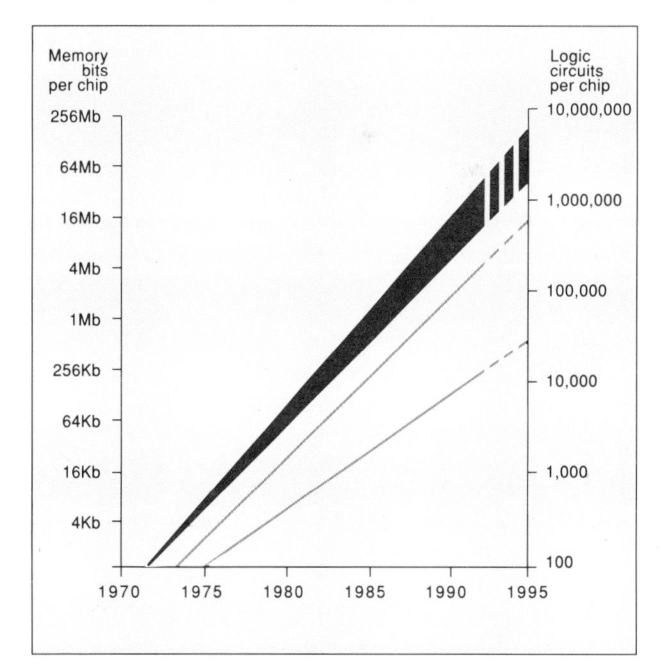

Above: The power available on a single chip has increased dramatically over the years, matched by a reduction in the size of powerful computers.
Left: The production of microchips is carefully monitored and controlled by computer. Here, a technician wearing overalls to keep the environment dust-free, changes a control tape.

and not much bigger than a postage stamp will by itself provide 2 Mbyte memory capacity. During the 1990s new generations of 64 Mbit and 256 Mbit DRAMs will in turn provide 8 Mbyte and 32 Mbyte per chip, while by the year 2001 the first gigabit DRAMs (1 Gbit = 1024 Mbit) will provide a colossal 128 Mbytes on a single chip.

Today's 16 Mbit memories require ultra-miniaturized transistors, each as small as the wavelength of light and as invisible, except through electron microscopes. With each new generation of DRAMs requiring a 30 per cent decrease in transistor size, by 2001 the new 1 Gbit DRAMs will have to be based on transistors not much bigger than 0.1 micron.

Fabricating chips with transistors this small demands incredible levels of technology: a single microscopic flaw or impurity, not to mention a minute speck of dust, will knock out a transistor and so make the whole chip defective. As a result, all operations must be carried out in ultra-clean rooms (dust levels down to 1 particle per cu ft, compared with 10,000 per cu ft in even a hospital operating theatre). Traditional liquid-based 'wet' chemical processes are similarly being replaced by 'dry' processing involving ionized gases and plasma. The microphotographic processes used to create circuits now have to use extreme ultraviolet light, and may soon have to be replaced by X-ray processing.

With all this advanced technology a new self-contained chip fabrication plant, known as a 'fab' module, now costs over $300 million to build and equip. With these capital costs increasing by 80 per cent with each DRAM generation, the plants required for 1 Gbit DRAMs will cost up to $2 billion each. Because of this, some forecasts predict that there will only be a handful of DRAM plants in operation by 2001, leaving the rest of the microelectronics industry to concentrate on less demanding products.

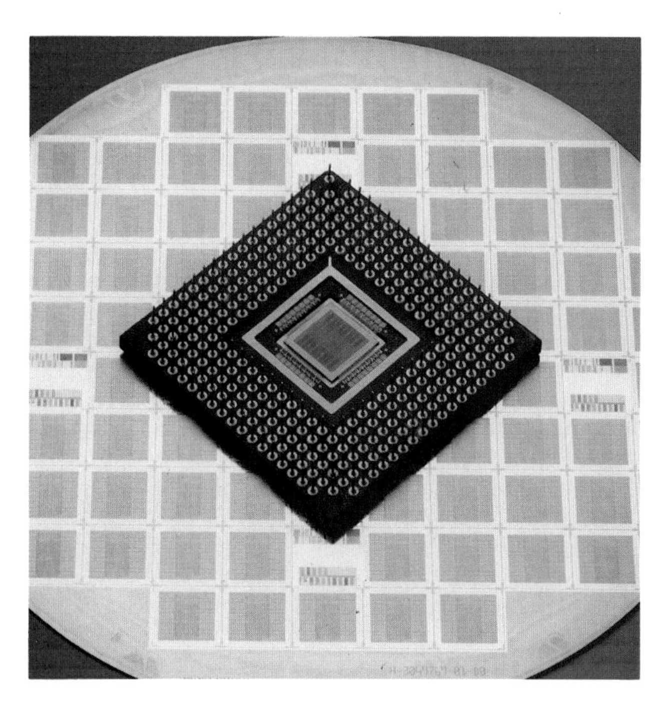

Above: A complex, state-of-the-art microchip such as might be used for advanced microprocessors. The chip is photographed on top of a wafer containing a number of microchip dies.
Below: A silicon chip, typically about ¼ in. square, viewed through a microscope so that its intricate patterns can be clearly seen.

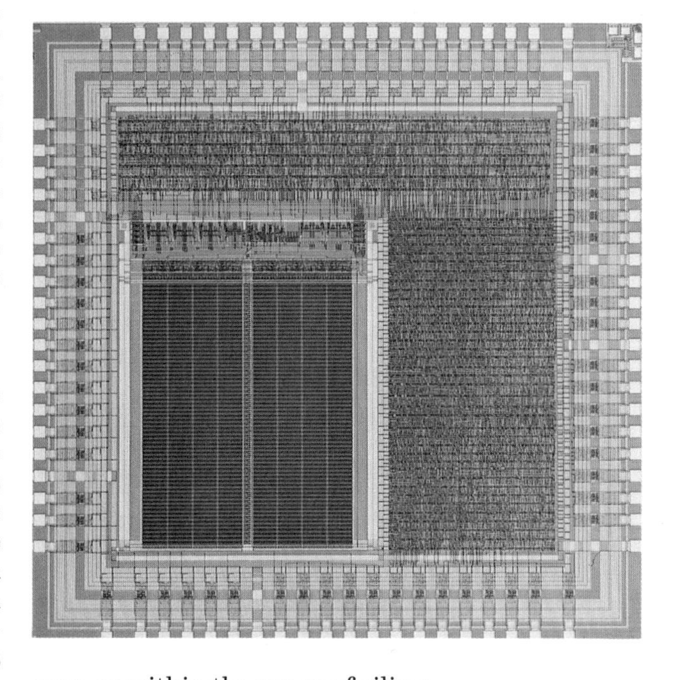

The future of silicon

Silicon, one of the earth's most common elements and the main constituent of rocks and sand, has proved more precious than gold for the microelectronics industry. It seems set to maintain its supremacy over several rival materials. In the quest for speed of operation, gallium arsenide (GaAs) was once thought likely to replace silicon for chips operating above 1 GHz, i.e., more than once every billionth of a second. Recently, however, silicon chips have been shown to operate at speeds 50 times faster than this, casting doubt on the need for a switch to GaAs at all.

Superconducting materials were once thought to be necessary to take memory chip densities up to the 1 Gbit level, a goal that is now once again seen as within the range of silicon.

The trend towards optical-semiconductor materials to form microelectronic lasers and all-optical computing chips is a role that, recent research results suggest, silicon itself may be able to fulfill.

Molecular biology

Molecular biology is one of the most exciting fields of life science in the 1990s. Many experts see it as the route to major discoveries that will have applications in medicine, industry, and farming.

During the 1950s, molecular biologists studied the BIOCHEMISTRY of large molecules in living cells. These were mainly proteins, and the building-blocks they are made of, known as amino acids.

Nowadays, molecular biology is more concerned with another group of molecules in living cells – the nucleic acids such as DNA (deoxyribonucleic acid), the "blueprint for life". GENETIC ENGINEERING and GENETICS both involve the nature of genes and manipulating DNA.

Most living things use DNA as the carrier of their genetic information. This huge molecule is a double helix, shaped like two intertwined spiral staircases. The information in the genes tells the cell how to make various proteins. Proteins are the molecules that build the structure of the cell and also, in the form of enzymes, control the hundreds of biochemical reactions happening inside each cell.

The genetic information is coded as a string of chemical subunits along the DNA molecule. The subunits are known as nucleotide bases or, more simply, bases. They are like letters in a sentence of instructions. However, in the case of DNA there are only four different "letters". They are adenine (A), guanine (G), thymine (T), and cytosine (C). There may be hundreds of thousands of bases along one strand of DNA. The bases are arranged in linked pairs with those in the other strand, like steps on the staircase of DNA.

A gene is a sequence of pairs of bases that makes up one unit of genetic information. A simple organism, such as the virus lambda, has relatively few genes. A complex organism such as a mammal has many thousands. In molecular biology, each gene is a sequence of bases that represents the code for making a structural or enzyme protein. ("Gene" is a term with different meanings, depending on the branch of science.)

Making a protein from its gene is known as protein synthesis. It involves intermediate molecules which translate the genetic code, the ribonucleic acids, or RNAs.

Making proteins from genes

In a DNA molecule, each base on one helical strand links, or pairs, with a base in the opposite strand. However, of the four bases, adenine can only pair with thymine, and guanine pairs only with cytosine. Therefore, when the two strands in a double helix of DNA are separated, each forms a template or "mirror image" from which the other

Above: A scientist examining an autoradiogram of a DNA sequence. Each group of four strips represents a sequence of the nucleotide bases adenine, guinine, cytosine and thymine in the DNA of the worm *Ophocera volvulus*, a parasite responsible for diseases like river blindness in tropical countries. The proportion and sequence of the bases determines the genetic properties of the organism.

can be constructed. If two DNA strands fit together with the correct bases cross-linking, they are known as complementary.

The first stage of protein synthesis involves separating the two DNA strands. Then a long strand-like molecule of messenger RNA, mRNA, is assembled, using one DNA strand as a template. The mRNA is also made of nucleotide bases. These are put together by the enzyme RNA polymerase according to the coded message in the DNA. This part of the process is termed transcription.

The mRNA carries a complementary copy of the coded base sequence to which a specialized cellular subunit, the ribosome, can attach. The ribosome tracks along the mRNA; each RNA molecule may have several ribosomes tracking along it in parallel. At the front of the mRNA, or "upstream", is a ribosome binding site so that the mRNA can link to the ribosome. Then comes an initiation site or promoter (the "go switch"), and the coded protein-building sequence. These are followed "downstream" by a terminator site where the coded sequence ends and the mRNA detaches from the ribosome.

There are 20 main kinds of amino acid subunits available for building proteins. Some proteins have relatively few amino acids, others have many thousands. Assembling them involves transfer RNAs or tRNAs. On the mRNA, three nucleotide bases or "letters" code for one amino acid. This three-letter code is known as a codon. Each tRNA has a corresponding complementary code, the anticodon. Within the ribosome each tRNA is bound whenever its three-letter sequence is matched in the mRNA passing through the ribosome. Attached to each tRNA is its specific amino acid. In this way the amino acids are lined up in the right order and joined to make the protein. This step of the process is called *translation*.

Manipulating genes

Modern GENETIC ENGINEERING techniques allow the isolation and detailed study of single genes. The entire set of DNA in an organism can be purified, and cut at specific sites by enzymes called *restriction endonucleases*. For example, the restriction enzyme known as EcoRI cuts DNA wherever there is a base sequence GAATTC. The HindIII enzyme cuts at AAGCTT. The resulting set of small DNA fragments, when cloned to a plasmid or phage vector, is known as a library, and can then be further manipulated.

Redundant and junk DNA

An organism's entire set of DNA is called its genome. Much of the genome, particularly in more complicated organisms, may not code for protein synthesis. Its function is often a mystery. It may divide the rest of the DNA into gene units, or be redundant and unused.

To get rid of this "junk" DNA, when making gene libraries for analysis, molecular biologists reverse part of the protein synthesis process. The starting point is the total mRNA in a cell. This has come only from sequences of DNA intended for protein synthesis. An enzyme called *reverse transcriptase* makes a single strand of DNA from the mRNA code. This complementary DNA is then made into normal double-stranded DNA by another enzyme, *DNA polymerase*. In this way, only DNA sequences which are active genes, coding for protein synthesis, are represented in the library.

Many similar or identical genes appear in widely differing organisms, and code for building similar or identical proteins. This is presumably

because they come from the same evolutionary ancestors. The degree of similarity is known as *sequence homology*, and it varies according to the evolutionary relationships between the organisms. Many of the essential proteins in ourselves, for example, show a high degree of homology with those of apes and monkeys, but less homology with other mammals.

Sequence homology can be used by the molecular biologist to isolate genes. First, the desired DNA sequence is purified and labeled by radioactive marker substances. This radiolabeled sequence is used as a probe to screen a DNA library from another species. The library DNA is multiplied in bacteria, the bacteria are stuck to a special membrane, and treated to expose their DNA in a single-stranded form. The membrane is then flooded with the radiolabeled probe DNA. The bases of the probe DNA pair to those of the library DNA where there is greatest homology (similarity).

The ability to determine the individual sequences of bases in a strand of DNA now allows molecular biologists to study the anatomy of genes in great detail. The technique involves taking a single-stranded DNA template and synthesizing a double-strand from it using the enzyme DNA polymerase. In separate reactions, the synthesis is terminated by special dideoxynucleotide forms of each of the four bases, adenine, cytosine, thymine, or guanine. These act as stop switches or "terminators". Using radioactive labels, the resulting "ladder" of randomly terminated fragments can be analyzed by the common laboratory method of electrophoresis, and compared directly to known sequences. A map of the nucleotide bases in the DNA is gradually built up.

Gene banks

A great many genes from a wide variety of organisms have been isolated and sequenced in this

Left: An automated DNA synthesizer, capable of producing lengths of high-purity DNA. The bottles at the bottom contain reagents needed for the synthesis.

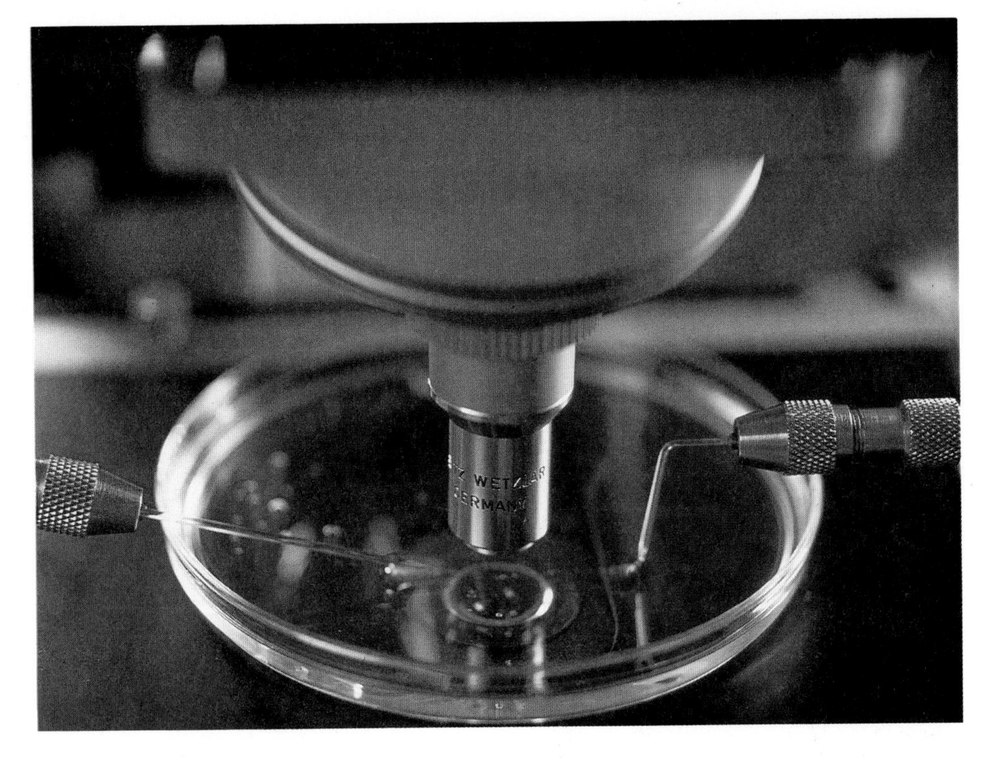

Right: A light microscope being used to view lengths of DNA in the petri dish while they are being manipulated.

manner. The huge amounts of information being produced by molecular biologists are stored in computerized databases - "gene banks". The information is widely used by researchers who wish to compare unknown and new DNA sequences with those from other sources. The use of computers will continue to speed the progress of molecular biology in the future.

Known DNA sequences may be used as a starting point for isolating homologous genes from other species of organisms. For example, a number of human genes have been isolated using an unlikely intermediary, the microscopic yeast *Schizosaccharomyces pombe*.

Short synthetic pieces of DNA, called oligonucleotides, are designed by genetic engineers and molecular biologists to be used as primers in the recent and very important technique, the polymerase chain reaction or PCR (see GENETIC ENGINEERING). PCR-synthesized fragments of DNA can in turn be used as probes for library screening, ultimately to identify and isolate a whole gene.

Many diseases have their roots in gene mutations or changes to the DNA sequence. A change in just one nucleotide base of the DNA can instruct the mRNA and tRNAs to build a completely different amino acid into the protein, thereby producing abnormal results. In deletion mutations, whole lengths of DNA are changed or lost, causing genes to disappear completely. These mutations may be detected using restriction endonucleases and restriction fragment length polymorphisms or RFLPs (see GENETICS).

Genetic changes and mutations can have particularly important implications if they arise in genes that control cell multiplication. Mutations arise naturally when DNA copies itself, and also more frequently under the influence of environmental agents such as ultraviolet radiation from the Sun, other radiations, or certain chemicals in the surroundings. In an organism such as the human being, the cells can normally deal efficiently with these changes as they arise. "Housekeeping" genes detect and repair the damaged DNA. Current research is concerned with how these "housekeeping" genes work. Defects in these genes have been implicated in the development of cancers, when cells multiply out of control.

The human gene map

In higher organisms, the huge lengths of DNA that represent genes are not floating around each cell. They are coiled and packed into structures called chromosomes. Each human body cell has 46 chromosomes, in 23 pairs.

One of the most ambitious of all scientific projects is a multi-national effort to make a chromosome map, a gene map, and ultimately a nucleotide base sequence map, of the entire set of human genetic material – the human genome. The large size of the human genome, between 50,000 and 100,000 genes, means that the project will take some time.

The first organism to have its entire DNA sequence determined was a type of virus, lambda. This virus infects bacteria such as *E. coli*, and is a

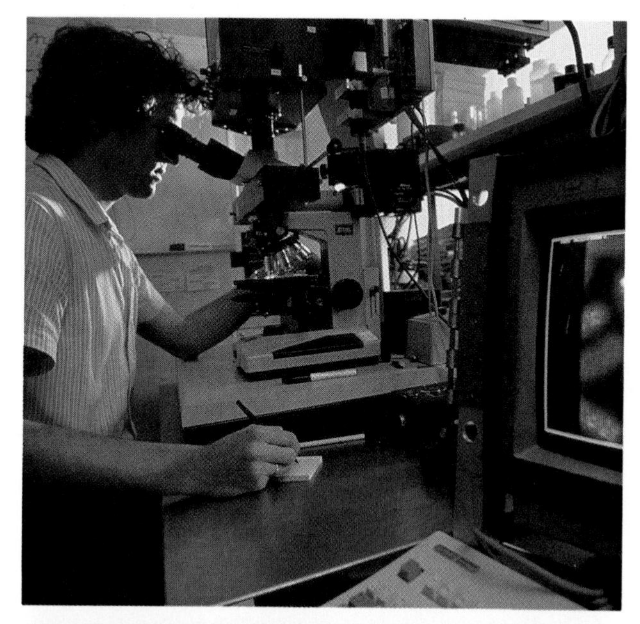

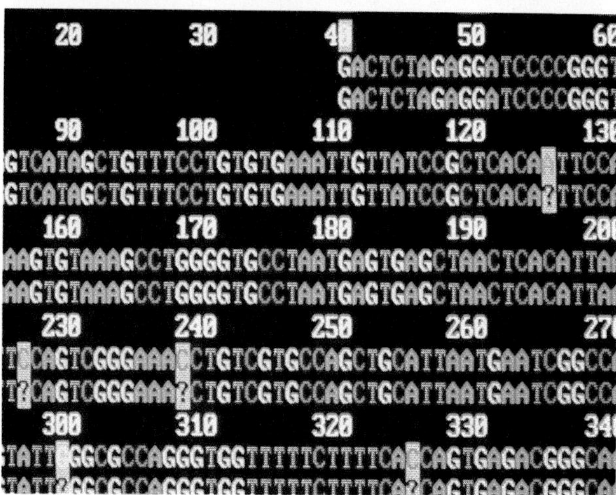

Worldwide research into the human genome. Top: A Yale University researcher uses a light microscope to map long DNA fragments on human chromosomes. The researcher is using a method known as radioactive in-situ hybridization. The chromosomes appear in red on the monitor screen while the DNA fragments (called probes) appear in yellow/green. The process involves a physical survey of each chromosome to find the location of genes and other markers. Above: A computer analysis of the DNA sequence of a human chromosome. The screen shows the amount and sequence in which the four nucleotide bases appear in a gene complex called HL-A, which has been implicated in transplant rejection. This research is being carried out at a hospital in France. Above right: DNA sequencing using gel electrophoresis, a technique used to examine the nucleotide base sequence of DNA. The fragments, contained in an agarose gel, are viewed under an ultraviolet light.

useful tool for molecular biological research. It provides a relatively simple model for the coordinated action of several genes.

A greater challenge has been the sequencing of the genome of *E. coli* itself. Molecular biologists are currently improving their techniques by studying the yeast *Sc. pombe* and the nematode worm *Caenorhabditis elegans*.

The end-product of the Human Genome Project should be a picture of the entire genetic make-up of a "typical" human individual. Compiled under the auspices of HUGO (the Human Genome Organisation), a vast database of information should result, providing a standard against which to compare the genes of individuals suffering from genetic disorders. The great hope is that by understanding the organization of the human being at the level of molecules such as proteins and DNA, we might better understand the mechanisms of inherited diseases and how to treat them.

Neurology

Neurology, the study of the brain and the multifarious disorders affecting it or arising within it, has been greatly aided by the development of new imaging techniques, particularly magnetic resonance imaging (see ANATOMY AND SURGERY). For example, MRI has made it possible to observe the inflammatory changes in the white matter of the brain that are typical of multiple sclerosis. Injecting a dye into the patient's blood and then observing the brain with MRI shows the areas of active inflammation. This should speed the development of new drugs for this disease: doctors will be able to see very rapidly whether drugs they are evaluating have any effect.

Further advances in the application of MRI to neurology are set to take place over the next few years. At present, one of the few treatments available to help those patients with epilepsy who cannot be helped by drugs, and whose seizures originate in the temporal lobe of the brain, is surgery. The temporal lobe of the brain houses nerve centers dealing with important functions such as memory and language. Therefore, before surgeons remove part of it, in the hope of cutting out the section causing the epilepsy, they need to know that they are not going to leave the patient with a worse disability than before.

The traditional way of doing this has been to inject barbiturates into, for example, the right hand side of the brain, to shut it down. If the patient retains his or her normal abilities, the surgeon can be reassured that it is fairly safe to remove the right temporal lobe. This procedure is risky: about one in every 100 patients having it has a stroke as a result.

Seeing into the brain

More recently, it has been possible to identify which parts of the brain are involved in which functions, using a technique called PET scanning. But this involves exposing the patient to relatively large doses of radiation and needs sophisticated and expensive equipment.

This problem could be solved, however, by MRI, in conjunction with a new technique that makes it possible to tell how well oxygenated the blood is in a particular part of the brain. If someone is reading, for example, the area of the brain involved in that activity will be using up oxygen quickly, which will show up on the scan.

This method should further improve the accuracy of brain surgery for epilepsy which cannot be controlled with drug treatment. Neurologists are now better able to pinpoint regions of the brain which are the origin of the electrical activity that causes fits. Clues can be obtained by filming someone during a fit: if the first symptom of a fit is

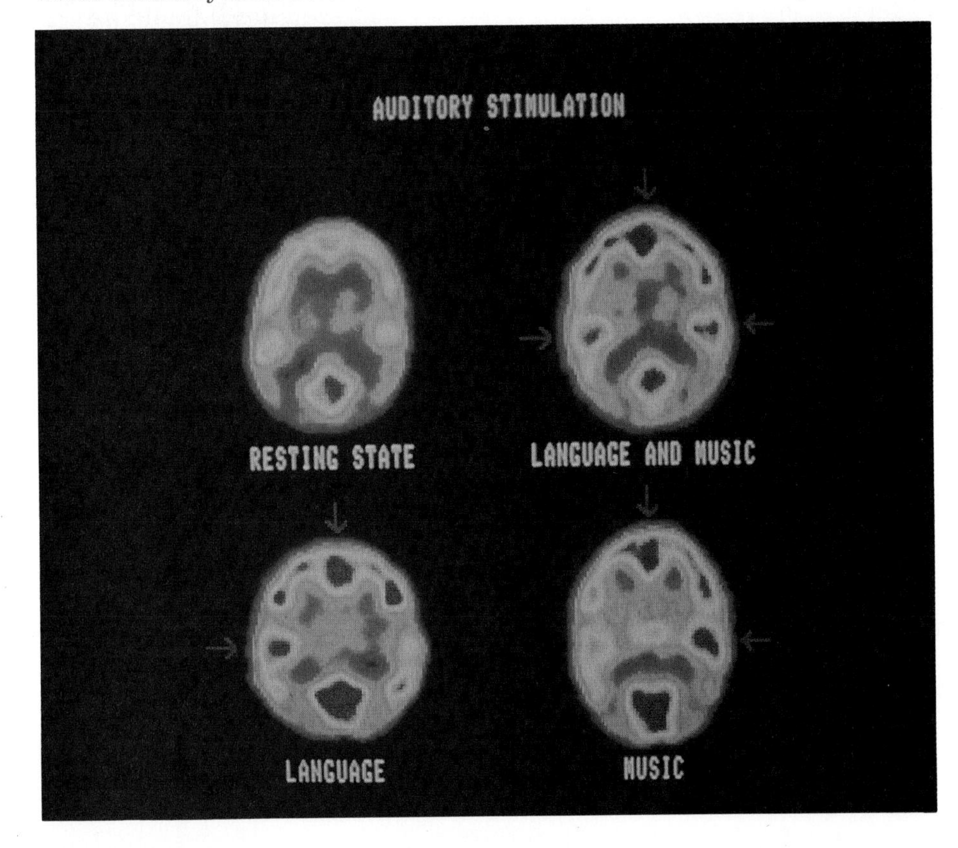

Left: These four scans, made using the technique of Positron Computed Tomography, show how various stimuli affect different parts of the brain.

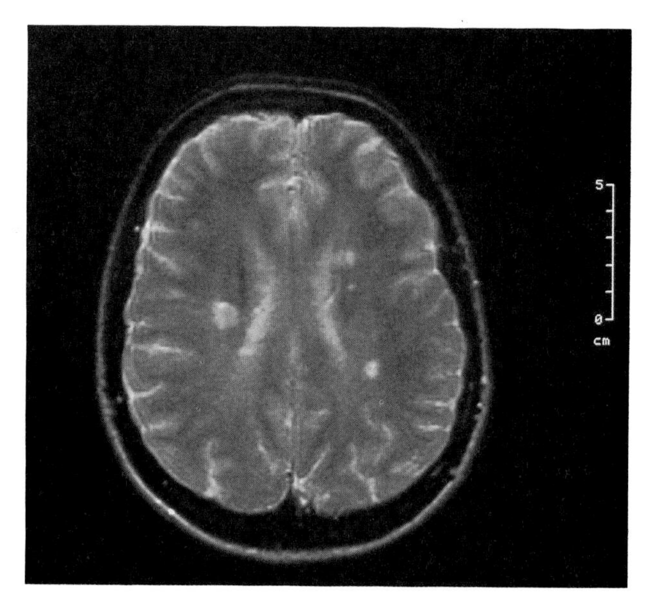

Above: This MRI scan of the brain of a woman suffering from multiple sclerosis shows bright circular regions which are characteristic of the disease.

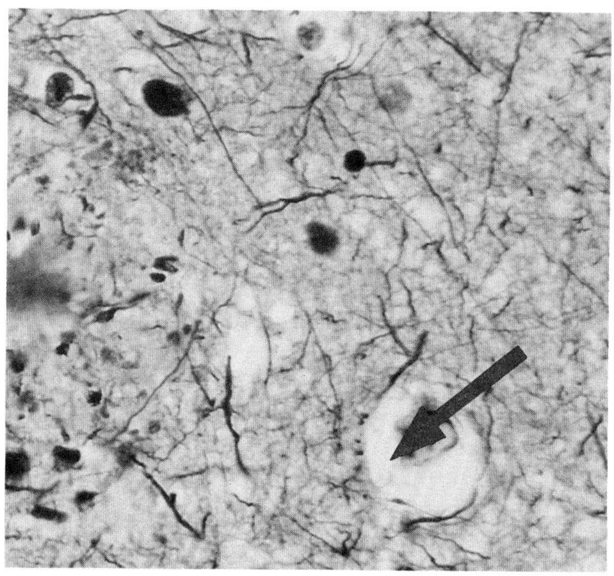

Above: Micrograph of the brain of an Alzheimer's disease sufferer. The circular lesion at the left (arrowed) is a characteristic senile plaque.

movement on the right side of the body, for example, then the left side of the brain is involved. Electroencephalograms – recordings of the electrical activity of the brain – can supply further detail.

The lives of many people with epilepsy have been transformed by a new drug called vigabatrin. The fundamental neurological fault in epilepsy is overexcitability of certain nerves. Vigabatrin has a calming effect by boosting the action of the neurotransmitter called GABA, which normally inhibits nerves from firing.

In Alzheimer's disease, there is also hope that new drug therapies may soon be developed. It is now known that people with this disease have an excess accumulation of the protein called beta amyloid in their brains. It may be possible to use this information to design an effective drug; the recent discovery of the gene associated with a very rare form of Alzheimer's disease may also hasten the development of new drugs.

An aspirin a day

The discovery that aspirin can help to prevent stroke should before long reduce the amount of disability suffered as a result of this disease. People who have a stroke have often suffered a transient ischemic attack (TIA) in the previous five years. A TIA lasts from a few minutes to a few hours, with symptoms such as dizziness, weakness of an arm or a leg, and inability to speak normally.

There is now good evidence that someone who has had a TIA is less likely to have a stroke if he or she takes an aspirin every day. In addition, the risk of a stroke in people who have had a TIA and whose carotid arteries are blocked by more than 70 per cent can be reduced if they have an operation to unblock the arteries.

Cure by transplant

Patients with Parkinson's disease suffer from uncontrollable tremor, rigidity, gradual loss of mobility, and inability to initiate movements. The symptoms are caused because an area of the brain, called the substantia nigra, stops producing a neurotransmitter called dopamine. Early studies of laboratory animals showed that transplants of cells into the animals' brains could survive and produce neurotransmitters. During the 1980s, researchers decided to try to find out whether they could use a similar technique to replace the failing supply of dopamine in Parkinson's disease.

Because it had been found, through animal experiments, that cell transplants derived from the brains of aborted fetuses were more likely survive, surgeons decided to try this strategy in humans. Progress in this line of research has been hampered by ethical and political issues. In the U.S., a moratorium imposed on any work using fetal tissue was lifted by President Clinton in January 1993.

But even in those countries where transplants of fetal brain tissue have been allowed to proceed under strict ethical guidelines, such as the U.K. and Mexico, it has been difficult to say how well the grafts work. Work reported in 1993 suggested that the spouses of sufferers from Parkinson's disease also displayed its milder characteristics. The study could lead to improved early diagnosis.

Number theory

Number theory studies the natural numbers – 1, 2, 3, and so on. It is one of the oldest branches of mathematics, dating back to the Babylonians of 1700 BC and before, an appealing recreational subject, and one of the deepest and most difficult branches of modern mathematics.

Consider, for example, the equation $x^2 + y^2 = z^2$, to be solved in natural numbers. Solutions, such as $3^2 + 4^2 = 5^2$, $5^2 + 12^2 = 13^2$, and so on, give the sides of right-angled triangles (by Pythagoras' theorem), so they are called Pythagorean triples. The Babylonians seem to have known the general rule for finding all these, which we can write as $x = p^2 - q^2$, $y = 2pq$, $z = p^2 + q^2$.

Back in the 17th century, number theorist Pierre Fermat claimed that there are no solutions in natural numbers to the equation $x^n + y^n = z^n$, where n is an integer greater than 2. Put another way, you cannot find any numbers that fit the equation $x^3 + y^3 = z^3$, for example.

This claim, known as Fermat's last theorem, remains unproved to this day, despite the best efforts of many professional mathematicians and not a few amateurs. It seems unlikely that Fermat had a valid proof of it, and that an elementary proof exists if the claim is true. It has been verified for $n = 4$ by Fermat himself, for $n = 3$ in the 18th century, and for $n = 5$ and 7 at the start of the 19th century, and is now known for every n up to 150,000. However, the theorem has still not been proved absolutely.

In 1922 the American-born mathematician L.J. Mordell, working in England, conjectured that

Left: The sunflower is one of many examples of mathematical series existing in nature – the flower's seed pods are arranged in a series of rings which conform to the Fibonacci series, in which each number is the sum of the two preceding numbers, as in 1, 1, 2, 3, 5, 8, 13... The series also appears in pine cones, animal horns, and the arrangement of leaf buds on a stem. It is named after medieval Italian mathematician Leonardo Fibonacci.

almost all equations in integers of higher degree than 3 (in a sense he made precise) have only finitely many integer solutions, if any. So there would not be an infinite number of solutions, if any, to Fermat's equation. The conjecture rested on the limited knowledge of examples that were available, but on no theoretical insight, and it remained unclear what its status was. In 1986, however, the German mathematician Gerd Faltings won the most famous international prize in mathematics (the equivalent of a Nobel prize) for confirming that Mordell was correct.

This leaves Fermat's last theorem unresolved, because it makes the stronger claim that there are no solutions to Fermat's equation. A new approach has recently been opened up, which rests on conjectures of French mathematician André Weil and Japanese mathematicians Shimura and Taniyama. It is now known that if these conjectures are true then Fermat's last theorem is also true. The evidence for these conjectures is considered to be strong, and rests in part on the evidence of computer-led studies of many examples. The conjectures fit into a program that is coherent and attractive; however, they remain unproved. It seems that number theory guards its treasures carefully.

Number theory interacts with computing in other ways. It is a fruitful source of problems with which to test the design of computers; specifically, their ability to handle very large numbers very quickly. One test concerns the search for what are called perfect numbers. These are numbers that are equal to the sum of their divisors, like $6 = 1 + 2 + 3$, and $28 = 1 + 2 + 4 + 7 + 14$. Euclid (300 BC) gave a formula for even perfect numbers (no odd ones are known, and if one exists it must be very large). It is $n = 2^{p-1}.(2^p - 1)$, where p is a prime number such that $2^p - 1$ is prime. Such primes are called Mersenne primes, after Marin Mersenne, a contemporary of Fermat who revived their study.

When $p = 2$, $2^p - 1 = 2^2 - 1 = 3$, which is prime, and $2^{p-1} = 2^1 = 2$, so the formula yields the perfect number $n = 6$, and when $p = 3$, $2^p - 1 = 2^3 - 1 = 7$, which is prime, and $2^{p-1} = 2^2 = 4$, so the formula yields the perfect number $n = 28$. Testing for primality is a time-consuming and sophisticated business; there are, for example, about 100 million primes less than one billion. This historical association has led to a benchmark for measuring the ability of computers to handle very large numbers with complete accuracy: the ability to discover large Mersenne primes. The current record, established in mid 1992, for a Mersenne prime has $p = 756839$; the prime $2^{756839} - 1$ has about a quarter of a million digits.

Another test is the evaluation of *pi*, which by 1992 was known to over 2 billion decimal places. There is a mathematically simple approximative process for doing this, but getting a computer to calculate *pi* requires programming it to select at every stage only the numbers in the present approximation that will affect the next stage. This is a subtle business, akin to hearing just the frequencies you want in a complicated piece of music. It has applications to many uses of computers, so it is helpful to develop it in areas where the mathematics is straightforward, as in the evaluation of *pi*, which is not itself of any interest at all.

Above: The 1990 Cray Computer is one of many supercomputers which have had their design and capacity tested through with large number theory calculations. The computer is currently in use in the United Kingdom Meteorological Office.

Above: A Babylonian clay tablet from 1800-1650 BC which provides evidence of that culture's interest in number theory. The tablet lists, in cuneiform script, what are now called Pythagorean triples. It is a forerunner of modern trigonometry tables.

Nutrition and food science

The concerns of the nutritionist and the food scientist are wide ranging. In the Third World they are concerned with developing strategies to solve the seemingly ever present food shortages and nutritionally related diseases (such as malnutrition, blindness, anemia, and goiter) that cause endless suffering. In western countries, on the other hand, they are researching the effects of a very different kind of diet on what are commonly called the diseases of affluence: obesity, heart disease, cancer, and even dental caries. Meanwhile, they are also concerned with meeting the demands of the modern consumer for high quality, nutritious foods that combine convenience with a long shelf life.

Antioxidant vitamins

With the advent of the 1990s Americans are being increasingly urged by nutritionists to eat more fruits and vegetables. The National Academy of Sciences in their 1989 report *Diet and Health* recommended that the U.S. population should eat five or more servings of vegetables and fruits per day, especially yellow and green vegetables and citrus fruit. This is not simply a call to add some color to the country's dinner table but has much more serious implications for the health of the nation. One vital reason is that fruit and vegetables are major sources of important antioxidant nutrients – vitamin C, beta carotene (a precursor of vitamin A), and vitamin E. There is clear scientific evidence, also, that these nutrients can protect the body from a wide range of degenerative diseases, such as cancer, atherosclerosis, coronary heart disease, and rheumatoid arthritis, that are thought to involve agents known as free radicals.

Production of Free Radicals

Sequential one electron additions to molecular oxygen

$$O_2 + (e^-) \longrightarrow \bullet O_2$$
(superoxide anion radical)

$$\bullet O_2^- + (e^-) + 2H^+ \longrightarrow H_2O_2$$
(hydrogen peroxide)

$$H_2O_2 + (e^-) + H^+ \longrightarrow H_2O + HO\bullet$$
(hydroxyl radical)

$$HO\bullet + (e^-) + H^+ \longrightarrow H_2O$$

Above: How free radicals – shown by the dot – are produced from molecular oxygen. Their unpaired electrons make them highly reactive.

Left: Fresh fruit and vegetables are increasingly recognized as a vital element of the American diet, helping combat a variety of disorders.

Right: Low-fat products depend on research into fat substitutes which can be used for food processing without adding extra dietary calories.

Free radicals are any chemical species that have one or more unpaired electrons yet exist independently. In living organisms the most important free radicals are derived from molecular oxygen, such as hydroxyl and superoxide, together with other highly reactive oxygen species such as ozone and hydrogen peroxide. Such free radicals are produced in the body as part of normal metabolism, and are generally dealt with by the body's own array of defense mechanisms. These include the antioxidant vitamins which are thought to prevent oxidation damage inside the body by stabilizing some of these free radicals and quenching the effect of others.

The greatest risk of disease seems to arise when production of these free radicals is increased by external factors such as air pollution, radiation, and cigarette smoke, and in such circumstances the need for antioxidant nutrients becomes even more imperative. Smokers, in particular, are more likely to be deficient in vitamin C, to such an extent that in 1989 the Recommended Dietary Allowance (RDA) of vitamin C for smokers was increased from 60 to 100 mg/day, while more recently research on American smokers has suggested that 200 mg/day may be more appropriate. Results of a scientific study published in 1991 also suggest that supplementation with vitamin E may partially protect against the harmful effects of ozone in smog.

Research into these complex and wide ranging areas is still in its infancy and much work needs to be done. Experts cannot agree, for example, whether supplements of antioxidant vitamins are as effective as increasing the intake of foods containing those vitamins (there may be other substances in the plant foods themselves that are also protective, such as glucosynilates found in green leafy vegetables). The exact mechanisms relating to specific disease processes are not fully understood.

Beyond cholesterol

Antioxidant vitamins are also linked with another important area in nutrition research – the role of cholesterol in atherosclerosis and coronary heart disease. High levels of vitamin E may play an important role in preventing free radical damage of cholesterol and the subsequent production of oxidation products which are more damaging to arteries than cholesterol itself. It has even been suggested that it may be low levels of antioxidant vitamins rather than high levels of cholesterol that are of greater importance in the development of heart disease.

The 1990s have certainly seen a move away from the view that dietary cholesterol is the "bad guy" in the heart disease story. While high levels of cholesterol in the blood are predictive of heart disease, this is not a result of eating foods high in cholesterol. Most cholesterol is, in fact, made within the body itself, with the most important dietary influences on heart disease being surplus weight and eating a diet high in fat, particularly saturated fats: meat and dairy fats. The introduction in the 1960s of unsaturated soft vegetable margarines and the increasing use of (again, unsaturated) liquid vegetable oils for cooking certainly heralded the start of a decline in rates of heart disease in the U.S. However, American diets are still seen as being too high in fat – a factor which increases the

Left: The ice-cream cone was an early example of an edible food packaging, followed in the 1990s by edible packaging for French fries and other savory products. The material is biodegradable.

tendency of blood to clot and hence the risk of heart attack.

Some of the most recent research in this field has shown that fish oils can protect against heart disease by mechanisms that do not involve lowering blood cholesterol. The specific protective agents are two unsaturated fatty acids called eicosapentanoic acid (EPA) and docosahexaenoic acid (DHA). Long term studies in several countries including the U.S. have shown that eating fish (especially oily varieties) just two or three times a week reduces rates of heart disease compared with eating none at all.

Fat substitutes

As Americans are increasingly urged to lower the amount of fat and energy in their diet, food scientists have been busy attempting to develop the perfect fat substitute – one that has all the texture, taste, and culinary properties of the real thing, but is either lower in calories or calorie-free. One such newly approved product is Simplesse (© The Nutrasweet Company), designed to simulate the mouthfeel of emulsified dairy fat but made out of spherical protein microglobules, specifically egg white and milk protein. Lower in calories than the equivalent amount of fat, the product still contributes to the energy cost of a food and is suitable only for a limited number of uses such as ice creams, frozen desserts, salad dressings, and spreads.

Another type of fat substitute that has yet to be approved for food use by the Food and Drug Administration (FDA) is the unabsorbable fat; for example Olestra (© Procter and Gamble), which is a polyester of sucrose with fatty acids from soybean, corn, or cottonseed oils. Unabsorbable fats of this type (and there are over 100 more in various stages of development) cannot be broken down by digestive enzymes and are therefore not absorbed or metabolized by the body. On the plus side they provide zero calories and are heat stable, so they can be used in a wide range of processed foods such as pastry, cakes, cookies, and for deep frying. They can also reduce absorption of unwelcome substances such as pesticides and cholesterol. On the other hand there are nutritional concerns that they might decrease the absorption of fat soluble vitamins A, D, and E, and reduce the efficacy of some types of drugs such as oral contraceptives. The amounts that might be consumed, especially by someone on a reducing diet, are also far in excess of those normally accepted for what is essentially a food additive.

Edible packaging

Another area where food scientists are carrying out considerable research is in the field of edible food packaging. This idea is not new – the Chinese were coating fruit and vegetables with wax hundreds of years ago, while sealing edible foods in fat as a preservative measure was well established in Britain by the 16th century. What is new is the recognition among food scientists that edible packaging can play a major role in environmental protection – providing the ideal solution to keeping food fresh while reducing, at least in part, the estimated 1500 lb (700 kg) of rubbish that each American generates in a year.

The 1990s have seen the launch of an edible savory food container for serving French fries. Based on potatoes, and soon to be available in a choice of flavors ranging from chili to chicken, the cups combine strength and taste with 100 per cent biodegradability. In the future it is hoped to adapt the technology to produce hamburger boxes, meat trays, and egg containers – the perfect replacement for polystyrene.

Most current research, particularly in the U.S., is centered on the development of edible films and

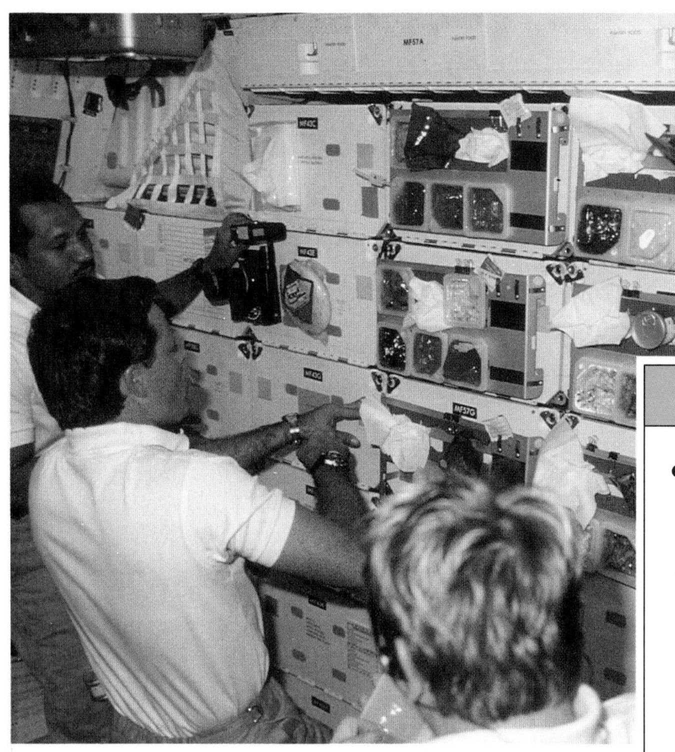

Left: Mealtime aboard a space shuttle. Much research remains to be done on methods of providing a sustainable food supply aboard long-duration missions, such as those to Mars.

coatings. Using proteins, fats, or starches as a base, it is hoped to develop films that will prevent the movement of moisture either in or out of the product. These films might be invisibly applied to freshly peeled fruit or vegetables, or to prepared foods such as sandwiches, snack products, ice cream bars, and pie fillings without affecting taste, texture, or appearance.

At the United States Department of Agriculture a shellfish extract called chitosan has been successfully combined with a fatty acid called lauric acid to produce a uniform film that is free from holes. Depending on its thickness, the film can also be formed into bags and pouches. To overcome the problem of the coating imparting a taste to the food, some of the product's natural flavor is included in the film formula – for example, if the product is raisins, the film emulsion is made with dilute raisin juice.

The drawbacks of such edible films seem to lie in their limited ability to cope with heat and humidity. The film can be heat sealed but only by very basic closing methods, and applying excessive heat could change the composition of the film, not only affecting performance but possibly introducing harmful toxins. There are also considerable problems in applying the film efficiently on an industrial scale. Given time these problems can be overcome but whether or not they are depends to a great extent on how willing the big food companies are to reduce their current reliance on unnecessary, environmentally damaging packaging.

• FACT FILE •

- Contrary to expectations that astronauts would have a lower energy requirement in space, weight loss is a common finding in astronauts returning to Earth. This weight loss occurs even among astronauts who do not suffer from space motion sickness and who maintain or increase their energy intakes above Earth levels. Muscle protein is also lost, together with bone calcium, despite a seemingly adequate diet. Research into the nutritional needs of astronauts to overcome these degenerative problems could also apply to nutritional interventions on Earth, for example in osteoporosis and aging.

- Astronauts tend to eat more carbohydrate and less fat when in space. Favorite foods are peanut butter, flour tortillas, and fresh fruit. Most space foods are preserved by canning, freeze drying, or thermovacuum packing. The only foods not allowed are alcohol, carbonated drinks, foods that produce excessive crumbs, and those that do not store well at room temperature.

- NASA encourages the use of food as the primary source of nutrients whenever possible, rather than using vitamin-mineral supplements. This is because natural foods contain essential non-nutritive substances such as fiber and carotenoids. Natural food also provides an important sense of psychological well being.

- The challenge is to develop in-flight food systems that will support missions of several years in duration. These will probably depend heavily on genetically engineered and synthetic food sources.

Obstetrics and gynecology

Obstetrics and gynecology are two closely related medical specialties concerned almost exclusively with women. Obstetrics is concerned with all aspects of pregnancy and childbirth; gynecology with the disorders that affect the reproductive system in women, whether or not they are pregnant.

Obstetricians are involved with pregnancies from the earliest stages to give maximum safety to mother and child. As soon as a woman becomes pregnant, the obstetrician wants to know as much as possible about her physical and psychological state and about the genetic health of the embryo.

Later, as the embryo develops into a fetus, it is vital to check that everything is proceeding normally. One of the most valuable ways of monitoring fetal development is by ultrasound screening. Modern, high-resolution ultrasound scanners can safely monitor fetal vitality and rate of growth, diagnose twin pregnancies, check the position of the fetal feeding organ (the placenta), detect various abnormalities, and, toward the end of pregnancy, check whether the fetus is lying in a suitable position for safe delivery.

It is not only when a woman is pregnant that check ups are needed. Gynecologists are often concerned with problems associated with menstruation. They also investigate and, if possible, treat many cases of infertility. They deal with many cases of pelvic pain and backache and of infection and tumors of the pelvic organs. Since the female reproductive system is so much under the control of hormones, the gynecologist must also be an expert on ENDOCRINOLOGY and will often prescribe hormone therapy.

Laser treatment

Women who suffer from menstrual problems may benefit from removal of the endometrium – the lining of the uterus, which normally comes away at each menstrual period. The former procedure involved dilation of the cervix so that the obstetrician could scrape away the endometrium using a sharp-edged wooden spoon. A technique that has become widely used in the 1990s is laser ablation of the endometrium. This involves only a fine catheter, which can be inserted with much less dilation and risk of pain, and a laser is used to destroy the lining.

In vitro fertilization

One way in which many infertile couples can have children is by the technique of "in vitro" fertilization – popularly called the "test tube baby" method. In this case, both partners have fertile eggs and sperm but the process of conception is prevented because, for one reason or another, the sperm cannot reach the egg. To overcome this, the woman's eggs are taken from her and placed in fluid in a warm sterile dish ("in vitro" means "in

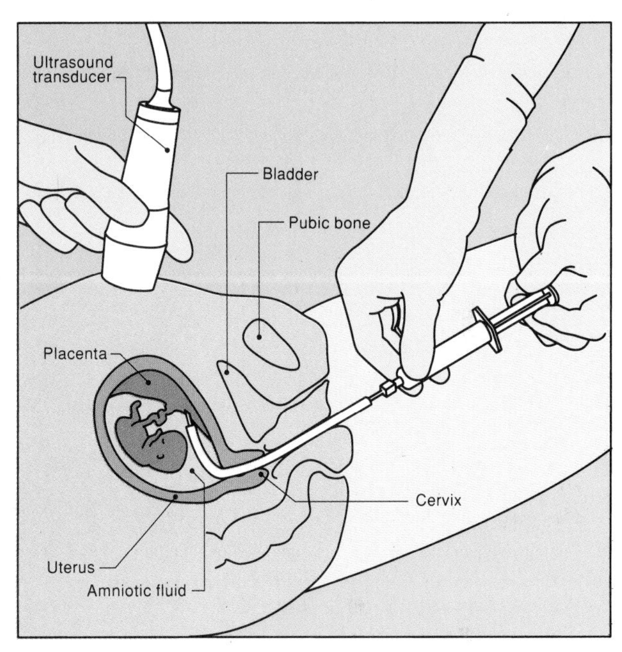

Top: Chorionic villus sampling may be carried out via the vagina, as shown here, or through the abdomen. The orientation of the fetus can vary considerably.

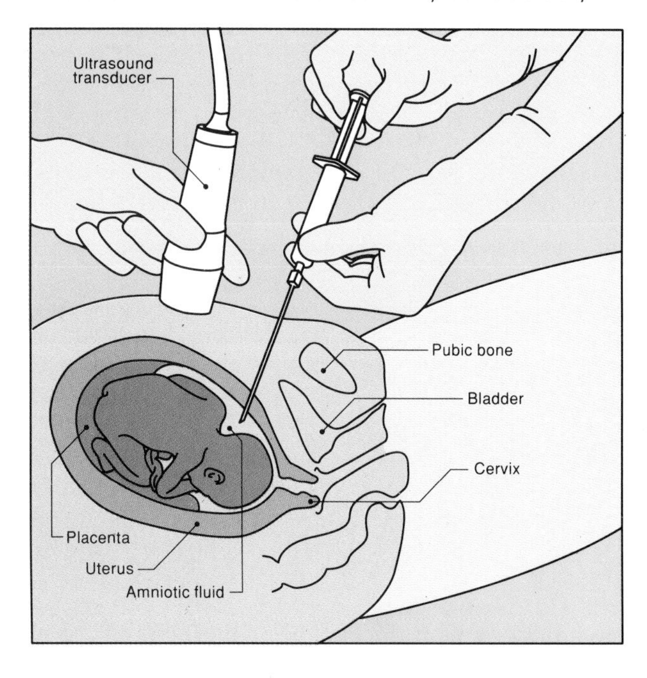

Right: Amniocentesis is particularly recommended for mothers over the age of 35, and carries a small risk of inducing a miscarriage. A sample of about 10 ml of fluid is needed from the amniotic sac.

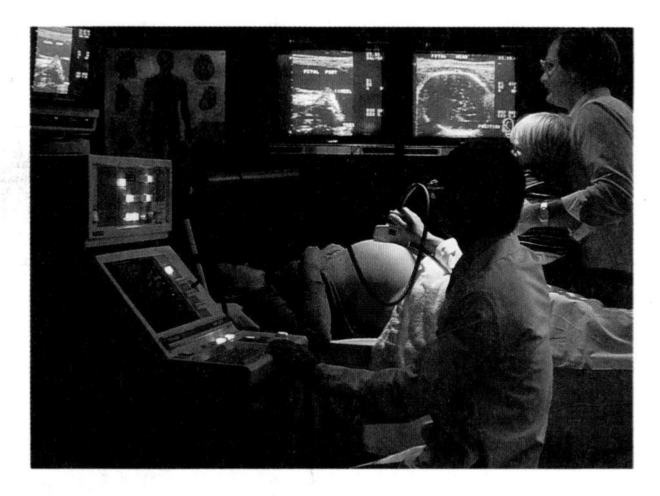

Above: Ultrasound imaging of the fetus is used to monitor growth and detect problems.

glass"). Her partner's sperm are then added and fertilization occurs in the dish. In a development announced in 1993, some clinics are offering a choice of the child's sex. This is based on the slight differences in behavior of the XX chromosomes in female-producing sperm and the XY chromosomes in male-producing sperm, but the reliability of the method has yet to be proved.

Obstetricians can watch the early development of the fertilized egg under a microscope. If all goes well, they place the fertilized ovum in the uterus to develop normally. The method is still somewhat experimental but results are steadily improving.

Chorionic villus sampling

Very early in pregnancy the fertilized egg divides into a part that will form the fetus and a part that will form the structure that nourishes the fetus throughout the pregnancy (the placenta). The latter starts off in the form of small fingerlike structures that grow out from the embryo into the wall of the uterus. These are called chorionic villi. Because both the villi and the fetus come from the same fertilized cell, they have exactly the same chromosomes. Therefore a microscopic sample of chorionic villi provides detailed knowledge of the genetic constitution of the future baby.

Chorionic villi can be obtained from about the eighth week of the pregnancy onwards, either by passing a fine tube through the neck of the uterus (the cervix) or by passing a needle into the uterus through the abdominal wall. The obstetrician can then study the future baby's chromosomes. Conditions such as Down's syndrome, in which there are visible chromosome abnormalities, can immediately be detected.

Other conditions that can be diagnosed by villus sampling at an early stage of pregnancy include sickle cell disease, cystic fibrosis, Duchenne muscular dystrophy, hemophilia, phenylketonuria, retinitis pigmentosa, and retinoblastoma. All these conditions are serious, and some may prove fatal. Chorionic villus sampling provides the parents with the possible option of agreeing to early termination of the pregnancy, a moral consideration that concerns obstetricians and parents alike.

Amniocentesis

Pregnant women over the age of 35 are now commonly advised to undergo an amniocentesis. The fluid that surrounds the growing fetus is called amniotic fluid. The fetus swallows some of this fluid. It also urinates and casts off skin cells into it. A sample of the amniotic fluid can thus provide material for testing for various abnormalities.

To obtain the sample the obstetrician passes a long needle attached to a syringe through the wall of the abdomen (which is under local anesthesia) and into the fluid in the uterus. A sample is then sucked out. The whole process can be viewed in real time on an ultrasonic scanner which shows the uterus, the amniotic sac, and the needle.

An important finding may be the presence of raised levels of a substance produced by the fetus called alpha-fetoprotein. Abnormal levels alert doctors to the possibility of such conditions as Down's syndrome or spina bifida.

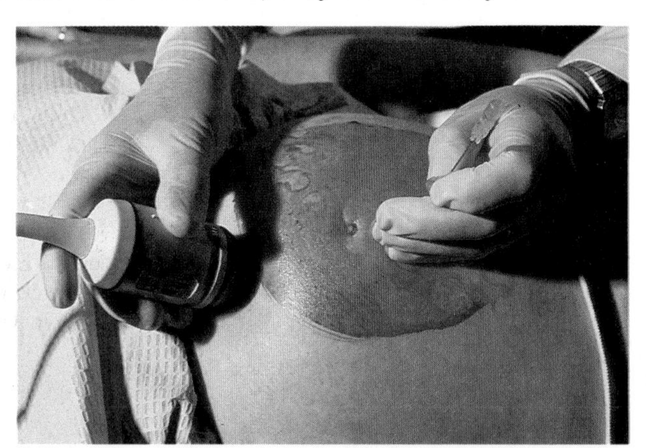

Left: Amniocentesis involves taking a sample of amniotic fluid from the uterus under local anesthetic to provide an early diagnosis of abnormalities.

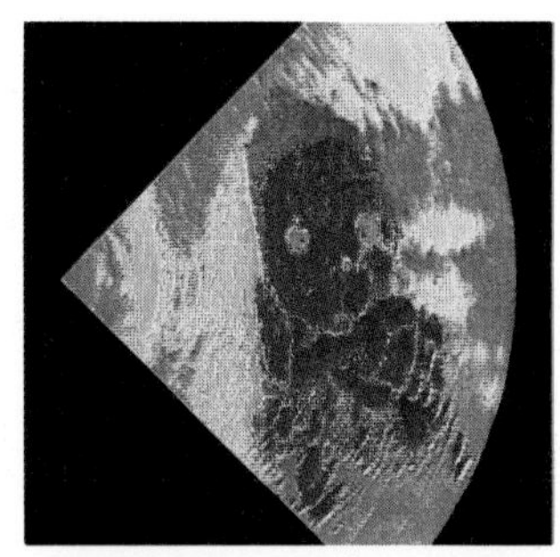

Left: This false-color ultrasound scan shows a frontal view of a human fetus in the uterus at approximately six months.

Oceanography

Oceanography is the science of the marine environment, so, like other branches of ENVIRONMENTAL SCIENCE, it draws on the basic disciplines of physics, chemistry, biology, and GEOLOGY to study its own subject – the sea. And it is collaboration among scientists from all these areas that has resulted in great advances in recent years.

It is not just the surface of the sea which is in motion. There is an overall deep circulation, called hydrothermal circulation. Sea water is drawn down through fractures and heated by contact with hot rocks deep in the Earth's crust. It rises again, to be ejected from the sea bed through vents at the mid-ocean ridges, in spectacular plumes of particle-laden water with temperatures up to about 750° F (400° C). Chemical reaction with the rocks transforms the composition of the water, removing some elements and adding others, so that the process is a major influence on ocean chemistry. The plumes also support colonies of animals (see MARINE BIOLOGY).

These "black smokers" make a substantial contribution to the dissolved substances that make sea water salty, once thought to be solely the work of rivers. But this raises the question of why sea water has basically the same composition throughout the oceans. The answer lies in its circulation and mixing. In high latitudes, water sinks from the surface, because cooling makes it denser, and then spreads through the ocean basins before diffusing back into the upper layers, mixing along the way with water from other regions. It takes several centuries, on average, to complete this journey.

Deep-sea sediment cores reveal that the concentration of minerals in sea water has remained roughly constant over geological time. How is this possible if dissolved material is continuously being added to the ocean by rivers and submarine volca-

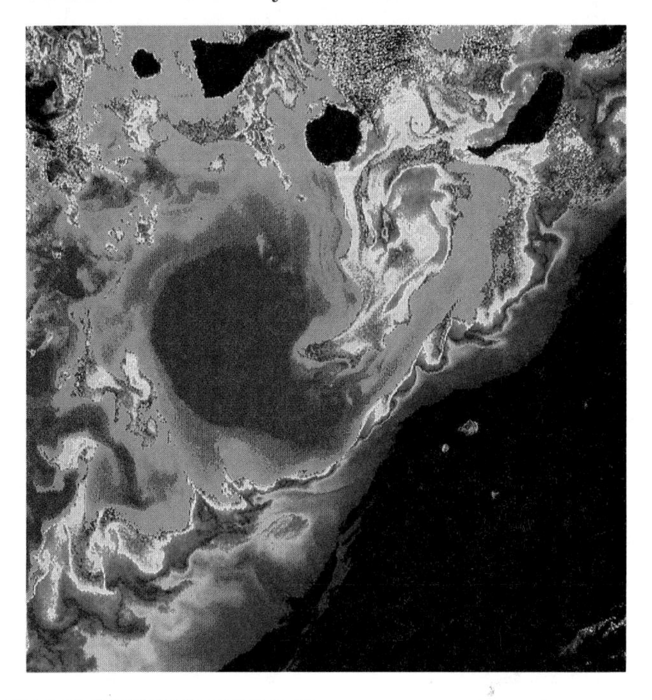

Right: Brightness temperature measurements include the effects of the atmosphere and clouds as well as sea temperatures. This image, from the ERS-1 satellite, shows the sea off the west coast of Africa with the Canary Islands at top (black). The large red feature is an ocean circulation known as a warm core ring, just a few degrees warmer than its surroundings, where cold water moving down from the pole mixes with warmer Atlantic water.

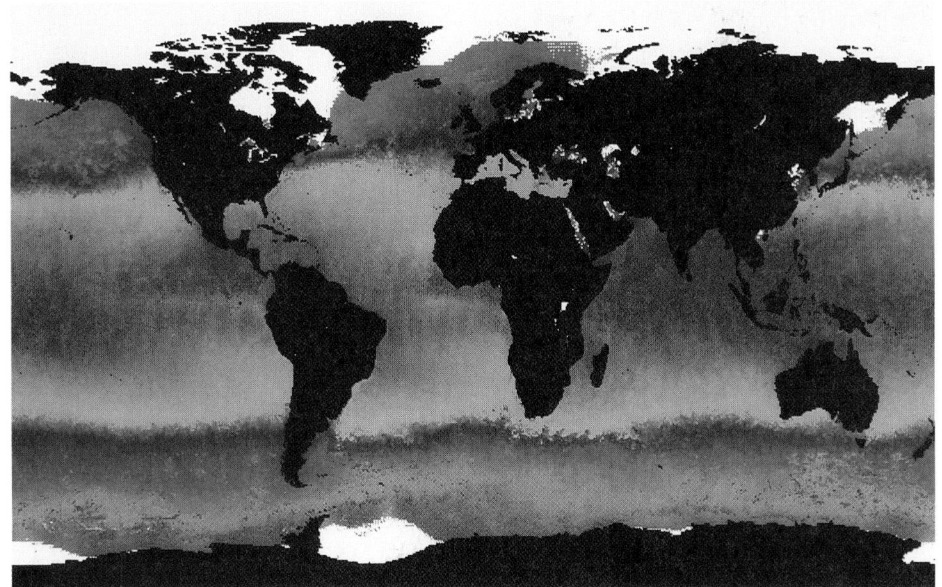

Left: Measurements of ocean temperatures are now easily carried out by satellite. Sea surface temperature measurements made by the ERS-1 satellite over the whole globe – shown here for the period April–May 1992 – reveal how hot and cold currents change over time.

noes? In most cases, they become absorbed by tiny sea creatures and eventually finish up in the sediments, up to 6 miles (10 km) deep, that accumulate on the ocean floor. Much of this material is biological in origin – the remains of microscopic organisms that flourished in the upper sunlit layers of the ocean. This organic detritus forms the sole food supply of animals living on the deep-sea bed, where photosynthesis is impossible.

Recent sea-bed photography has emphasized this dependence by revealing a previously unsuspected feature of the rain of particles – its strongly seasonal nature. In temperate latitudes the tiny drifting plant cells (the phytoplankton) "bloom" in the spring in response to increased sunlight. As a result, there is a temporary carpet of greenish "fluff" on the ocean floor, signaling an upsurge of feeding and breeding activity among the bottom-dwelling animals.

Another finding has come from an unexpected source. By studying the concentration in sea water of manufactured chlorofluorocarbon (CFC) gases, oceanographers have been able to trace water movements in the depths of the ocean. CFCs have been produced in large quantities only since about 1950. The proportion in the atmosphere has been measured year by year. The ratios found in a water sample from the deep ocean therefore provide an estimate of the year when it left the surface.

The concentrations involved are extremely small – less than a millionth of a gram per ton of sea water. It turns out that even the very slow bottom currents flow at around 500 yards (0.5 km) per day. Photographs taken of the changes in the soft sediments of the sea bed have revealed "abyssal storms", caused by powerful eddies in ocean currents such as the Gulf Stream. At these times the deep water can flow over 50 times faster than normal.

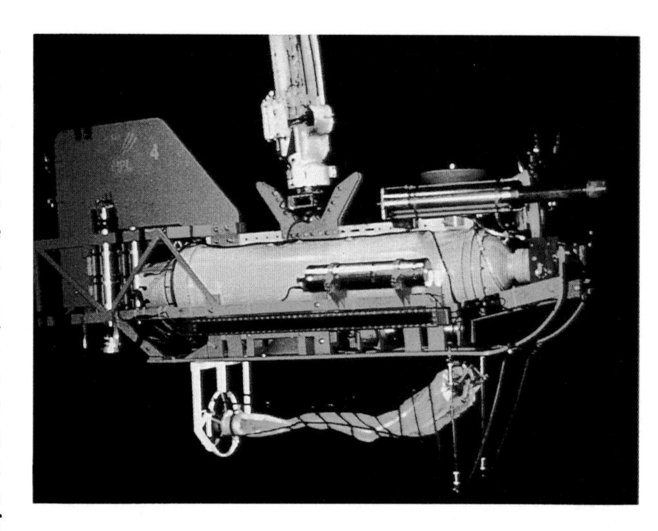

Above "Deep Tow" is an oceanographic research submersible which is towed by a surface vessel. Below: Ocean currents are tracked at depth by this ALACE probe, at the Scripps Institute of Oceanography in La Jolla, CA. The self-powered probe sinks to a depth of 3300 ft (1000 m) where it floats in the prevailing current. Eventually it returns to the surface and reports its position to a weather satellite so that it can be recovered.

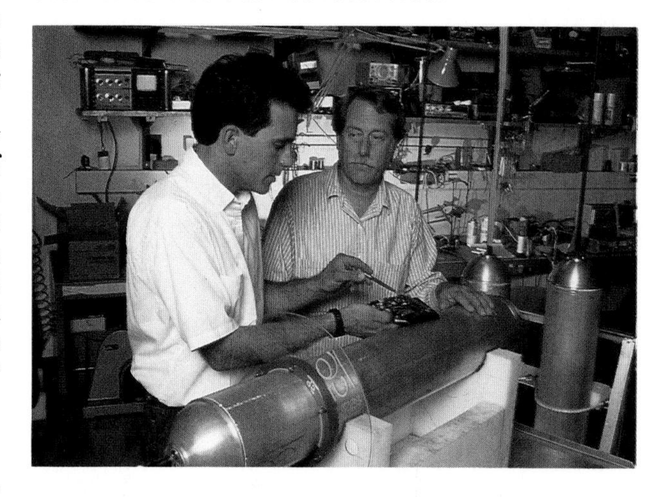

The human impact

So far the deep sea has been relatively undisturbed by human activity, but the same cannot be said of surface waters. The exploitation of fisheries increased rapidly after World War II, so that now there is hardly a major fish stock in the world that is not under pressure. But most important from a global point of view is the role of the oceans in climate change.

The principal greenhouse gas is carbon dioxide (CO_2). Perhaps a quarter of the extra CO_2 released into the atmosphere by the burning of fossil fuels is removed to the deep ocean, either by physical absorption in sinking water masses or by conversion to organic matter by photosynthesis in phytoplankton. The ocean is therefore a significant buffer against the greenhouse effect, at least in the medium term. But eventually this water will return to the surface, bringing with it both the absorbed CO_2, and CO_2 produced from the organic detritus by the respiration of the bottom-dwelling animals that feed on it.

Moreover, if global warming continues, from whatever cause, there will be a rise in sea levels due to a combination of partial melting of the polar icecaps and thermal expansion in the upper layers of the ocean. Current predictions suggest a rise of 1-3 ft (30-100 cm) over the next century if nothing is done to restore the situation. This would threaten with flooding much of the most valuable land on Earth, the coastal margins, together with the homes and livelihoods of millions of people.

Oncology

Oncology is the study and treatment of cancer. Though cancer rivals heart disease as a common cause of death, up to a third of all cases can be cured using the latest treatments.

The body is made up of approximately a thousand billion cells. Cancer can start in any one of them and scientists have now discovered why. Each cell has as many as 80,000 genes, which are small segments of DNA (the long threadlike molecule in a cell that carries genetic information – see GENETICS). Among the genes are particular sequences of DNA which are responsible for the control of cell growth. Normally, these segments, termed oncogenes, are under the control of other genes which act as on/off switches. It is when one of these switches fails to work, perhaps because it has become damaged by radiation or by chemical carcinogens, that cancer develops.

There are three approaches to therapy: surgery, RADIATION MEDICINE (radiotherapy), and drugs (chemotherapy). Surgery and radiotherapy are effective at treating cancer confined to a specific place in the body: the tumor can be removed or killed by radiation. But when the cancer has spread, it must be treated using drugs that circulate around the whole body.

The drugs used may be synthetic hormones which mimic the natural substances that control the growth of certain kinds of cell. Breast cancer, for example, can now be treated using a drug called tamoxifen, which blocks the action of estrogen. Clinical trial data published in 1992 showed that this new form of anti-estrogen therapy reduced deaths from breast cancer.

More frequently, therapy employs drugs called cytotoxics which actually kill cancer cells. Childhood leukemias, testicular cancer, and certain lymphomas (cancers of the cells that make up the lymphatic system) were once invariably fatal but can now be cured in up to 75 per cent of cases. However, cytotoxic drugs are less effective in other forms of cancer, such as those of the lung and colon.

Above: False-color scanning electron micrograph of cancer of the human bronchus.

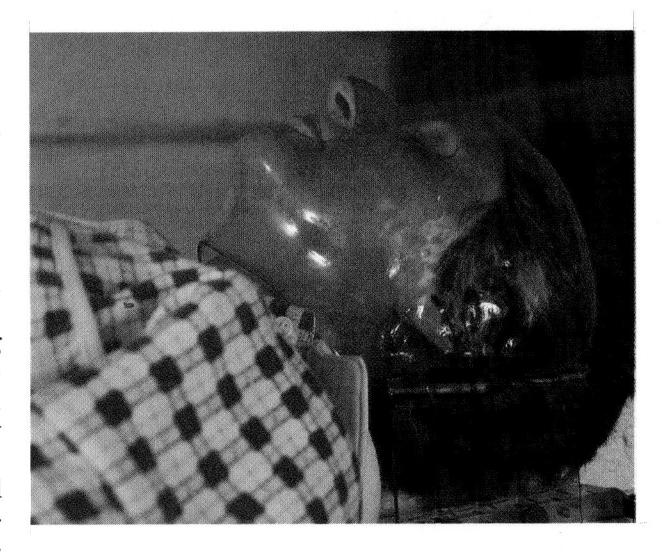

Above: Red laser beams are used to align the head of a patient undergoing radiotherapy for an intracranial tumor. So that the radiation beam is delivered accurately, the head is immobilized in a plastic mask.

Targeting cancer cells

This resistance to drugs cannot be overcome by increasing the dose since cytotoxic therapy is limited by its side effects. Anti-cancer drugs work by blocking the division of tumor cells. But healthy cells also divide. The blood-forming cells in the bone marrow, cells in the hair follicles, and those lining the intestine are particularly severely affected by cytotoxic drugs. This causes the familiar problems of anti-cancer therapy – susceptibility to infection, hair loss, and nausea.

There is now hope that these problems will be overcome by new means of directing cytotoxic drugs specifically at cancer cells. One technique, still not in widespread use, involves combining an anti-cancer agent with antibodies from the human immune system which recognize tumor cells and home in on them. The antibody does the targeting and the drug then kills the cell it becomes attached to. Work carried out in 1987 pioneered the use of photosensitive drugs such as psoralens which are toxic only when activated by exposure to light. This offers the possibility of confining the toxic effects of the drug only to the tumor itself.

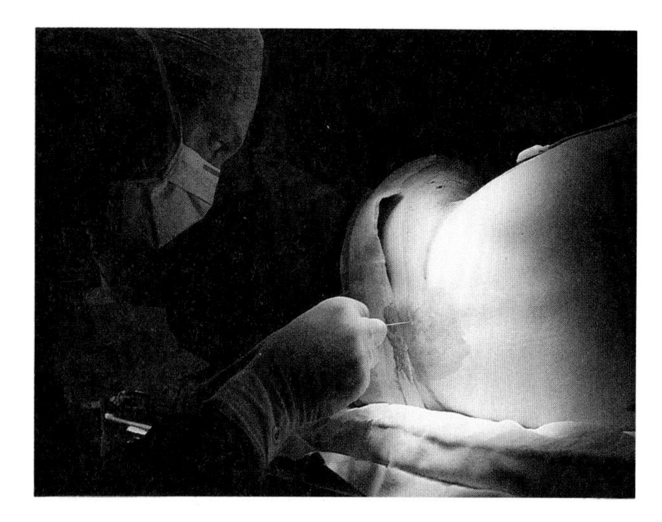

Above: A lumbar puncture being carried out prior to bone-marrow transplant. Cerebrospinal fluid is drawn off and cancer-killing drugs injected. These rapidly enter the brain, where they destroy any tumors which are present.

Bone marrow transplants

Cancer therapy is limited by the damage such treatment does to the patient's bone marrow, which forms vital cells that make up the blood and fight infection. Bone marrow transplantation can overcome many of these problems and is increasingly used in cases of leukemia.

Over several days, the patient is given large doses of drugs and radiation with the aim of eradicating all traces of cancer, including tumor cells in the brain. Such treatment destroys the bone marrow, which also harbors cancer cells.

Marrow is then harvested from a close relative by sucking it up through large bore needles from the center of the hip bones. This marrow is concentrated and infused into the patient's bloodstream. The cells find their way into the bone spaces where they lodge and start to divide, so creating new marrow.

To aid this process, substances termed colony stimulating factors can now be given. These are genetically engineered human proteins which speed the regeneration of marrow cells. In 1990, at the Washington meeting of the American Society of Clinical Oncology, the first promising results of this new form of therapy were reported.

As an alternative to taking bone marrow from a compatible donor, a small amount of the patient's own marrow can be removed before cytotoxic treatment. The marrow is deep frozen for the period of drug therapy, thawed, and then reinfused. This technique has the advantage of reducing any problem of rejection. The disadvantage is that cancer cells may be reintroduced to the patient along with the marrow. Doctors are therefore developing means of using antibodies to "launder" marrow before it is returned.

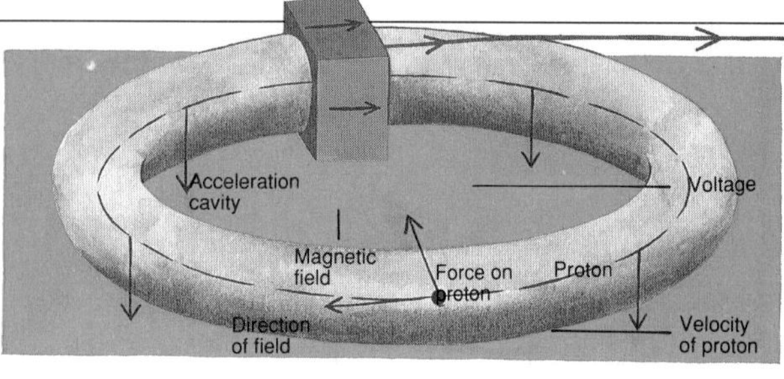

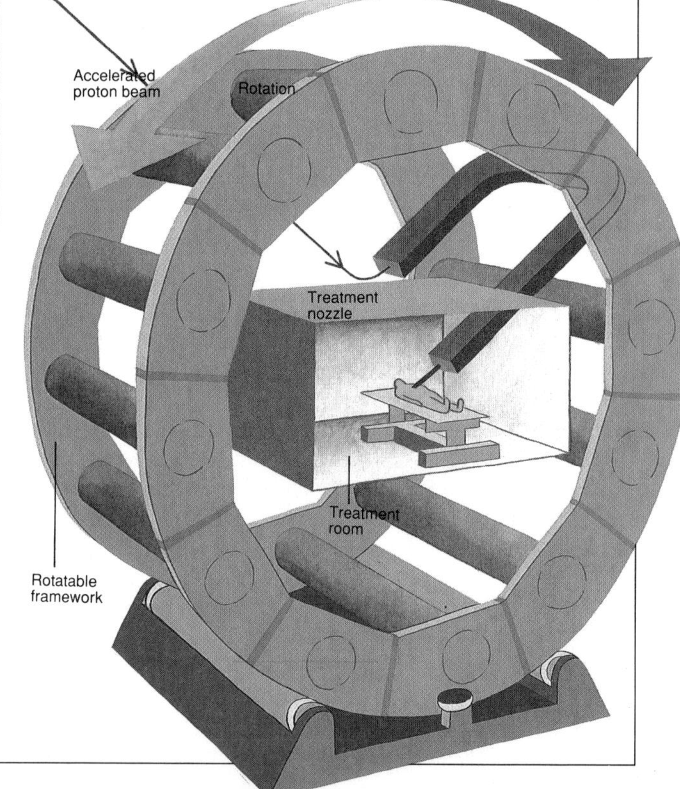

One recent development in cancer treatment are proton accelerators – vast machines which create fast-moving streams of protons. The accelerator is an enormous circular device, resembling a Ferris wheel, which surrounds the treatment room and has a magnetic nozzle protruding from it. The nozzle is attached to an acceleration system (pictured above), and can be pointed at specific parts of the body. The system creates an intense magnetic field which drives the protons faster and faster until they reach a critical speed, at which point they are diverted out of the acceleration tube and into the nozzle. The concentrated proton beam kills the tumor, which the body then breaks up and excretes. The depth to which the beam extends into the body can be varied to within a fraction of an inch.

Ophthalmology

Ophthalmology is the medical specialty concerned with the diagnosis and treatment of eye disorders. All ophthalmologists are doctors. They are sometimes called "oculists" but should not be confused with optometrists, who are people who test vision and prescribe glasses and contact lenses. Optometrists are not primarily concerned with eye diseases.

The range of equipment used by ophthalmologists has increased greatly in recent years. It includes *slit lamp microscopes* to examine the outside and front interior of the eyes under high magnification; *automatic refractors* to check whether glasses are needed; various kinds of *ophthalmoscopes* to examine the insides of the eyes; *visual field analyzers* to check how far the field of vision extends outwards and to see whether there are any defects in the visual fields; *ultrasound eye measurement equipment* to work out the power of lens implants needed after cataract surgery; lasers to treat a range of conditions and to seal holes in the retina; *cryopexy* equipment to freeze parts of the eye and secure attachment of detached retinas; and *diathermy* equipment to control minor bleeding in the eye.

Eye operations

Eye operations have always called for great skill. Today, new equipment means that not only is it easier to carry out basic operations, but new operations are possible which were once only dreamed of. Microsurgery, using binocular-operating microscopes and instruments of remarkable delicacy and precision, is now established and almost all ophthalmic surgery is done using the *operating microscope*.

As in any operation, the eye surgeon wears sterile operating clothes and gloves and must not touch anything other than sterile equipment and

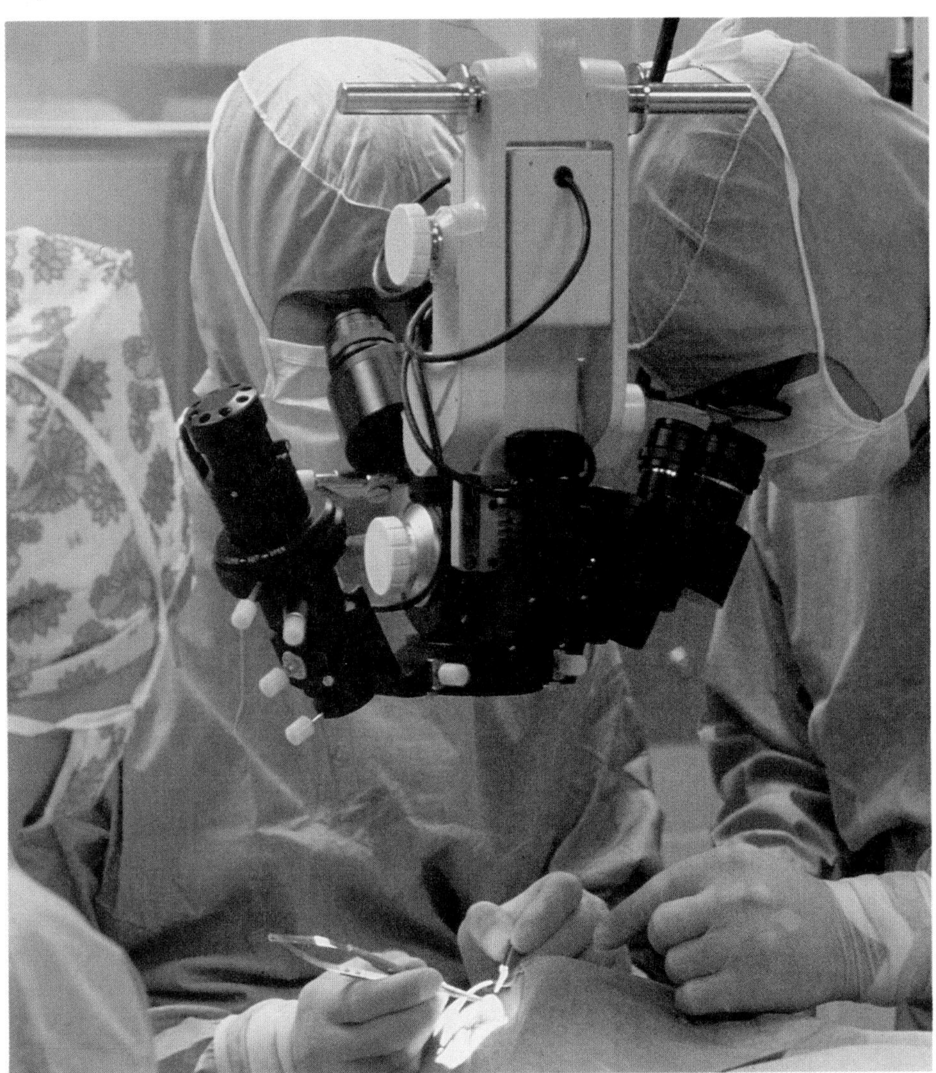

Left: Surgeons use a binocular operating microscope during an eye operation while students follow the operation's progress using the other sets of binoculars.

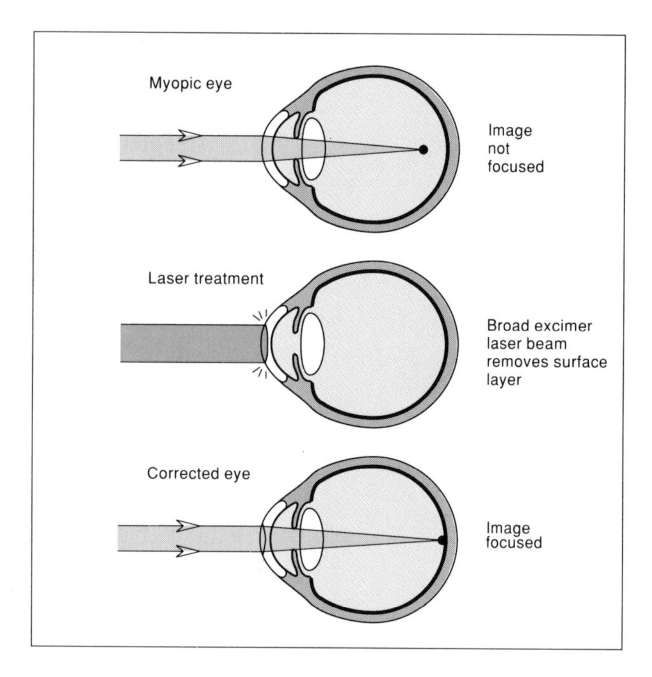

Left: The excimer laser removes a thin layer – here exaggerated – from the cornea to alter its focal length. The ultraviolet light from the laser cannot penentrate the cornea so has no effect on other parts of the eye.

instruments. The surgeon controls the basic movement of the operating microscope by a panel of pedals; most kick off their rubber boots when they are comfortably seated at the microscope. The pedals control axial and other illumination, focus, zoom magnification, and up, down, and sideways position shift. The microscope and the latest operating instruments, such as diamond scalpels, allow a degree of precision which would otherwise be impossible.

With such equipment it is now a routine operation to remove cataracts – opaque internal eye lenses – and replace them by tiny but very precise plastic lenses. In contrast to the heavy magnifying and distorting glasses which were previously necessary, many patients now do not need glasses after cataract surgery.

The excimer laser

This is one of the most recent developments in ophthalmology. The excimer laser is a new instrument used to reshape the surface of the external lens of the eye (the cornea) in order to abolish nearsightedness (myopia) and other focusing errors. People who are nearsighted have corneas that are effectively too strong for the length of their eyeball, so that the image of distant objects is brought to a focus in front of the retina and appears blurred. They can, however, see close objects clearly.

The excimer laser uses a mixture of argon and fluorine gases to produce a narrow, concentrated beam of intense but invisible ultraviolet light. This light energy does not generate heat in the tissues but vaporizes them with great precision.

To treat myopia, the cornea is flattened by removing a thin layer of tissue centrally – up to about 10 per cent of the thickness. The laser beam does not penetrate the cornea and there is no danger to the internal parts of the eye. The surgeon has to estimate the amount of tissue removed from the cornea with great care in order to correspond to the previous focusing error.

Once the surgeon has reduced the curvature by just the amount needed, the image of distant objects falls exactly on the retina at the back of the eye so the patient can see them clearly. Near objects are focused by the normal process of accommodation, using changes in the curvature of the internal lens.

After the operation, which takes about ten minutes, and which is performed painlessly in the office using anesthetic eyedrops only, the patient feels some discomfort for about 24 hours. After about three to six months the eye's focusing becomes fully stabilized, but from the time of the operation most patients can see clearly without glasses or contact lenses.

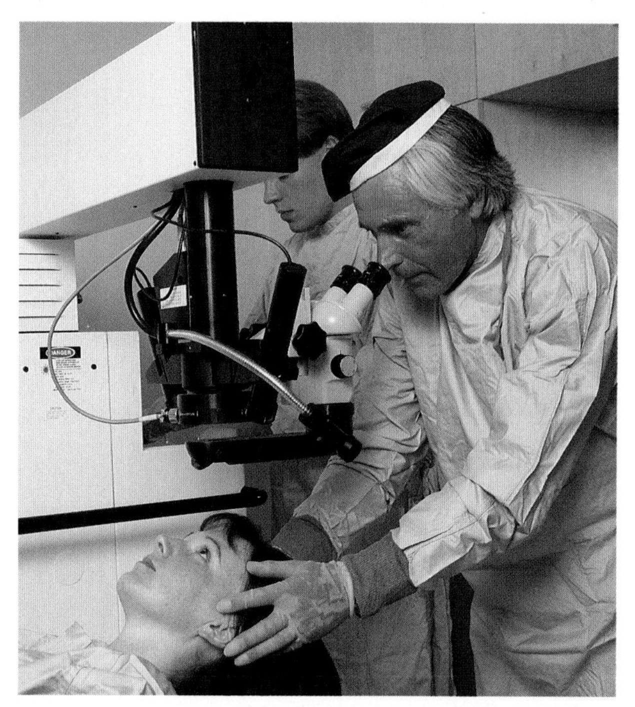

Left: A patient at the Cromwell Hospital in London, England, receiving excimer laser treatment for nearsightedness. If treatment is successful, the patient's eyesight will be corrected and she will not need to wear glasses or contact lenses again.

Optics

Optics is a branch of physics that has seen a considerable revival of interest in the last two decades. This has been sparked off by the introduction of cheap and reliable lasers which has encouraged the development of holography and what is called non-linear optics.

Interactive color holographic displays

Animated, full color holograms are commonplace in popular films such as *Star Wars*, but only very recently have scientists been able to create them in reality. In 1991 a breakthrough from the Massachusetts Institute of Technology Media Lab made it possible to produce color holographic images that move.

At the moment, the original images are color computer graphics. The images are sent to an "acousto-optical" crystal which modulates the intensity of the laser beams, and are finally displayed on an optical system. One major problem with real-time animated holograms is the huge rate of information transfer needed. A typical display hologram contains about 10^{10} bits of information; to make this move at film or TV rates the computer would have to handle up to 10^{11} bits per second, too much even for today's supercomputers. To reduce the information rate, only small holograms are possible, with no vertical parallax and only a limited depth range.

Using a Connection Machine supercomputer, a data rate of 5 x 10^8 bits per second is sent to the acousto-optic crystal and the image is built up one line at a time. The result is a 3D image floating in space. Three different laser beams allow animated, shaded, color images to be displayed. The system can react to an image edit command in about one second so an operator can interact with the image. In the near future faster computers will allow higher resolution and faster interaction. Such a system may be used to visualize complex scientific data, such as images from medical scans.

The phase conjugate mirror

One of the key developments in the last decade has been the practical exploitation of "non-linear" optical effects. We expect optical materials to behave in a linear fashion; that is, if we shine red light into a piece of glass, we expect to get red light out of it. With the advent of the laser, which can produce very high brightness, non-linear effects become important; some of the light might double in frequency, with red light emerging as blue, for example. In one of the most interesting effects, the mixing of light beams in a non-linear medium (such as barium titanate) produces a polarization

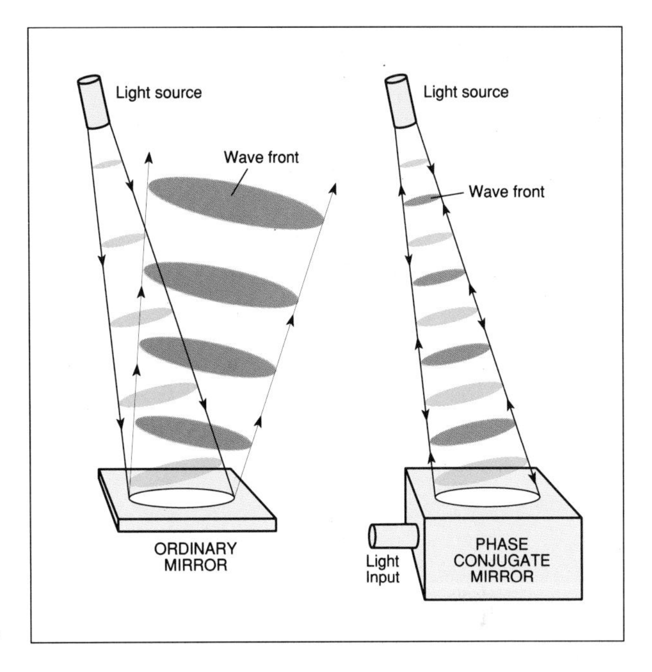

Above: A phase conjugate mirror reflects light back to its source. Unlike retro-reflectors (such as car tail reflectors) it preserves the phase of the light.

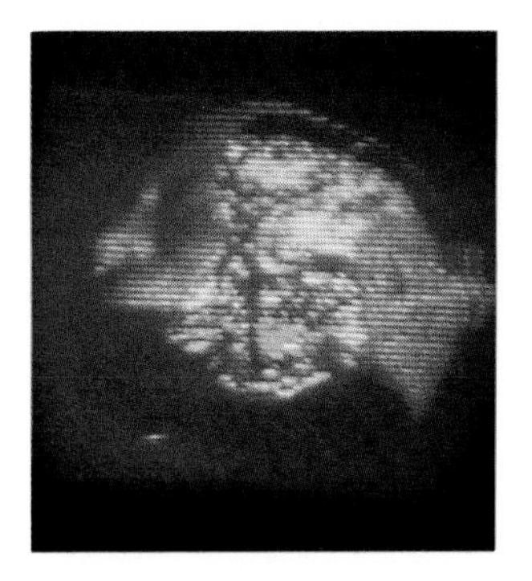

Left: An image of a patient's head produced on a display system which creates a color hologram. The image is built using a scanning system similar to those used in laser displays to create line images with laser light by rapidly moving the beam.

which will reradiate the input beam in a time-reversed form known as the *phase conjugate*.

Phase conjugation has one extraordinary effect. An ordinary plane mirror merely deflects the spreading (diverging) light beam, but a phase conjugate mirror redirects the beam back along its original path and changes it to a converging beam. Some interesting practical applications arise: because exact reversal occurs, distortion, such as that produced by turbulent air or by imperfect optics, can be corrected as it happens and undistorted images produced. One application for this is in making very tiny computer chips, which are produced by optical projection. The effect can also be used to make a hologram in real time without the need for a permanent recording medium.

The X-ray microscope

Ever since the optical microscope was invented there has been an unending quest to increase the

Above: In use, the interactive color hologram reacts to controls from the viewer, just as in a virtual reality setup, but in this case the image is seen without the need for a heavy headset. The 3D image is about 1.5 x 1.5 x 22.5 in (40 x 40 x 570 mm).

Above: The interactive color holographic display setup, on an optical bench in the Massachusetts Institute of Technology Media Lab. The image, seen through the large lens at the left, appears apparently floating in the air.

resolution; that is, to allow finer and finer details to be seen. The electron microscope has improved resolution by up to 1,000 times, but the specimens must be placed under high vacuum. This rules out many biological samples whose internal structures change in a vacuum. Very recently, a combination of several technical advances has led to the development of X-ray microscopes with a resolution of ten times the best optical microscopes, and with the potential to be 100 times as good.

Improvements in integrated circuit fabrication technology have allowed researchers to build a very fine X-ray focusing lens called a "zone-plate". This consists of many concentric rings of an X-ray absorber (usually gold) on a thin support. The gap between the outermost rings is about a millionth of an inch (20 nanometers).

As well as this new lens, the synchrotron electron accelerator has dramatically increased the brightness of X-ray sources; X-ray detectors are now more sensitive and have higher resolution than before.

The new microscopes have another special advantage: specific chemical elements absorb X-rays of different wavelengths – they have different X-ray "colors". By taking pictures of the same sample at two or more different X-ray wavelengths, the different known elements show up as different tones. This can provide very important information about processes in MICROBIOLOGY, and can be carried out without damaging the cell.

Right: An image from a scanning X-ray microscope at the National Synchrotron Light Source, New York, detailing a rabbit muscle. The sample was in a cell which reproduced its natural environment.

Multiple mirror telescopes

Among the largest optical systems are those used for astronomical telescopes. Making these giant mirrors has never been easy, but one possible solution is to make the large primary mirror out of a mosaic of smaller, more manageable pieces. Such an approach has been used in the new Keck telescope on Mauna Kea, Hawaii.

The primary mirror, 386 in (9.8 m) across, is made out of a "fly's eye" assembly of 36 smaller hexagonal mirrors of more manageable size and weight. Each mirror is polished until it is close to the correct concave figure, and the remaining error is corrected by a computer-controlled system of precision actuators and a fixed mechanical "warping" harness. This combination of passive and active control allows the shape to be corrected as the telescope points to different parts of the sky. Each actuator can move in steps of one six millionth of an inch (4 nm), over a range of 1/25 in (1 mm).

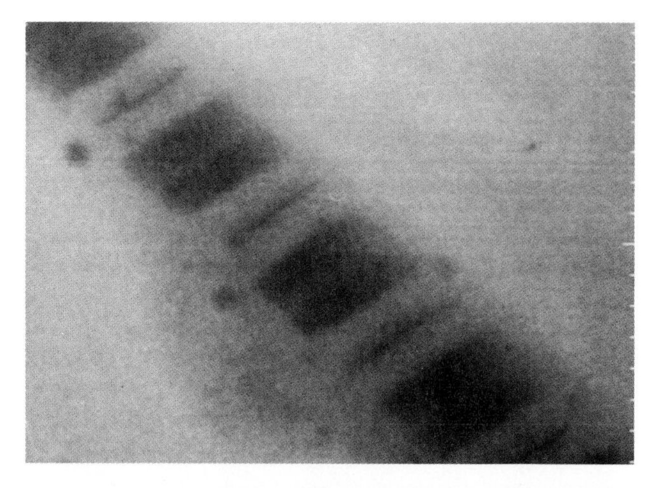

Organic chemistry

To the scientist in the early part of the 19th century the word "organic" referred to chemicals that could only be made by living things. Everything of mineral origin was termed inorganic. Organic compounds were thought to be special, as a "vital force" was necessary for their production. However, in 1928 all that changed when the German chemist Wohler succeeded in making an "organic" compound, urea, in the test tube from simple "inorganic" materials. The vital force theory was discredited and one of the most powerful sciences of modern times began.

Organic chemistry is now taken to mean the study of those compounds containing carbon, but not the simple metal salts, which remain part of INORGANIC CHEMISTRY. Some carbon-containing compounds do not fit neatly into either category; these fall into the domain of ORGANOMETALLIC CHEMISTRY.

Once chemists recognized that they had the ability to make organic compounds in the laboratory, they began exploiting their new-found prowess. As the end of this century approaches, the rate of discovery of methods of synthesizing, extracting, identifying, and applying organic chemicals is still increasing. The Chemical Abstracts Service in Washington, D.C. recently catalogued the ten millionth chemical, of which over two million are organic compounds.

Chemical synthesis

Chemists have a multitude of techniques at their disposal for manipulating organic compounds from the simplest, methane (CH_4), to the most complex of polypeptide anticancer antibiotics and supramolecular structures.

The real breakthrough in organic chemistry came in the 1960s, when Harvard University professor and Nobel Laureate Elias J. Corey developed the methodology of *retrosynthetic analysis*. It is one of the most powerful tools at the chemist's disposal for building large complex organic molecules from smaller, more readily available, and cheaper starting materials.

The method works by picturing the target molecule to be constructed as if it were a jigsaw puzzle. By working backward from the target it is possible to find chemical components that, when reacted together, form the complete puzzle. The modern organic chemist is still using retrosynthetic analysis to design everything from insect antifeedants for "greener" farming, more environmentally friendly detergent molecules, dyes and paints which are brighter and safer, and better drugs with fewer side-effects (see PHARMACOLOGY).

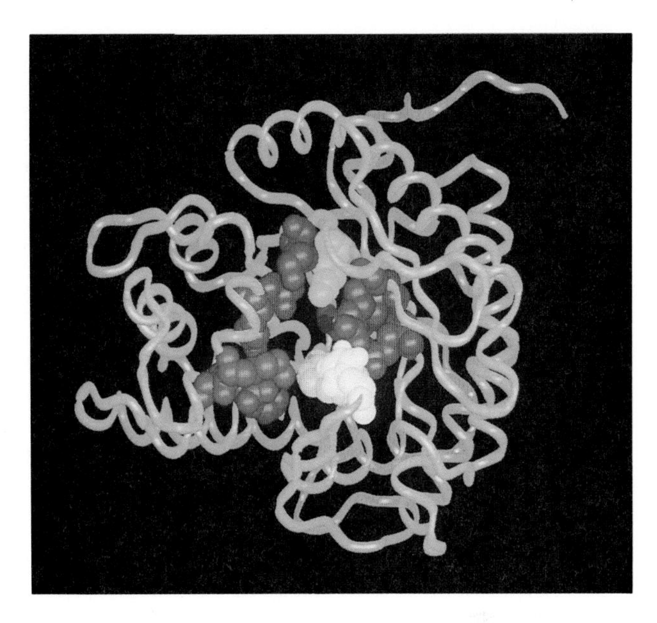

Above: Carbon-carbon bond-forming enzymes such as this one, aldolase, shown here as a computer structure, are increasingly being used as catalysts in organic or "biotransformation" reactions.

Enzymes in synthesis

There are problems with traditional organic synthesis, not least the number of steps often required before simple starting materials can be converted into a useful compound. For example, many reactions need to be carried out at high temperature

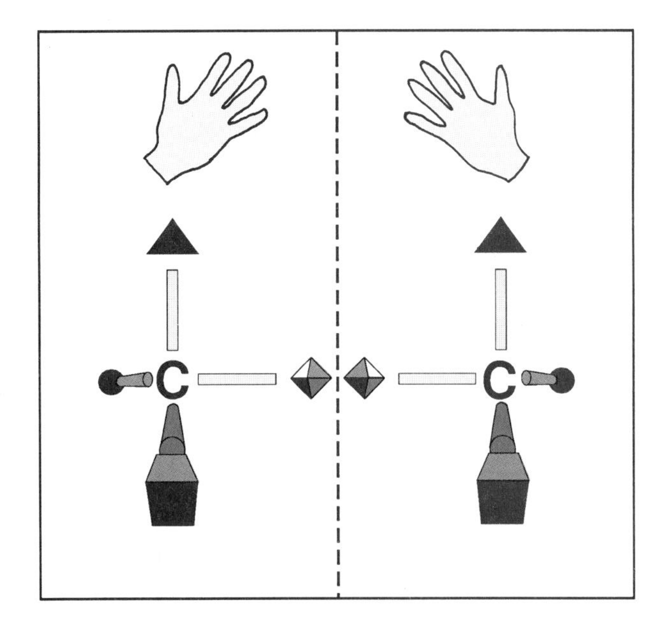

Right: The principle of chirality. A molecule can have two structures which are identical in chemical makeup but which are mirror-images, like left and right hands, with different properties.

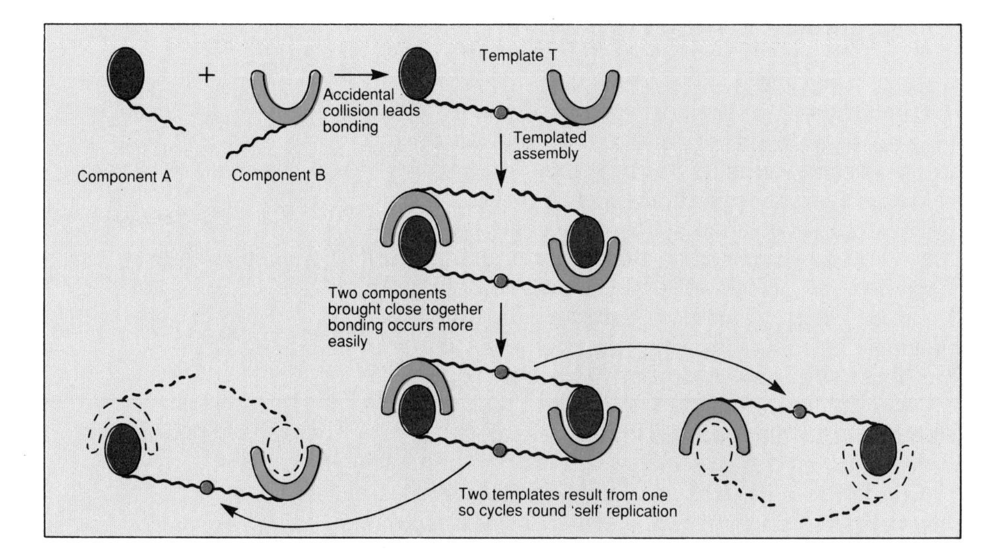

Right: How molecules can assemble themselves. A chance linking of two components, A and B, provides a template which makes it easier for other such molecules to form.

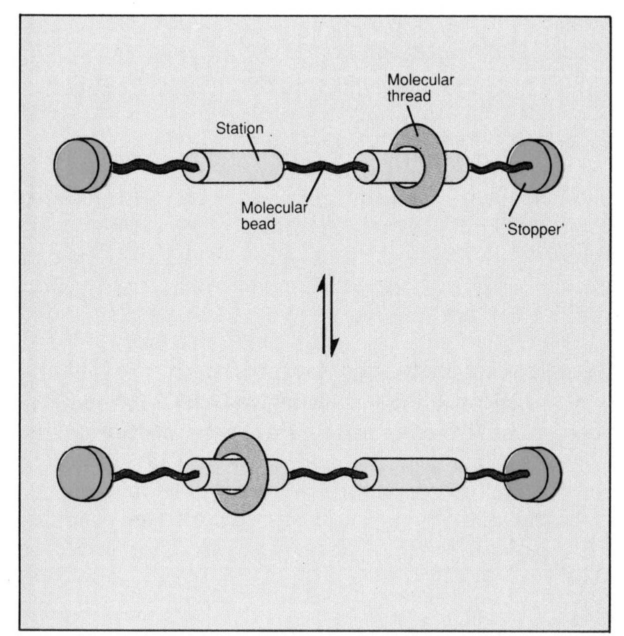

and pressure in order to proceed at a useful rate. Artificially constructed catalysts, which assist reactions without being themselves consumed, have come to the fore as a means of speeding up some reactions, such as the conversion of methane (natural gas) into industrially useful products such as alkenes and aldehydes. But the cost of such catalysts is high, as many are based on precious metals. They also have a limited lifespan, due to "poisoning", despite the fact that theoretically a catalyst is retrieved unchanged at the end of a reaction.

Organic chemists have now turned to nature to help solve such problems. Nature has its own catalysts in the form of enzymes, complex protein structures found in all living things. Enzymes have many advantages over manufactured catalysts. First, they operate at much lower temperatures and therefore need less energy input.

Second, enzymes are very specific. This means that each type will only catalyze a certain type of

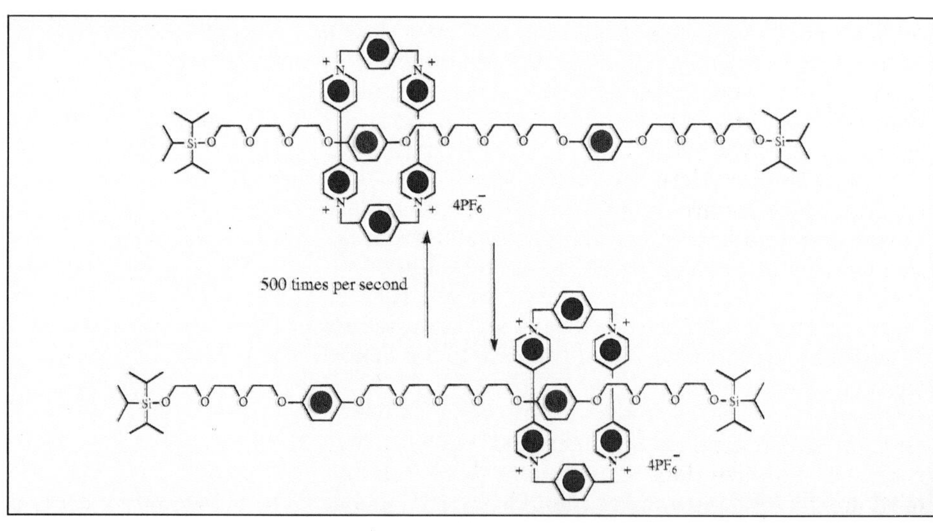

Above and right: This molecular shuttle could act as a switch in a future computer. It acts as a bead oscillating between two "stations", which could be controlled by an external signal such as light.
Right, the chemical structure of the shuttle.

reaction on only a certain class of molecule, thus reducing the number of possible by-products in a reaction. Fortunately, this specificity is not a limiting factor because there are well over 10,000 enzymes known so far and GENETIC ENGINEERING is able to increase this still further.

One other way in which the selectivity of enzymes makes them special catalysts is that they can distinguish between the right- and left-hand forms of a molecule. Some chemicals exist in two discrete forms known as *enantiomers*, with the chemical groups arranged around a carbon center in such a way that one is a non-superimposable mirror image of the other – like a pair of hands. Such molecules are said to be *chiral*, from the Greek for hand.

Chirality is very important in biology because often one enantiomer can behave differently from the other when interacting with chiral biomolecules. For example, the left-handed form of the painkiller ibuprofen is a highly effective analgesic while the other is only mildly so. Occasionally one enantiomer of a drug turns out to be harmful rather than beneficial, thalidomide being a well known example. The left-handed form of the drug is an effective tranquillizer while the other enantiomer severely disturbs fetal development.

Using enzymes as catalysts in synthesis allows the chemist to manipulate the handedness of reaction products. The starting material which is to undergo conversion will only fit into the so-called active site of the enzyme if it is the correct shape – like a left hand for a left glove. Many industrial syntheses now rely on enzymes.

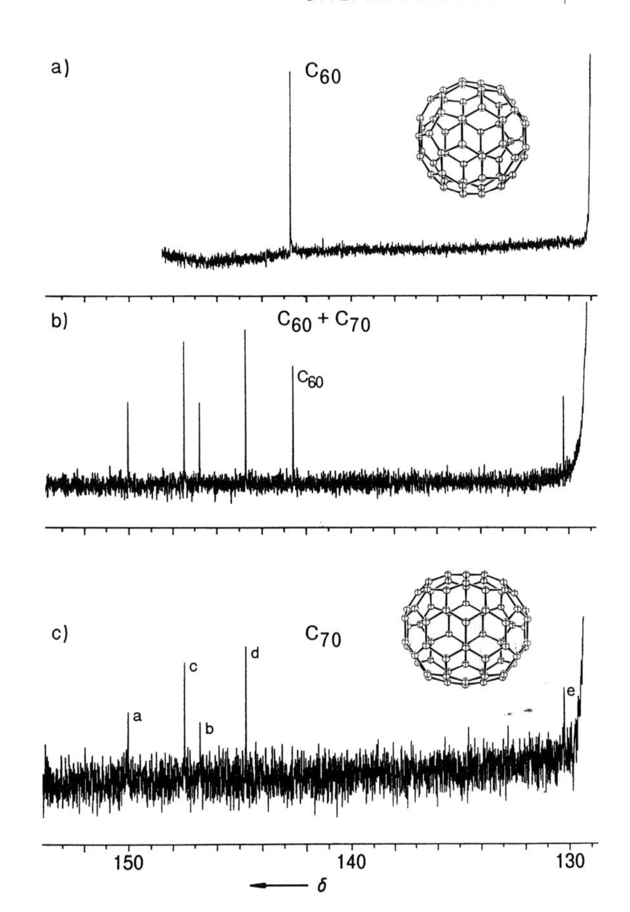

Above and left: These laboratory NMR spectra revealed to researchers the differences in structure between samples of the two fullerenes, C60 and C70. The samples themselves are shown (left); the pale pink extract is C60, the red one C70.

Molecular recognition

But organic chemistry is not just about designing new ways to make drugs. Some researchers are making compounds with the eventual aim of building molecular machines. Tiny switches and transistors that respond to light, molecular wires and diodes that carry signals, and other devices might be incorporated into the supercomputers of the future. With such a reduction in scale one could easily imagine a supercomputer fitting into a space the size of a briefcase.

One of the properties of some molecules, which organic chemists are exploiting to their advantage in designing molecular devices, is molecular recognition. Certain molecules, for example so-called macrocyclic rings and cages, which are relatively large molecules, often demonstrate the ability to "recognize" and trap smaller molecules or ions in their cavities.

A simple example are the crown ethers, simple rings of alternating carbon and oxygen atoms. The rings vary in size depending on the total number of atoms in the ring and it is the size of the hole in the middle that determines what chemical species the crown ether will recognize. The smallest crown ether can recognize and trap lithium metal ions but nothing larger, for instance. It can therefore be used to detect lithium in the presence of other metal ions such as sodium and potassium, by incorporating the crown ether or a chemical relative into an electrode sensor.

A second property that is very important to the chemist designing molecular devices is so-called *self assembly*. Taking the smallest crown ether as an example again, not only will the complete ring recognize lithium ions, but if the component parts of the ring are simply mixed in a solution contain-

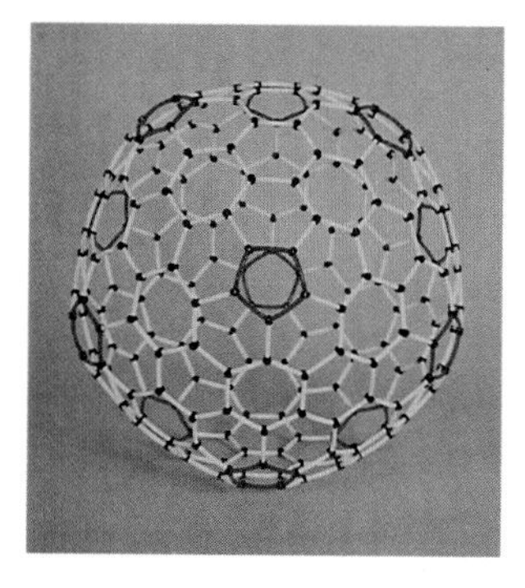

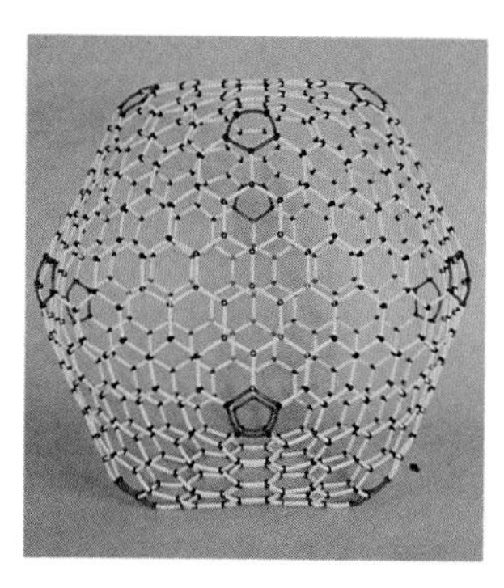

Above: Molecular models of large fullerene molecules, made by their codiscoverer. These showed that C240 and C560 would not be spherical, as had been assumed, but polyhedral.

ing lithium ions the parts will spontaneously assemble around the ion and form the crown ether ring. The metal ion is said to be acting as a "template" in the self assembly of the crown ether.

When the properties of recognition and self assembly are extended to more complex chemical structures the basis of devices becomes apparent. Researchers such as Professor J. Fraser Stoddart at Birmingham University, England, Nobel laureate Professor Jean-Marie Lehn, at the University Louis Pasteur, France, and Julius Rebek Jr., of the Massachusetts Institute of Technology, among many others, are all working on designing molecular structures that can undergo recognition and self-assembly processes.

Stoddart and his co-workers have recently been focusing on making molecules to order and have made startling progress towards molecular devices. Recently, they have built a number of long chain molecules with ring-shaped molecules threaded onto them – like beads on a string. By incorporating various chemical groups along the thread's length they can make the molecular beads "shuttle" backwards and forwards between these groups, which Stoddart calls "stations".

The next aim of Professor Stoddart's team is to discover a method by which they can control the shuttling movement using an external input such as light. Ultimately, such structures or their descendents could become the switches in optoelectronic computers., which could usher in a new era of computers even smaller than those of today, and are based on purely electronic components.

Lehn and his research team have been using macrocyclic rings, which are related to the crown ethers, to mimic various biochemical processes. The aim is to understand nature better and to develop useful chemical sensors and devices. For example, they have devised a chemical system that will emulate the formation of the energy molecule ATP in our bodies. Another self-assembly system uses copper as a template to mimic the formation of double helices.

Meanwhile, Rebek and his colleagues are bringing organic chemistry full circle. In 1992 they reported a chemical system that could be a major clue in explaining the early processes of replication in the origins of life. They have designed a molecule that undergoes molecular recognition and self assembly leading to a larger molecular structure. This "supermolecule" can then act as a template molecule, bringing together two more of the original components and allowing them to self assemble more rapidly, the result being that the first template catalyzes the formation of a second. The two templates can then readily split apart and catalyze the next round of assembly.

The process is a very primitive analogy of the way in which DNA, the chemical that carries the genetic code, self-replicates when cells divide. In DNA a single helical strand acts as a template for the self assembly of the DNA base units forming a double helix. These two entwined templates then uncoil resulting in two single-stranded templates, and so on.

The early organic chemists removed the need for a "vital force" to explain carbon compounds. Now the chemist is reinventing this force in the test tube.

• FACT FILE •

- One important aspect of organic chemistry is the realm of fullerene or buckyball research. These are the all-carbon compounds with, for example, the archetypal fullerene-60 (buckminsterfullerene) having 60 carbon atoms joined together to form a sphere.

- A great deal of money and time is being invested in buckyball research by academic researchers and multinational corporations alike. They have huge potential not only as fascinating new chemicals to play with but also because of their novel materials properties, everything from superconductivity and non-linear optical effects to properties such as superlubricant ability.

- Every possible reaction and manipulation of buckyballs and the related buckytubes are being investigated. These molecules, that were first postulated as existing in outer space, could take organic chemistry to the stars.

Organometallic chemistry

Organometallic chemistry (OM) involves making and studying molecules which contain a direct link, or bond, between a metal atom and a carbon atom. This branch of chemistry encompasses both organic and inorganic chemistry. It has resulted in many useful materials for the academic chemist and industrialist. Almost every day, people come into direct contact with an OM compound or with materials manufactured using OM chemistry. For example, many plastics (including polythene) are manufactured using an OM compound. The "lead" in gasoline is in fact tetraethyl lead, an OM compound.

Organometallic chemistry is a rapidly developing field and as 83 out of the 103 elements in the periodic table are metals, there is a vast potential for making new materials with interesting and useful properties.

Sandwich compounds

Major developments in OM chemistry took place following the chance discovery in 1951 of ferrocene, which opened up a field of research of immense variety. The metallocenes are compounds in which a metal atom such as iron or cobalt is sandwiched between two flat, aromatic rings such as cyclopentadienyl or benzene. The chemistry of these unusual compounds is still rapidly developing while the study of their properties has led to the use of half sandwich complexes, which contain only one aromatic ring, in the synthesis of fine chemicals and drugs. For example, an efficient synthesis of *β-lactams*, which are found as part of the structure of penicillins, involves the use of a half sandwich complex of iron closely related to ferrocene.

Catalysis

The emphasis now is on understanding how and to what extent OM chemicals react. Of these, catalysts are especially important. Many industrial processes, including those used to turn crude oil into useful chemicals, rely on catalysts. Likewise, the conversion of synthesis gas (a mixture of hydrogen and carbon monoxide) to higher hydrocarbons, alcohols, and aldehydes uses *heterogenous* catalysts. These are often metals supported on an inert material or finely dispersed metal oxides or hydroxides. Investigation of OM complexes of the metals involved gives an insight into the reactions which take place between organic molecules at the metal surface of a catalyst.

Chemists now believe that the mechanisms proceed via intermediates similar to some stable OM

Above: Catalytic cracker units lie at the heart of all oil refineries. Chemists are striving to produce improved catalysts.

materials. For example, the polymerization of ethene to give polythene uses the *Ziegler-Natta catalyst* which is based on a mixture of titanium chloride and an alkylaluminium. The intermediates formed during the reaction are all organotitanium compounds, so the study of related, stable organometallics helps to reveal the mechanism of this important industrial process.

Future developments in this area will certainly involve making catalysts for efficiently converting

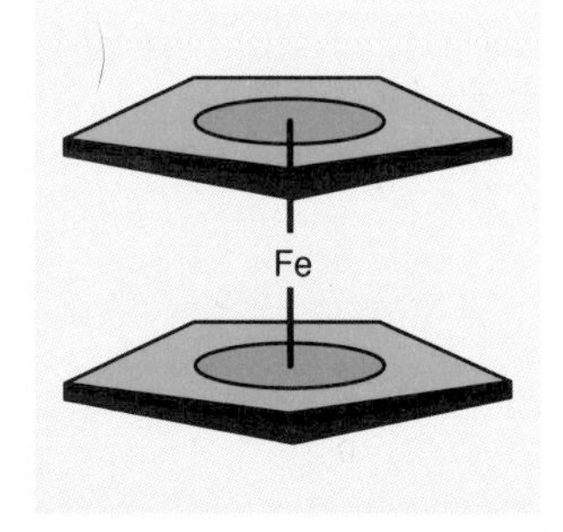

Left: Ferrocene, the pioneer organometallic compound, consists of an iron atom surrounded by flat aromatic molecule rings.

Left: The reactor cell of a research MOVPE system, where the gaseous molecules pass over a heated substrate on which they are deposited.

methane, the most abundant fossil fuel, into higher hydrocarbons and value-added chemicals. Methane can be directly converted into methanol by oxidation using methane oxygenase enzymes. The enzyme acts as a very efficient catalyst, so organometallic compounds are being designed to mimic its action. The development of mild, selective, and efficient catalysts for the conversion of synthesis gas is economically important and presents a great challenge to academic chemistry.

Fine chemical synthesis

Another use of organometallic materials is in the synthesis of fine chemicals such as organolithium, silicon, copper, magnesium, aluminum, and boron. Many transition metal organometallics are also involved, particularly by pharmaceutical companies for producing chiral molecules – that is, molecules that can have different properties when their shape is mirror-imaged (see ORGANIC CHEMISTRY). In the 1990s, experiments are continuing in using organotin derivatives as intermediates in producing fluorinated nucleotides which have possible antiviral or anticancer activity.

A new use for volatile organometallic derivatives is in *Metal Organic Vapor Phase Epitaxy* (MOVPE). This technique is used in the synthesis of compounds in groups III and V of the periodic table, such as gallium arsenide and indium phosphide, which are important in the semiconductor industry. The method involves passing a gaseous mixture of, for example, trimethyl gallium and arsine (AsH_3) over a graphite plate in a heated chamber. The organometallic compound decomposes at the high temperatures used (about 600° C) and the metal atoms produced combine to give very thin, pure, uniform layers of the semiconductor.

Help from bacteria

Complex organisms, such as humans, take in food containing large molecules, break these large molecules down into their constituent components, and from these build up aminoacids and proteins. Certain bacteria, including the methanogens and halobacteria, however, make all their proteins from very simple molecules such as hydrogen, carbon monoxide, carbon dioxide, and nitrogen – they literally "live on air".

Other bacteria, found in the gills of a species of mussel, use methane as an energy source. The bacteria are able to build complex organic molecules, on which the mussel feeds, from methane. These bacteria are rich in nickel-containing enzymes, and convert simple molecules into more useful complex systems via catalytic processes involving organometallic intermediates.

Similar organometallic intermediates are observed in industrial processes such as the Monsanto acetic acid synthesis. By studying and attempting to mimic the biochemical processes used by these very ancient bacteria, scientists are able to improve industrial methods for synthesizing useful chemicals.

Osteopathy

Until the 19th century medical doctors often used spinal manipulation to treat back pain, but their official position thereafter was that it had no value. Osteopathy and, in particular, chiropractic, which both involve manipulation of the body, were dismissed as quackery. This has changed in recent years as controlled studies have shown that manipulative therapies have value in some types of muscle and joint ailments. Many doctors of conventional medicine have sought additional training in this area, as have physical therapists.

A 1991 study by a Rand Corporation panel of medical doctors, osteopaths, and chiropractors concluded that patients with low back pain who showed no signs of spinal nerve damage or abnormalities in X-rays could benefit from manipulative therapy. Studies showed that these patients returned to work sooner than those given conventional treatment, such as pain-killing drugs. Back pain is the greatest single cause of time off from work for Americans under 45 years of age.

The panel also agreed that for patients with certain neurological symptoms, such as weakness or numbness in a limb, manipulative therapy would be useless or even dangerous.

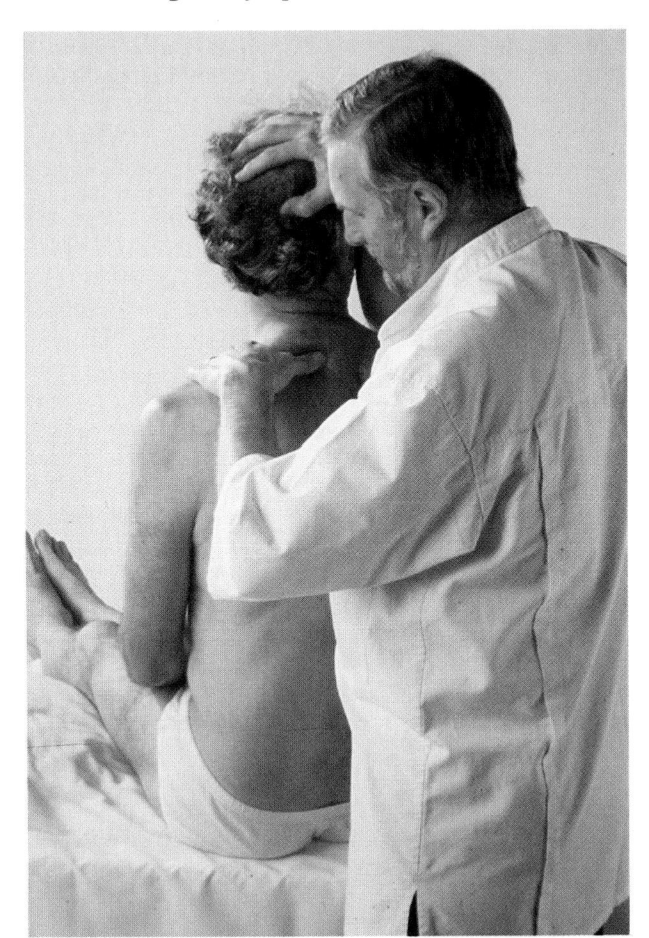

Until 1976 the American Medical Association forbade its members to refer patients to chiropractors; it is now common practice, but the AMA still argues that there is no scientific evidence that manipulative therapy is appropriate for such ailments as essential hypertension, cancer, heart disease, stroke, and diabetes.

Osteopathy

Osteopathy is a therapy which involves manipulating the bones, joints, muscles, and ligaments. Osteopathy (from the Greek *osteo*, bone, and *pathos*, disease) is founded on the belief that a disturbance in one function of the body can alter the balance and affect another, quite separate, function. The osteopath claims to be able to treat a wide range of illnesses besides bone or joint disorders. However, osteopaths will not treat some conditions, including fractures, malignancy, acute arthrosis, various diseases of the bones, severe cases of disc prolapse which cause neurological problems, or tuberculosis.

Dr. Andrew Taylor Still, the inventor of osteopathy, founded the first osteopathic training organization in the world, The American School of Osteopathy, in 1892. There are now 15 osteopathic medical schools and 169 osteopathic hospitals in the country, and 29,000 practitioners.

Osteopathic training resembles that for the M.D. degree, including four years of schooling, internship, and residency. Osteopaths are familiar with, and use many, conventional medical techniques along with manipulative therapy.

The power of touch

After a conventional physical examination, including an assessment of posture and range of movement of the joints, an osteopath will conduct an examination by touch, seeking to locate such problems as fractionally misaligned vertebrae, and may then massage the muscles or manipulate the spine or other joints.

To treat a fixed or misaligned joint, the osteopath may perform a high velocity thrust, moving the joint quickly through its normal range of movement. This often produces the clicking noise that people associate with osteopathic treatment, which is the result of a vacuum forming within the joint as it is moved.

Cranial osteopathy is a specialized manipulation of the head and upper neck to re-establish a balanced relationship between the structure of the

Left: Touch is a key factor in osteopathic diagnosis. Osteopaths conduct examinations by touch in order to identify problems such as misaligned vertebrae.

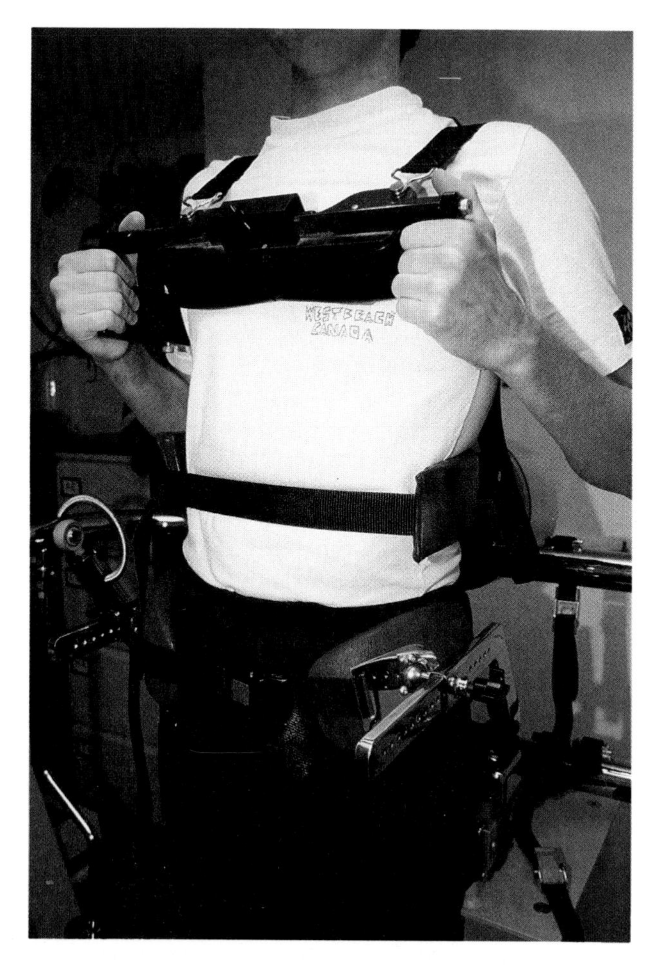

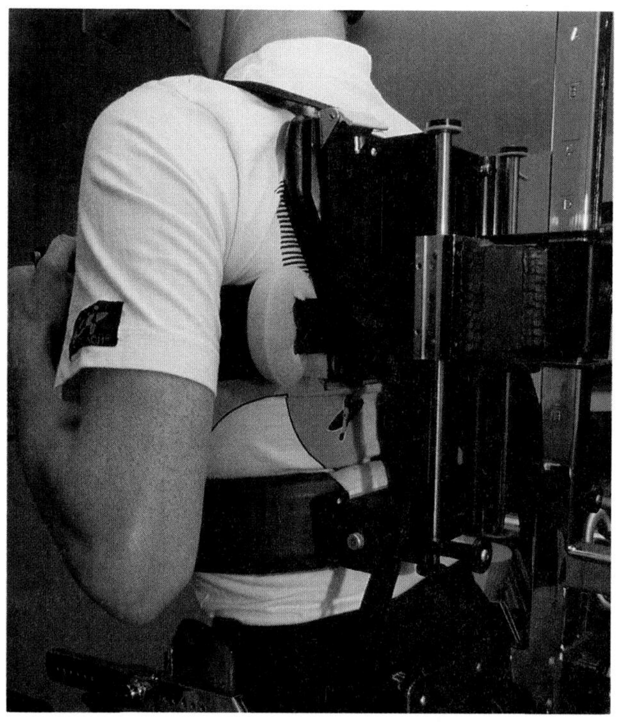

Left and above: A patient takes tests in a computerized diagnostic machine – a controversial new device which is intended to measure the patient's lower back movement patterns, thus helping the osteopath to identify any problems and measure progress in treatment.

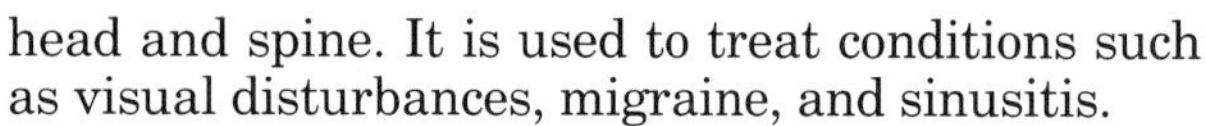

head and spine. It is used to treat conditions such as visual disturbances, migraine, and sinusitis.

Computerized diagnostics

Some osteopaths have recently adopted a computerized diagnostic machine which is claimed to identify disorders of the lumbar region of the spine. It also acts as an exercise machine for rehabilitation of injured patients.

The patient is placed in a restraint system which limits movement to the lumbar spine and performs a series of tasks against varying resistances. The machine monitors the patient's force, speed, and range of movement; this information is then summarized on a computer-generated report.

When used for rehabilitation, the machine supplies movement exercises which assist in the healing of soft tissue. Many osteopaths still regard this method of diagnosis and treatment as controversial, but some insurance companies favor it as a means of providing an objective verdict on a claimant's condition.

Chiropractic

Chiropractic is another form of manipulative therapy. The word chiropractic translates literally as "done by hand". Chiropractors treat 8 to 10 million Americans annually.

Developed by a Canadian, Dr. Daniel David Palmer, chiropractic is based on the theory that illness causes an imbalance in the structure of the body, and in turn, imbalance can cause illness. Chiropractors concentrate on spinal imbalance and posture.

Like osteopaths, chiropractors also view the body as a machine, but while the osteopath makes more use of leverage techniques and often makes adjustments further away from the problem area, the chiropractor makes more use of manipulative techniques, concentrating on the spine. A procedure called spinal adjustment – a quick thrust to the vertebrae – is central to chiropractic treatment.

At one time spinal adjustments were the only treatment given by chiropractors. Today they have expanded their scope to include counseling on nutrition and exercise. Chiropractors who specialize in sports medicine also offer advice on equipment and observe athletes in the performance of their sport to advise on the proper technique to avoid injuries. Since the 1980 Lake Placid Olympic Games, a chiropractor has served on the U.S. Olympic Committee's Sports Medicine Council.

Otolaryngology

Otolaryngology is the study of the ear, nose and throat. Recent advances in medical technology have helped alleviate the suffering of people with problems in this area. One advance that has affected the lives of thousands of people suffering from deafness has been the ability to make smaller and smaller hearing aids, with the help of modern microchip technology. Yet the challenge remains to develop a hearing aid that will magnify the sound of speech but not of background noises.

Hearing aids that stimulate the auditory nerve directly, so-called cochlear implants, have successfully helped many deaf people (see BIOENGINEERING). The deaf person has an operation to insert a sound receiver under the skin behind the ear, which is connected to a wire that stimulates the nerve. He or she also has to wear a microphone to pick up sound, which is connected to a device worn behind the ear. This transmits the sound to the receiver under the skin.

Cochlear implants are only suitable for people who are totally deaf, even though the auditory nerve functions normally. Only people who remember being able to hear are likely to benefit from having one, as they need to be able to relate to the sound they "hear" via the implant.

Another problem dealt with by the otolaryngologist is that of blocked sinuses. This condition affects millions of people, who can now be helped by a simple operation that involves none of the major incisions in the face that used to be necessary for surgery on the sinuses, with all the bruising and scarring that these caused.

The sinuses are a honeycomb of cavities in the bones of the face. They are found between the eyes and behind the nose, within the cheekbones, and within the bones of the skull. These passages are

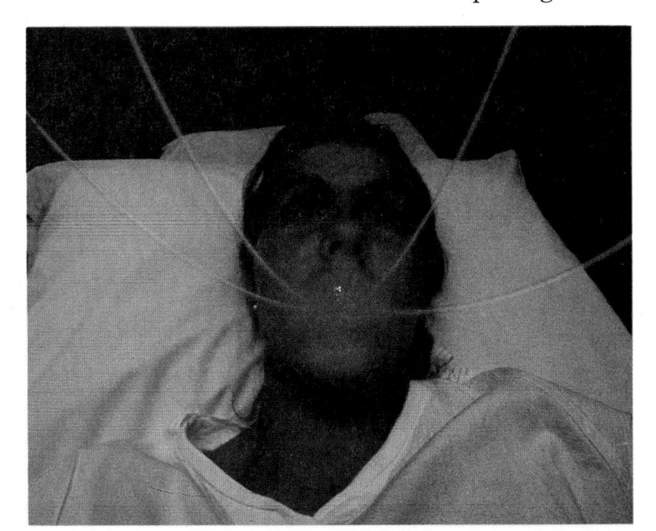

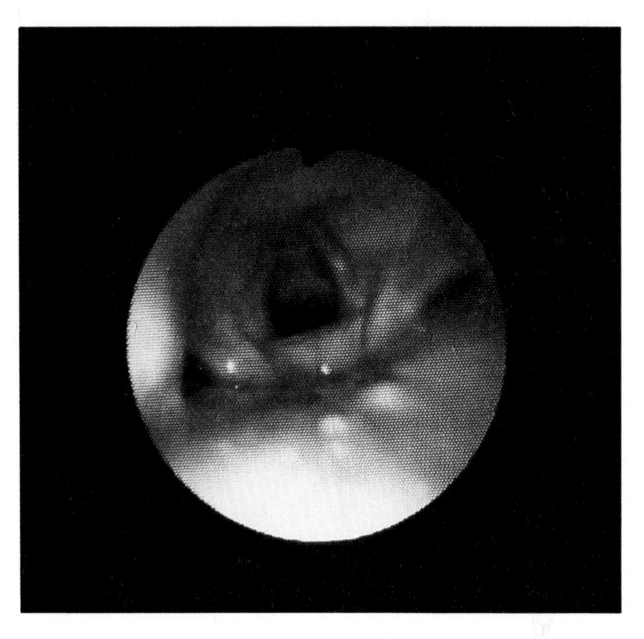

Above and below: Endoscopic views of an open (above) and closed larynx. The endoscope is vital to modern ear, nose, and throat surgery, giving surgeons an illuminated view of the area they are operating on without the need to make unsightly incisions.

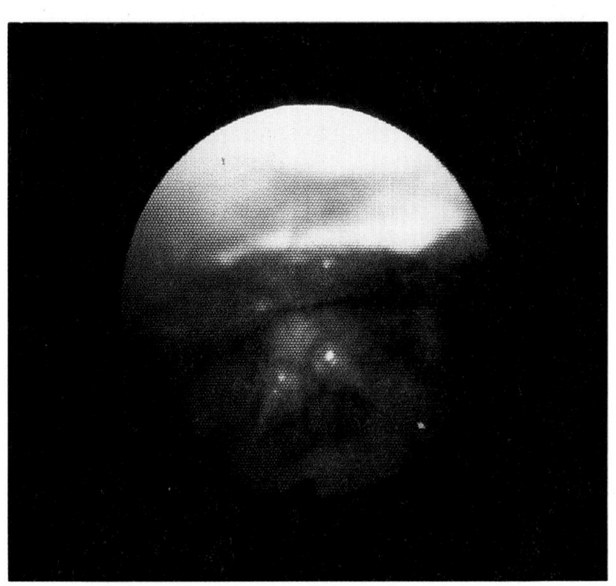

Left: A patient receives laser-activated cancer therapy. The use of lasers has been one of the greatest of recent breakthroughs in the treatment of throat cancers. In this case, a low-power red argon laser beam is being used to activate a drug, hematoporphyrin derivative (HPD), previously injected into the patient. HPD does not affect normal cells but is highly toxic to cancer cells, which strongly absorb it.

lined with same kind of membrane that lines the nose. They sometimes become blocked by swelling, by polyps (small outgrowths of tissue), or even by malignant growths. As a result, the person may find it difficult to breathe, have a continually "stuffed up" feeling, or a constantly running nose.

Endoscopic surgery

Endoscopic sinus surgery has made it much easier to diagnose and treat such conditions. The surgeon first looks at detailed CAT (see ANATOMY AND SURGERY) scans of the head to find out the exact anatomy of the patient's sinuses, as their position and mass vary greatly from patient to patient.

The surgeon then inserts a fine optical tube called an endoscope, which has a light at the end of it, up the nose and into the sinuses. Angled lenses make it possible to see around corners. This provides an excellent illuminated view of the sinuses, making it easy to remove polyps and open up blocked passages.

The operation is very quick to perform, so that patients need spend only a few hours in hospital. Some have the operation under a local rather than a general anaesthetic.

For the larynx, a major advance has been the removal of growths from vocal cords with the laser. The people to benefit most from this development have been those suffering from persistent hoarseness. This is common and extremely disabling, particularly for those who rely on their voices at work, such as teachers and lawyers.

The hoarseness can have many causes, ranging from polyps, swelling, and benign growths through to pre-cancerous growths and malignant tumors. Children may suffer from papillomata of the larynx, a viral infection that causes a rash of growths on the vocal cords. These growths may threaten to block the airway and endanger the child's life.

These conditions can now easily be treated with the help of the carbon dioxide laser. The properties of this laser allow it to vaporize cells down to a very shallow depth on a structure, without affecting the tissues underneath.

Vaporization of swollen areas and benign or malignant growths can alleviate the symptom of hoarseness in adults. Children with papillomata of the larynx, who often used to need a tracheotomy (a surgical procedure to allow them to breathe through an opening in the neck), can now be treated by laser in a virtually bloodless operation, with a stay in hospital of less than one day.

Treating cancer

People who have surgery for conditions such as cancer of the nose and sinuses need no longer experience the effects of the severe disfigurement that often followed such operations.

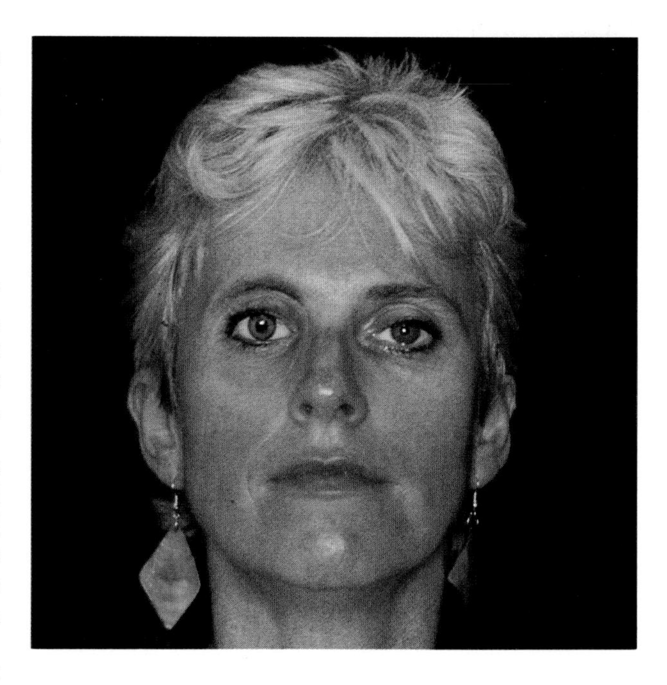

Above: Extensive cancers of the nose and sinuses sometimes necessitate the removal of the nose or even an eye. This woman has had her left eye replaced by a prosthesis.

Cancers of the nose and nasal sinuses is very rare; it accounts for less than one per cent of all cancers. Without treatment, it causes gross disfigurement, blindness, and severe pain. The sufferer is unable to eat or sleep.

The treatment for such cancers used to involve a large incision around the cheek, removal of the cheekbone, and, often, removal of the roof of the mouth. The patient had to wear a plate in place of the roof of the mouth and suffered severe disfigurement, with all the associated social and psychological problems.

Two new developments have revolutionized treatment for cancers of the nose and nasal sinuses. One is a new surgical technique. An incision is first made in the mouth. The surgeon removes the tumor and surrounding tissues from the inside, leaving the skin covering the face intact. A prosthesis can be fitted inside the mouth, so that the patient looks completely normal.

With extensive cancers of the nose and its associated sinuses, it is not always possible to avoid removal of the nose or, sometimes, the eye. These patients can be helped by a new generation of extremely lifelike prostheses.

The surgeon inserts tiny screws made of the metal titanium (which the body does not reject) into the bone that remains around the area removed. Onto these can be fitted a custom-made removable prosthesis that is undetectable except after close examination.

Parasitology

Parasitology is the scientific study of parasites and their way of life. Parasites are plants and animals that spend part or all of their lives living on or within, and at the expense of, another animal or plant, called a host. Because parasites usually harm their hosts, it is important to study them. When the hosts are ourselves or our food, parasites can cause immense suffering and damage.

Often, different plants or animals will live in close association with each other, but with neither damaging the other, or even with some mutual benefit from the association. This is called *symbiosis*. In parasitism, the host always suffers, although the actual damage may sometimes be very slight. After all, a parasite that severely damages, or worse, actually kills its host has deprived itself of a living and created prematurely the problem of finding its next host.

Plant parasites

Some ordinary plants, including the world's largest flower, Rafflesia, are parasites. All fungi are either parasitic or saprophytic, which means

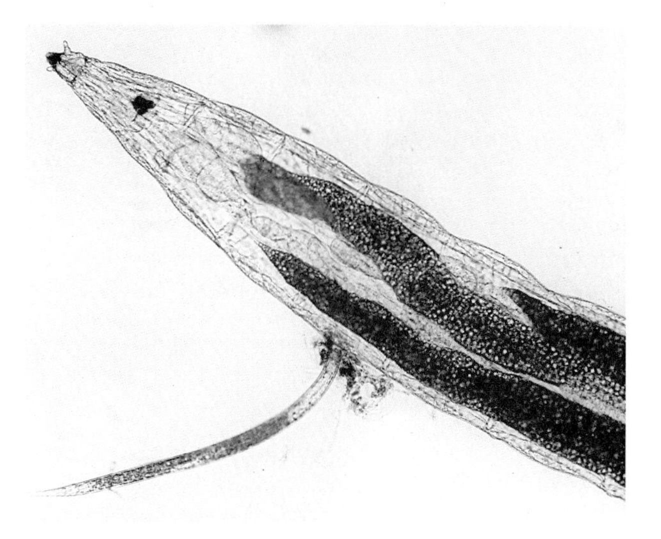

Some parasites have functions which are helpful to humans. Above: A parasitic nematode invades the larva of a mushroom scarid fly. The fly is a major pest to mushroom growers, boring through the stems of the fungi. Below: The tiny parasitic wasp Encarsia emerges from the pupal case of a glasshouse whitefly that it has destroyed. The whitefly is a major crop pest.

that they feed from dead tissue. Most fungi have a mass of root-like threads called hyphae that absorb food and water. In parasitic fungi, the hyphae penetrate host plant cells and absorb the cell contents.

Many fungal parasites do not cause much damage, but some, such as the honey or bootlace fungus *Armillaria*, can kill even huge trees. Others, like *Pythium*, are devastating to seedlings, while the mildews and rusts are harmful and unsightly on ornamental plants and very damaging to crops.

Fungal parasitism tends to be most damaging in crops grown in monoculture, as in the American Corn Belt. Whêre both parasite and host are native and in natural surroundings, evolution has seen to it that a reasonable balance is maintained. Where humans have intervened to modify the situation by introducing monocultures of specialized crop plants, often alien in origin and lacking the natural defense mechanisms evolved by native wild plants, pests can be devastating.

Researchers are seeking to identify other fungi that inhabit the plant surface without doing the plant any harm. The hope is that encouraging the harmless fungus will crowd out the parasite. *Armillaria* may be successfully combated by another non-parasitic, root-inhabiting fungus called *Trichoderma*.

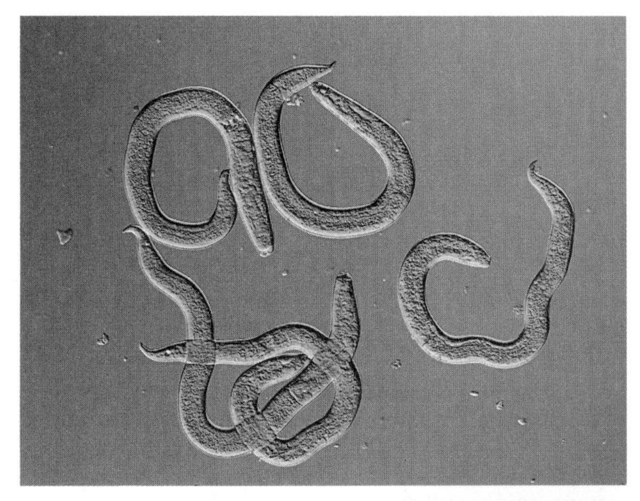

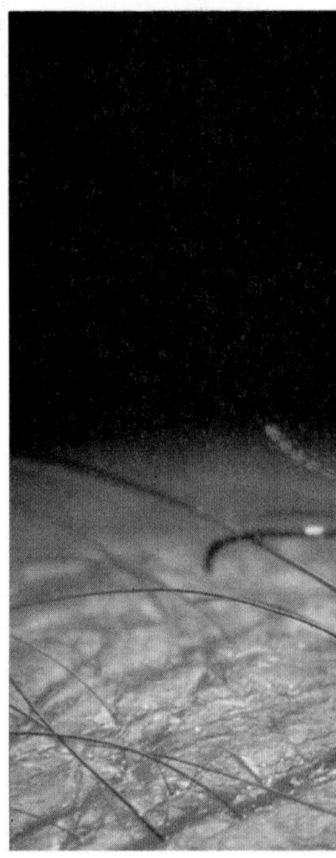

Above: The nematode *Heligosomoides polygyrus*, which is a parasite on rodents but does not affect humans
Right: Mosquitoes are one of the worst of human parasites. While feeding on human blood it transmits potentially fatal diseases such as malaria and yellow fever. In this picture, blood from a human arm can be seen flowing up the proboscis of a female yellow fever mosquito.

Parasites on our side

Some parasites are now being employed as pesticides. The fungus *Verticillium lecanii* can be applied in water, just like a chemical spray, to control a range of pests such as aphids. Parasitic nematodes are being used to control soil pests such as weevil larvae. Pesticide treatment of soil is difficult, expensive, and uncertain; there is no guarantee the chemical will reach the depth at which the pest lives. Nematodes sprayed onto the soil, however, move through it under their own power to find their prey.

On their own, the nematode parasites would slowly incapacitate their weevil-larva host, but this takes many weeks. Many parasitic nematodes carry symbiotic bacteria in their guts which enter the host and kill its cells, making them easier for the nematode to digest. Careful selection has provided a nematode-plus-bacterium combination lethal in a couple of days. GENETIC ENGINEERING has the potential to enhance the speed of kill of the bacteria still further.

Not all nematodes are so helpful. The appropriately named root-knot nematodes attack many tropical crops, some of great commercial value, such as cotton, citrus, corn, and tobacco. As they feed, they inject the roots with saliva containing biochemicals which drastically alter cell growth. Around the embedded head of the feeding nematode the cells enlarge dramatically, causing the crumpled root swellings that give the nematode its name. Researchers have now found soil-dwelling fungi that naturally attack the nutrition egg masses of the nematodes, and are seeking to enhance their effectiveness as biological control agents.

Unlike the broad spectrum toxic effect of chemical pesticides, such biological agents can be precisely targeted only at harmful pathogens.

Animals as parasites

In the animal kingdom, most parasites are so-called "lower" animals with comparatively simple anatomy. Parasitism is commonplace among insects, flatworms (or flukes), tapeworms, and roundworms (or nematodes). Most parasitic insects, such as ticks and mites, live on the outer

Left: A close-up of the nematode *Toxocara vitalorum*. Most nematodes are parasitic, affecting either plants or animals. Among the nematode diseases found in humans are hookworm, threadworm, maw-worm, and toxocariasis.

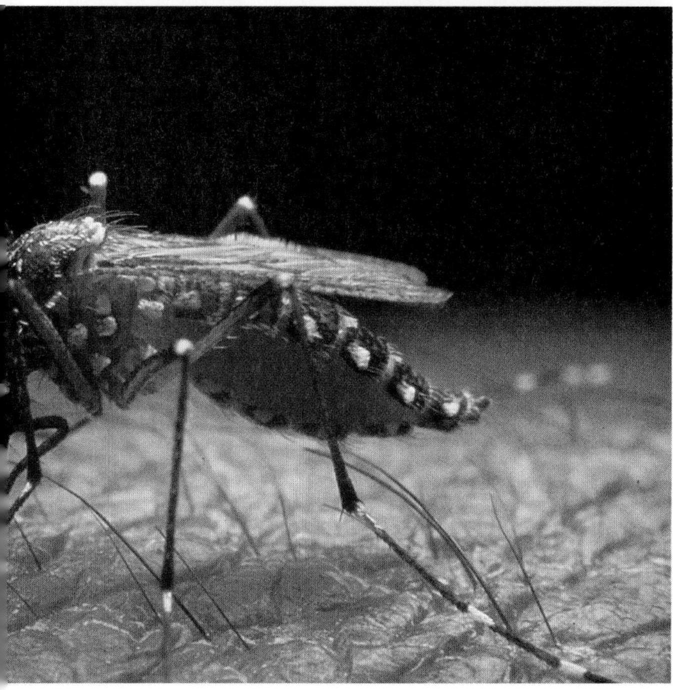

surface or skin of their host, while most flatworms, tapeworms, and nematodes live within their host. Most animal parasites are small, many microscopic, but a few can grow to a substantial size, tapeworms occasionally growing as long as 10 ft (3 m).

Parasites need a method of getting from one host to another. In many cases this is "passive" – the eggs or larvae are left in places where they stand a chance of being picked up by the host. For example, chickens pick up the eggs of a nematode worm, *Ascaridia galli*, when feeding and pass on the next generation of eggs in their droppings. But other parasites need vectors – that is, other agents which unwittingly transport the parasite from one host to the next.

A classic example of a vector at work is the mosquito, which carries the tiny protozoans that cause malaria. For many years the disease has been well controlled both by anti-malarial drugs and by killing the vector – the mosquito – with insecticides. Now, however, malaria is on the increase again. The protozoan parasite has developed resistance to the drugs, and pesticides such as DDT that initially controlled the mosquitoes so well are now considered to be too persistent and too environmentally damaging to be used.

One novel approach to the problem is currently being researched at the National Insititutes of Health. It aims to interrupt the life cycle of the protozoan when it is actually within the mosquito. A vaccine has been developed which will do this, but it will not protect the person bitten by a mosquito. Instead, a mosquito which bites a vaccinated person will not then transmit the protozoan to other people that it bites. Although it will still be necessary to protect the human carrying the vaccine using conventional methods, the hope is that the protection will gradually spread throughout the community.

The advantage of blocking the transmission of the disease at an early stage in the parasite's development is that there is less risk of particularly robust parasites surviving to pass on their successful genes and so create a resistant strain. The method was initially tested only in mice, with safety trials on humans scheduled in 1993.

Multi-host parasites

The life cycles of parasites can be fascinatingly complex. Gall wasps which attack oak trees begin their cycle in late summer when fertilized females lay their eggs on the undersides of leaves. Injected with the egg are biochemicals which manipulate the leaf tissue to produce characteristic galls. One causes pale spangle-like outgrowths, another, golden galls resembling microscopic silk buttons. Within the gall, which in fall drops to the forest floor, the egg develops into a larva by feeding on the plant tissue. The larva pupates, and in spring an asexual wasp emerges, quite different in appearance from its parent. This, without mating, flies to the newly opening tassels of oak flowers and there lays its eggs. Again these are accompanied by chemical secretions, but in this case the gall that forms is fleshy and spherical, closely resembling a red currant fruit. From these eggs hatch the males and females that will mate on the wing before the female lays her eggs in a leaf for the cycle to start again.

Left: A close-up of part of an oak tree. A gall, caused by an unidentified parasite, can be seen near the center of the frame.

An understanding of the mode of action of the biochemicals injected by the gall wasp could be of great value in manipulating tree growth, and research is being actively directed to this goal both in orchard fruits and in hardwood timber trees.

Schistosomiasis, a disease that afflicts 200 million people worldwide, is caused by worms that begin life as tiny larvae swimming in fresh water. The larvae first infect snails and multiply in them, then escape again into the water. If a person steps in the water they burrow through the skin and enter the bloodstream. After growing for a few weeks in the lungs they travel to veins that drain the intestine or bladder and remain for 20 to 30 years, constantly laying eggs. Some of the eggs burrow into the intestine or bladder to be excreted and, if they reach fresh water, start the cycle again.

Recent research at the University of California at San Francisco has revealed that at least one species of the worms has evolved to respond to a human hormone that calls immune system cells to the site of bacterial infections. The hormone is always present in veins that drain the intestine, because these veins contain waste products from intestinal bacteria. The presence of the hormone tells the worms they are in the right place to lay their eggs.

In many cases parasitism is extremely damaging to us and our crops, and may even be life-threatening, but a detailed understanding of its modes of action will help resolve the problems caused, and should also lead to a steadily increasing range of environmentally friendly pest and disease control strategies.

• FACT FILE •

- A single drug that cures a range of parasitic diseases may seem far-fetched, but work reported in 1989 could make it a possibility. The work, carried out by researchers at Imperial College in London, could help control some of the worst Third World infections.
- Several different parasites, spread by insect bites, are reponsible for the diseases African sleeping sickness, Chagas' disease, and leishmaniasis. Worldwide, 100 million people suffer from these diseases. But while the parasites are different, their effects all involve the same enzyme, called alkaline peptidase.
- Although the enzyme's role is still unclear, it is believed to aid the parasite in its attack on the host's blood system. If its effects can be curbed, the parasites will not be able to infect their hosts. Furthermore, the enzyme does not occur in humans, so any such drug would not harm them.
- The team, now based at Washington State University, is aiming to synthesize a molecule that will bind with the enzyme, thus inactivating it.

Particle physics

Particle physics is the study of the basic building blocks of the universe and the forces that act upon them. The field is one of the most exciting in modern physics, and each new discovery improves our overall picture of how the universe works. This view is known as the Standard Model of particle physics, which has been developed over more than two decades of research. According to this model, there are three groups of particles called quarks, leptons, and gauge bosons.

The Standard Model

The particles which make up the universe are held together by just four basic forces. In order of increasing strength these are gravity; the weak force, responsible for reactions that fuel the Sun and some forms of radioactivity; the electromagnetic force, which binds electrons to nuclei within atoms; and the strong force, which binds quarks together within protons and other particles. The Standard Model includes three of these four forces – gravity alone remains excluded for now.

According to the Standard Model, these three basic forces operate through carrier particles – gauge bosons – which are exchanged between interacting particles. In the case of the electromagnetic force, when electrically charged particles interact they pass between them a photon, the massless particle of light. The weak force acts through a heavier carrier – the charged particle known as W, or the neutral particle called Z, both of which are roughly 100 times heavier than the proton. The strong force acts between quarks through the exchange of eight varieties of massless carriers called gluons.

Quarks make up the protons and neutrons that form atomic nuclei. They also make up the short-lived particles produced naturally when cosmic rays – energetic particles from outer space – collide with the Earth's atmosphere. These exotic, unstable particles are also created in particle accelerators, where synthetic collisions mimic the effects of cosmic rays.

Lastly, there are the leptons, which do not feel the strong force. They include the electron, together with the muon and the tau, which are charged like the electron, but which are respectively 200 and 3600 times heavier. There are also three types of electrically neutral lepton, called neutrinos, which are associated with the electron, the muon, and the tau. Neutrinos weigh much less than their charged partners, and may even be massless.

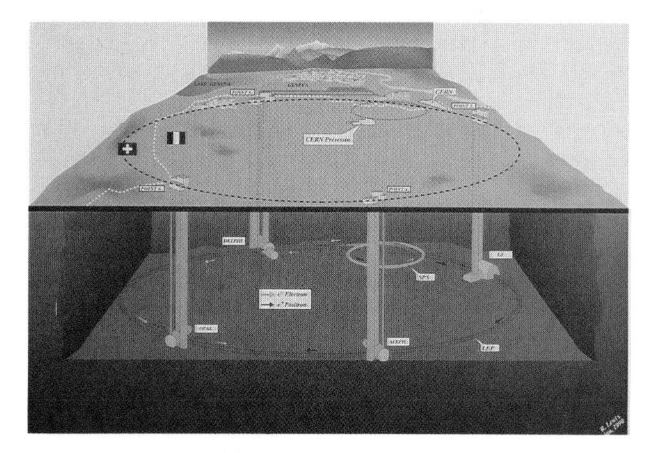

Above: Schematic view of the facilities at CERN, Geneva, which lies in both Switzerland and France. The main ring, the LEP tunnel, has a circumference of 17 miles (27 km), with various points around it at which particles can be extracted for experiments. The smaller ring, the SPS tunnel, is over 4 miles (7 km) in circumference.
Left: The outline of the CERN ring can be seen on the landscape.

Left: The collider detector at the Fermi National Accelerator Laboratory, near Chicago, is a collaborative U.S., Japanese, and Italian project. Calorimeters containing photomultipliers surround the region where collisions between protons and antiprotons take place.

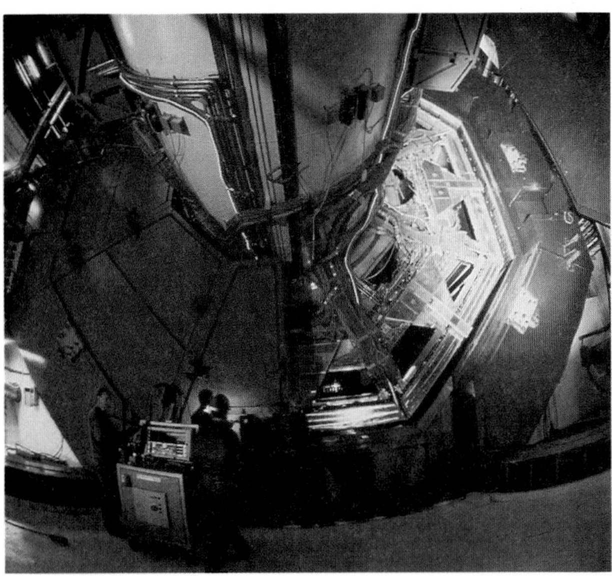

Right: The L3 detector at CERN, where electrons, moving one way round the ring, collide with positrons, moving the other way. A large magnetic field surrounds the detector, which is enclosed within enormous iron doors.

In 1989, experiments at CERN, the European Organization for Nuclear Research, near Geneva, and at the Stanford Linear Accelerator Center in California, revealed for the first time a limit to the types of quark and lepton. The experiments produced many Z particles, which enabled the physicists to study how readily this particle decays. The results showed that there can be no more than three types of neutrino for the Z particle to decay into – and these must be the three neutrinos we already know. This is an important result, for it implies that the number of charged leptons is also no more than three; and through the symmetry implicit in the Standard Model, there must be only three pairs of quarks – six quarks in all.

Missing ingredients

The Standard Model works remarkably well in accounting for the results of many experiments in particle physics. However, there are several missing ingredients. The symmetry underlying the theory implies six types of quark, but so far experiments have revealed the existence of only five. The protons and neutrons of everyday matter are made from the lightest pair of quarks, called "up" and "down"; particles created in high-energy collisions have revealed the existence of another, heavier pair called "charm" and "strange". A fifth quark, "bottom", the heaviest so far, has also been found. But its predicted partner, the sixth quark, called "top", is still missing.

Another missing ingredient has to do with the way that particles, in particular the W and Z gauge bosons of the weak force, acquire their masses in the Standard Model. The model assumes the existence of a new particle, which is called the Higgs particle after one of its inventors. The theory is that the other particles gain their masses through their interactions with this new particle, but so far there is no experimental evidence for its existence.

Beyond the Standard Model

One unsatisfactory feature of the Standard Model is that it is an amalgam of two theories. One of these is the electroweak theory, which successfully unites the weak force and the electromagnetic force. In electroweak theory, the weak and electromagnetic forces derive from a single underlying electroweak force; they appear different only in our low-energy everyday world.

The other component of the Standard Model is the theory of quantum chromodynamics, which deals with the strong force and its actions on quarks and gluons. The structure of this theory is similar to that of the electroweak theory, and this has led physicists to search for a "Grand Unified Theory" in which the strong as well as the weak and the electromagnetic forces are all derived from a single force.

One problem that occurs in trying to build such a theory is that the quarks and the leptons tend to

Left: The interior of the LEP tunnel at CERN.

acquire huge masses, making them 10^{16} (10,000,000,000,000,000) times as heavy as a proton. But this problem can be resolved by introducing what is called "supersymmetry".

Particles have an intrinsic property known as "spin", with quarks and leptons having half a unit of spin, and gauge bosons having whole units of spin. Supersymmetry brings extra symmetry into this picture by predicting that all the known particles have partners with spins differing by half a unit. When the interactions of these new particles are included in a grand unified theory, the quarks and leptons turn out to have sensible masses. These ideas are supported by recent studies at CERN, which have investigated the way the strengths of the electroweak and strong forces vary with energy within the Standard Model. It appears that at very high energies, the strengths will become equal – but only if supersymmetry is included in the calculations.

Experiments in the 1990s

Particle physicists are already searching for the top quark. It seems likely that it could weigh about 130 times as much as a proton, and there is a good chance that it could be produced at Fermilab, a laboratory west of Chicago. A machine there, called the Tevatron, accelerates protons and antiprotons before bringing them into head-on collisions at total energies of 2 TeV (2 tera electron-volts, or 2 million million electron-volts). When the protons and antiprotons meet, they turn into pure energy in an act of mutual self-destruction known as annihilation. The energy then rematerializes as many kinds of particles, and the physicists at Fermilab hope that in this debris they will discover particles that contain the top quark.

The Higgs particle presents more of a problem, for there is less agreement not only on its mass, but even on whether or not there is more than one type of Higgs particle. The idea of the Higgs particle may even be completely wrong. However, physicists know that they must discover some new effect in experiments at total collision energies above about 10 TeV. At these energies, some of the predictions of the Standard Model become nonsensical, so it is clear that some new ingredient must be found.

There are two proposals to build machines to explore this new high-energy region. The Large Hadron Collider, proposed for CERN, would produce collisions at a total energy of about 15 TeV. This machine would be built in the tunnel, 17 miles (27 km) in circumference, that already houses LEP, CERN's Large Electron Positron collider. In the U.S., preliminary work has already begun on a completely new machine, the Superconducting Super Collider, or SSC, in Texas. The SSC, with a tunnel 54 miles (87 km) in circumference, will reach collision energies of 40 TeV, subject to full funding from the U.S. government.

These colliders, if they are built, will not be completed until the late 1990s, but they are guaranteed to reveal new vistas in particle physics. They may yield one or more Higgs particles, or some other clues to the origin of mass. They could produce the first examples of heavy, supersymmetric partners to the particles already included in the Standard Model.

The final frontier

Even if research over the next decade leads to a successful grand unified theory relating the weak, electromagnetic, and strong forces, that will still exclude gravity. So far, gravity has defied all attempts to include it at the subatomic, quantum level with these other forces. However, one approach that appears to hold promise is the theory of "superstrings". This theory incorporates supersymmetry, and treats elementary particles not as points in space but as extended "stringlike" objects in a strange multidimensional space. At present, such theories seem to have little connection with the experiments of particle physics, but they may well hold the key to the next successful Standard Model.

Another great mystery concerns the origin of

matter in the universe. Whenever quarks and leptons are created in interactions in the laboratory or in cosmic rays, equal numbers of antiquarks and antileptons are produced. These are particles with the same masses as the quarks and leptons, but with opposite charges. All the matter we know in the universe seems to be built only from particles, and this raises the question of what happened to the antiparticles that should have been created at the same time in the early universe. The present Standard Model has no answer to this question, but it could be that a peculiar lack of symmetry in the weak force is related to the universal lack of symmetry between matter and antimatter.

• FACT FILE •

- Some limitations of the Standard Model of particles and forces are seen in particle physics experiments and in astrophysical observations of the structure of the universe itself. Evidence suggests that 90 per cent or more of the mass of the universe exists as "dark matter". This is non-luminous matter that we can detect only through its gravitational effects; for example, in the motion of galaxies and clusters of galaxies. It is a challenge for particle physicists, as well as astrophysicists, to identify the nature of this dark matter. It may, for instance, consist of particles predicted by supersymmetry, but which have not yet been observed in experiments.

- This important puzzle has also stimulated experiments to search for naturally occurring dark matter particles, away from the large particle colliders. Such particles do not yet have a name but they are being referred to collectively as WIMPs – weakly interacting massive particles. Because they are weakly interacting, they are hard to detect. Though they may have masses a few times that of a proton, if they exist billions of them could pass through a person every second without that person feeling a thing.

- Experimenters at the University of California at Berkeley are hoping to detect WIMPs through the minute recoils they would produce in sensitive materials at very low temperatures, where other movements are reduced to a minimum. These experiments are to be buried underground to shield them from the effects of cosmic rays. By the end of the decade, the search for WIMPs may be successful.

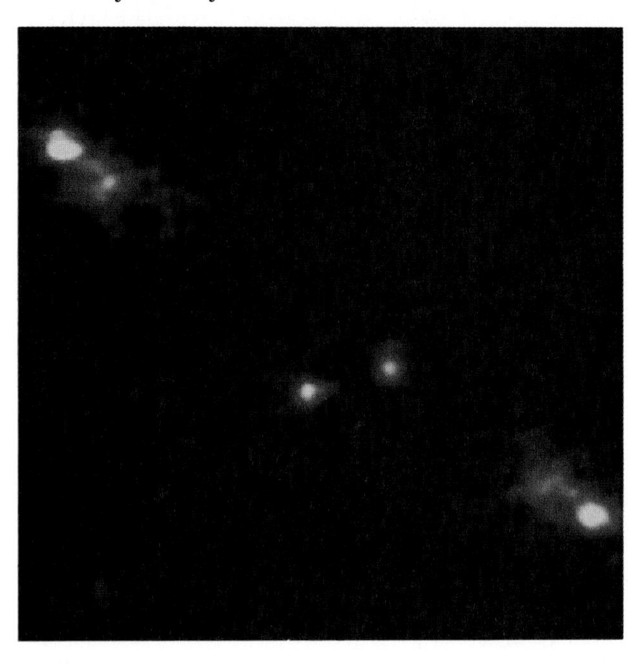

Above: Evidence for dark matter in the universe comes from the Hubble Space Telescope. The image of a single galaxy has here been split into two mirror images by a cluster of nearer galaxies, center.

Above: Graduate students at Berkeley, CA, working on a dilution refrigerator that will be used to search for particle dark matter. It cools the detectors to 5 milliKelvins – virtually absolute zero.

Pathology

Almost anyone who has been in hospital will have been helped by the skills of a pathologist. Pathology in its broadest sense is the scientific investigation of disease; for example, what effect a disease has on levels of different chemicals in the blood or on the cells and tissues of the body. Pathologists help other doctors to diagnose a patient's illness and, often, help them to decide the best treatment for the patient.

Over the past 30 years, pathology has broadened from one specialty into many. Experimental pathology involves trying to discover previously unknown causes of diseases through experimentation in the laboratory. Molecular pathology is the study of how molecules bring about disease and how their appearance and behavior then change during it. Another branch, chemical pathology, is the investigation of how chemicals in the body change in response to disease.

Histopathology is what most people think of when they think of pathology. It involves analyzing samples of tissue taken from patients. These are either embedded in kerosene wax or frozen before being finely sliced. The sections are placed on a microscope slide and stained in order to show the structure of the different cells, which are visible when viewed through a microscope.

New technologies have revolutionized histopathology. One advance was the development of the electron microscope, which allows much greater magnification of the sample. Its main application in pathology has been in diagnosing kidney disease. Looked at under the light microscope, a section from a sample of a diseased kidney often looks perfectly normal.

The electron microscope makes it possible to see deposits of protein in the tiny blood vessels, or glomeruli, that filter blood passing through the kidney. If these deposits are present, the histopathologist can advise the doctor that the outlook for the patient is poor and that a kidney transplant may be needed within a few months or years. Conversely, if the kidney looks normal, it may be possible to reassure the patient that there is nothing seriously wrong.

A second development allows histopathologists to distinguish between tumors which have cells that look extremely similar. For example, three different types of tumor (a non-pigmented malignant melanoma, a large-cell lymphoma, and an undifferentiated carcinoma) can look virtually the same when viewed under the microscope. But in each case, the treatment recommended for the patient is very different.

This breakthrough came when researchers discovered that tumor cells have specific proteins on their surfaces. As a result, histopathologists now

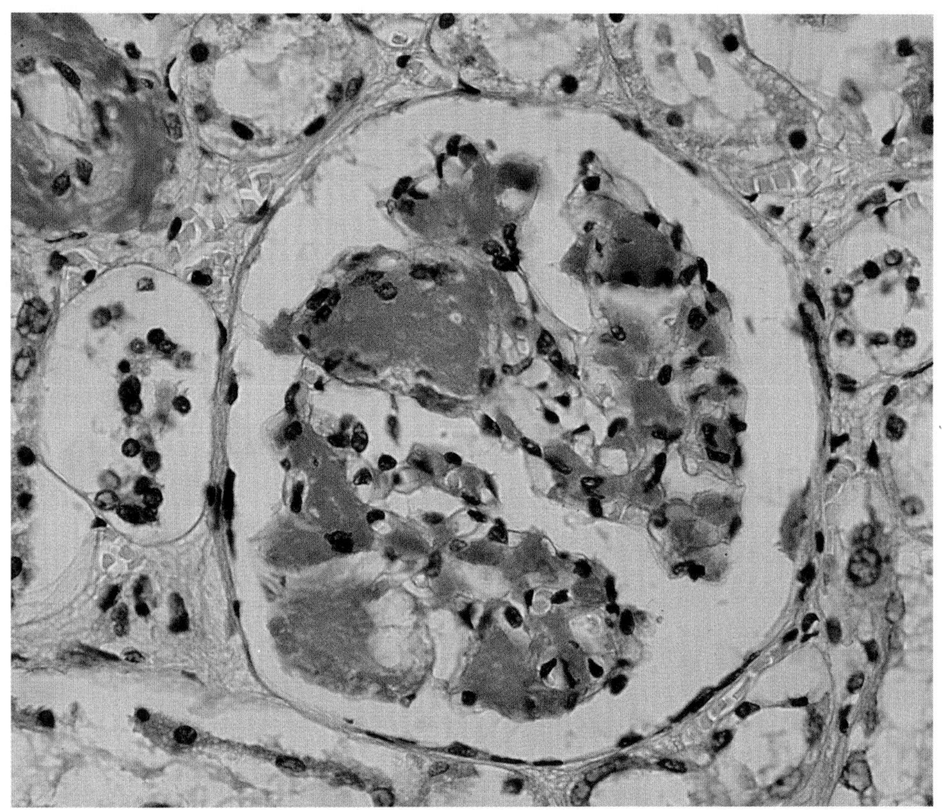

Left: The development of the electron microscope has led to huge breakthroughs in the diagnosis of kidney disease. This light micrograph of a human kidney shows amyloid deposits (pink). Amyloid is composed of protein. Its presence causes disruption of tissues, loss of functioning cells and, if arteries are involved, a reduction in blood supply. It is associated with diseases such as rheumatoid arthritis and some cancers. This specimen is from a person with a 20-year history of rheumatoid arthritis.

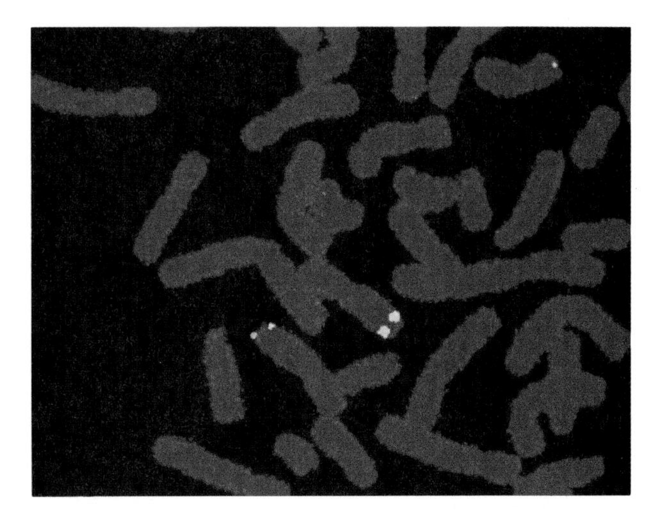

Above: Fluorescence micrograph of human chromosomes showing the mapping of DNA probes.

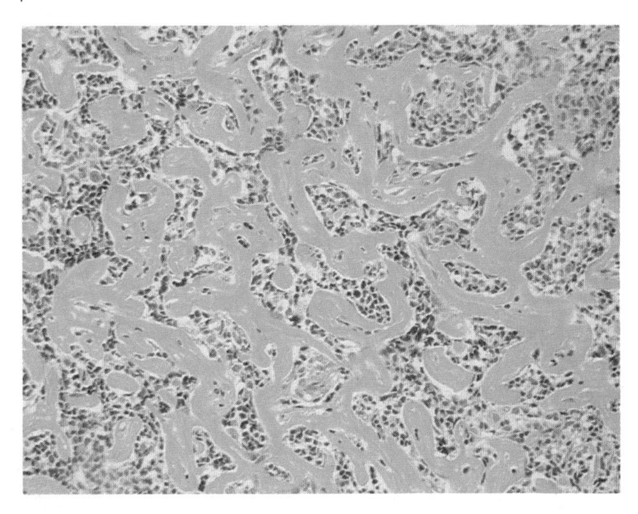

Above: Light micrograph of a human lymphoma (a cancerous tumor of lymphocytes).

have at their disposal a range of antibodies, each one capable of binding to one of these specific tumor proteins. They can tell whether the antibodies have bound to the cells in the tissue section because the antibodies are linked to chemicals which are colored or which fluoresce in ultraviolet light.

The role of genes

A third advance has come from new techniques which allow histopathologists to study the way in which individual genes make proteins in various tissues of the body. This can be helpful because a cell may produce a particular protein only if disease is present.

In addition, in cancer, genes that drive the abnormal cell division typical of a tumor, called *oncogenes*, may be activated. Knowing that such an oncogene is active may help to determine the best treatment for the patient.

The starting point for this latest technique is the fact that the genetic information needed to make a protein is held in the nucleic acid, DNA, which is found in the nucleus of the cell. The cell transcribes this blueprint into messenger RNA (mRNA), which then acts as a template for the structure of the protein (see MOLECULAR BIOLOGY).

It is therefore possible to identify which protein a cell is making, by detecting the mRNA for the protein. This is done by *nucleic acid hybridization*. For this, chemists synthesize short lengths of DNA which, because they are the same as the DNA template from which the mRNA is made, bind or hybridize to the mRNA.

The short lengths of DNA are called DNA probes. Pathologists can tell when the probes have hybridized because they carry a chemical or radioactive label. A probe can be synthesized for any protein, as long as its genetic sequence is known. A computer will take just a few seconds to check that the probe selected is unique to the protein being investigated.

Parathyroid disease provides an example of how DNA hybridization can help in diagnosis. The parathyroids – four glands near the thyroid in the throat – produce a hormone involved in regulating calcium metabolism. In parathyroid disease, the glands become overactive, producing abnormally large amounts of the hormone. The hormone itself, however, cannot be readily detected in the cells because they export it as soon as it is made. The problem of identification can be solved by using a DNA probe for the mRNA that codes for the protein.

Automating smear tests

The cervical smear test is a good example of how pathology is applied. In a smear test, the doctor takes a small sample of cells from the cervix (the neck of the uterus). In the pathology lab it is stained with chemicals and looked at under a light microscope. Abnormal cells have larger nuclei and take the stains more readily.

Unfortunately, checking the slides can be open to human error. It can be difficult for a laboratory worker to stay alert enough to spot the two or three abnormal smears in every thousand. Researchers have therefore been trying to automate the process. Prototype machines use pattern recognition devices to spot the darkly stained abnormal cells.

It may soon be possible for a machine to scan all slides, alerting a technician to any that have suspicious-looking cells on them. This would allow cytologists to concentrate their diagnostic skills on smears that especially need attention.

Pediatrics

The first years of a person's life can be the most dangerous ones. Children are particularly prone to many diseases which an older person would shrug off. The science of pediatrics deals with the care of children and, in particular, the diseases from which they suffer. The days when infectious diseases such as smallpox, poliomyelitis, and whooping cough used to kill many children before they reached adulthood are over – in developed countries, at least. Effective vaccines and antibiotics have eliminated some diseases and greatly reduced the threat of others.

But as the menace of many infectious diseases has subsided, other conditions have assumed greater importance in determining the health of children. These include congenital abnormalities, inherited diseases, and childhood cancers.

There are many different congenital abnormalities; that is, defects with which a child is born. Those affecting the spinal cord include neural tube defects such as spina bifida (in which the spinal cord may protrude from the spine), hydrocephalus (excess fluid on the brain), and anencephaly (absence of the brain, a condition which is incompatible with life). In most developed countries, prenatal screening for neural tube defects has resulted in a drop in the number of children born with these conditions. Where the fetus is found to be affected, the pregnant woman and her partner are offered the option to terminate the pregnancy.

In the case of congenital heart disease, in which the child is born with a deformed heart, new surgical techniques may now make it possible to correct the abnormality. Alternatively, if the defect is very severe, it may be possible to carry out a heart transplant. Such operations have been carried out on infants just a few days old, with donor hearts the size of plums. In one case, in 1987, the abnormality was diagnosed by ultrasound while the baby was still in his mother's uterus. When a suitable donor heart became available, doctors at the Loma Linda Transplant Center in California immediately carried out a Caesarean section and the transplant operation was performed within three hours of baby Paul Holc's birth.

Inherited diseases

The most common inherited disease among Caucasians is cystic fibrosis. The disease makes the body produce unusually thick and sticky mucus. This clogs up the lungs, making the sufferer prone to chest infections, and blocks the duct leading from the pancreas, so that food is not digested properly.

As recently as the 1970s, many children with cystic fibrosis died before they reached their teens. Modern treatment involves antibiotics to prevent and treat infections, chest physiotherapy to drain the sticky secretions, and enzyme supplements to assist digestion. As a result, many cystic fibrosis sufferers now live into their mid-20s. Heart-lung transplants have also helped some teenagers and young adults suffering with cystic fibrosis, although it is too early to say what

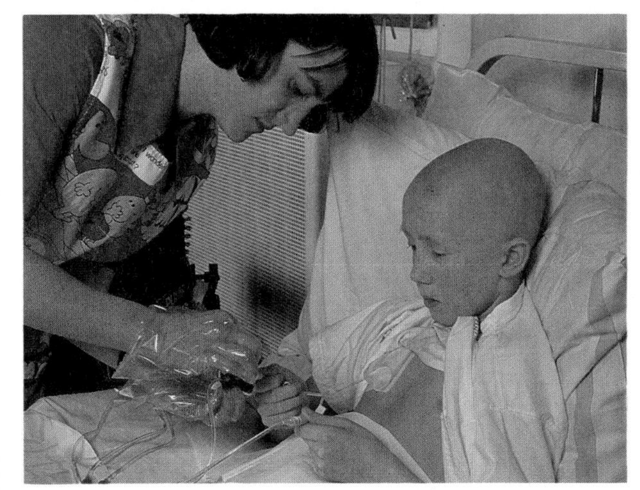

Left: A physiotherapist giving percussion treatment to a three-year-old cystic fibrosis patient. This loosens the mucus, which is coughed up.
Above: A pediatric nurse adjusting an intravenous line being used to deliver chemotherapy to a young boy with leukemia.

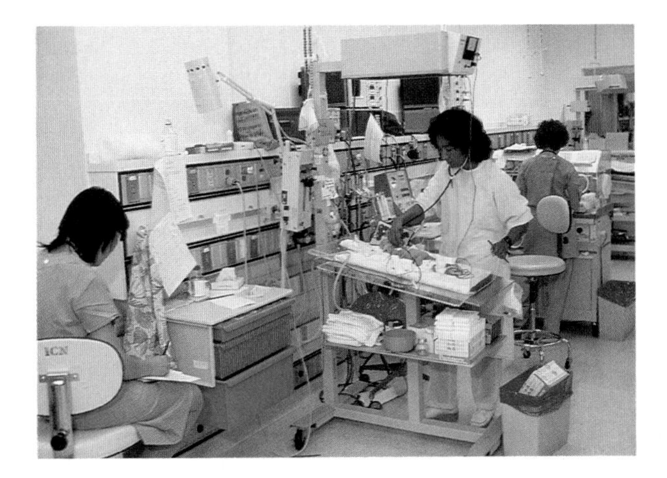

Left: Nurse attending a premature baby in a pediatric inensive care unit at Stamford Hospital, CT. The baby's condition is constantly monitored.

the overall effect of these operations will be on long term survival.

The discovery in 1989 by researchers at the universities of Toronto and Michigan of the gene for cystic fibrosis, which codes for a protein that controls the excretion of salt and water from cells, holds out the hope that more effective drugs may be on the horizon to treat this disease. Such a therapy may well be available in time to affect the survival of children being born with cystic fibrosis today. Hopefully, however, the practice of screening for carriers of the defective gene, together with prenatal diagnosis and the option of termination of affected pregnancies, will mean that fewer children will be born with cystic fibrosis in the future.

Childhood cancers are relatively rare, affecting about one in 600 children below the age of 15. In children, leukemias are the most common cancers, followed by brain tumors, then lymphomas (including Hodgkin's disease).

More effective combinations of anti-cancer drugs, developed with the help of large-scale clinical trials comparing the effects of similar treatments, now mean that half of all new cases of childhood cancer diagnosed each year can be cured. Such children are likely to have a normal life expectancy.

Some of the most striking advances have been made in the treatment of leukemia. In the 1960s, leukemia in children was almost always fatal, usually within 6 to 12 months. Fewer than 1 per cent of children with this disease lived for any length of time. In the 1990s, thanks to new medical discoveries, three out of four children who develop the most common form of childhood leukemia can be cured.

Saving premature babies

Better intensive care of premature babies means that such a baby born today has a much better chance of surviving than he or she would have had in the 1970s. The main improvement has been in methods of mechanical ventilation to help the baby's breathing. In addition, miniaturization of equipment has made it much easier to insert intravenous drips into a newborn's tiny veins to deliver food and medicines. Equipment designed to monitor the concentrations of gases in the baby's blood through his or her skin (without using needles to sample the blood), has made it possible to deliver the correct amount of oxygen.

Babies born 12 weeks early now have an approximately 80 per cent chance of survival, rising to 90 per cent for those 11 weeks early. Babies born 16 or 17 weeks early can survive, but, the more premature the baby, the greater the risk of its suffering disability. About 40 per cent of those who arrive 16 or 17 weeks early suffer some degree of disability.

Apart from advances in mechanical ventilation, two types of drug treatment have also helped many more premature babies to survive. One is the discovery that giving a pregnant woman steroids for 48 hours before a pre-term delivery greatly reduces the respiratory problems that the baby will experience once born. This is possible because some babies have to be delivered prematurely for their safety, the safety of the mother, or both. It cannot be done, however, when delivery is sudden or unexpected.

Second, a substance called a surfactant can be given to the premature infant. Because this reduces the surface tension of water, it helps to keep the lungs inflated. Without it, the air pockets in the lungs tend to collapse.

Cot deaths

With improved health care, infant mortality has declined over the years. But some infant deaths remain unexplained and are attributed to Sudden Infant Death Syndrome (SIDS). Less than two per cent of babies die in this way, mostly before the age of six months, but research has failed to find any single cause for this distressing problem. Experts now recommend that babies are placed on their back or side to sleep, that the parents should not smoke, that the baby should not get too hot, and that the doctor should be called if danger signs appear.

Many parents buy devices which monitor their baby's breathing and movement, but as yet there is no evidence that they reduce the incidence of cot death. Over 50,000 monitors are now in daily use in the U.S., but there has been no decline in the SIDS rate.

Petrology

Petrology is the materials science of the geological world. What chemical compositions do rocks have, what minerals are they made of, and under what conditions do they form? These are the basic questions a petrologist asks.

Petrology is above all an practical science, and it is by combining laboratory experiments, thermodynamic analysis, and field observations, that the petrologist hopes to understand how geological processes lead to the formation of rocks, thereby enhancing our knowledge of the solid Earth. The subject has much common ground with MATERIALS SCIENCE, which means that someone with a knowledge of petrology is not limited in scope to GEOLOGY, but may also be employed on materials development in industry.

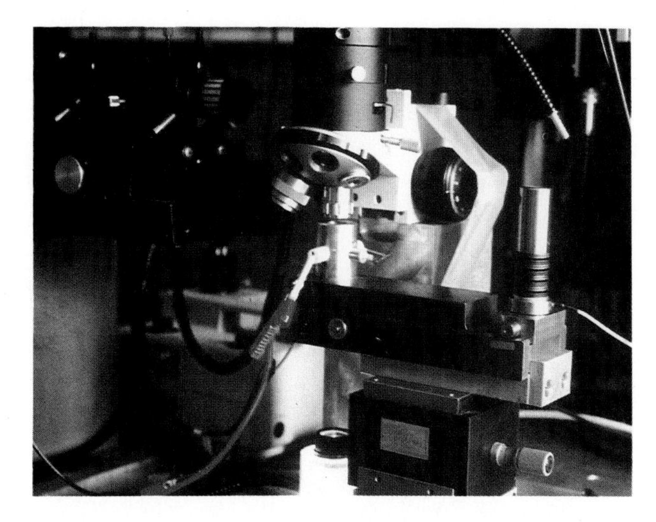

Above: A diamond anvil cell – a small amount of material is pressed between diamonds, subjecting it to a million times atmospheric pressure, emulating the conditions under which rocks are formed deep in the Earth.
Below: A piece of material which has been subjected to extremely high pressure in the press. The red area has been superheated using a laser.

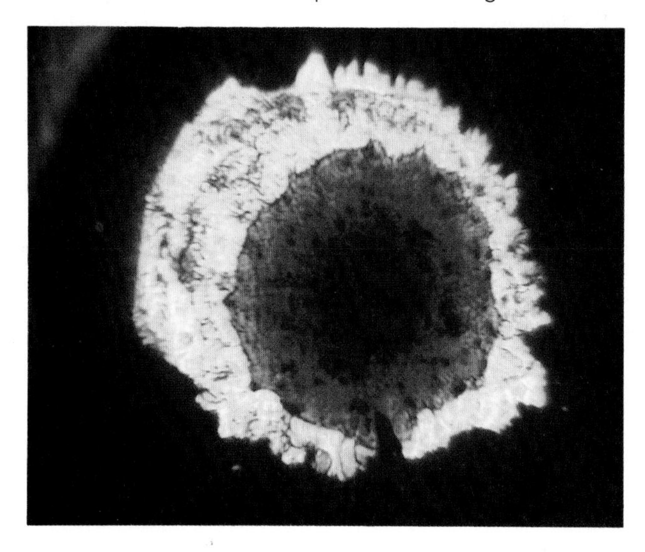

The memory of rocks

The idea of thermodynamic equilibrium lies at the heart of petrology. This means that a rock of given composition at equilibrium, under the same conditions of temperature and pressure, should always have the same mineralogy. As a simple example, consider the chemical element carbon which normally exists as the mineral graphite under the standard conditions of room temperature and one atmosphere of pressure. At much higher pressures, carbon is transformed into diamond whose structure is more compact. The rocks that we can collect at the Earth's surface have all, at some time in the past, experienced conditions within the interior and acquired mineralogies corresponding to conditions of higher temperature and pressure. The processes that continually reshape our planet have subsequently brought them to the surface.

Rocks still possess this mineralogical memory of these earlier conditions because mineral transformations and chemical reactions between minerals are very slow at surface temperatures, requiring geological time scales. This is why we can mine diamonds at the Earth's surface, and why diamond rings and necklaces in jewelers' shops do not transform into graphite.

Studying the Earth's deep interior

Petrologists can actually create artificial rocks in a small capsule surrounded by strong confining materials, using high pressures and temperatures. In this way they can map out the combinations of pressure and temperature where minerals are stable. Such a map is known as a *phase diagram*, the stock-in-trade of the petrologist. In the last few years a range of remarkable new tools has become available. Particularly powerful among these is the diamond anvil cell. This consists of a press which subjects a small sample of material, confined between diamonds, to a million times atmospheric pressure. The transparency of the diamonds allows the sample to be heated by a laser beam to a temperature of several thousand degrees, and allows X-ray CRYSTALLOGRAPHY to be taken under the conditions of the experiment. Experts believe these to be the conditions existing deep inside the Earth.

Armed with these results, petrologists can now compare the properties of the minerals obtained in the laboratory with, for example, a knowledge of the deep structure of the globe provided by SEISMOLOGY. So even without going there, it is possible

Left: Two scientists take measurements of the temperature and velocity of gases escaping from a vent on Mt. Etna, Italy. The gases were highly corrosive and measured more than 1800 °F (1000 °C), hence the red coloring in the vent's walls. In recent years, petrologists have borrowed techniques used in physical chemistry in order to gain a greater understanding of the properties and behavior of magma.

to explore the compositions and the phase diagrams of the materials making up the deep Earth, and to make contributions to the study of important problems such as how the liquid iron outer core is slowly crystallizing to produce the solid inner core, and how it is stirred by vigorous motions. These processes are responsible for the generation of the geomagnetic field, showing how the study of regions, seemingly so remote, can lead to understanding of phenomena of everyday significance such as the direction in which a compass needle points.

Molten rock, known as magma, is the stuff of volcanic eruptions. Petrologists have learned how to combine their measurements of the thermodynamic properties of magma with fluid dynamic models of how it flows beneath volcanoes. Although volcanologists have known for some time that small amounts of gases (mainly water and carbon dioxide) are dissolved in magma, it is only in the last few years, by borrowing and adapting a number of techniques from PHYSICAL CHEMISTRY such as infrared absorption spectroscopy, that petrologists have measured how much of these species can be dissolved in silicate melts. Moreover, they have determined how the solubilities of these species increase with pressure, and so can predict how magma tries to degas as it rises through the Earth's crust beneath volcanoes.

This process by which bubbles form in the melt as it decompresses, causes a large expansion which accelerates the rising magma towards the eruption vent. This, in turn, determines whether the magma is expelled as a lava flow or as a violent jet, injecting volcanic gases and aerosols high into the atmosphere, and is ultimately responsible for the environmental impact of volcanic eruptions.

Links with other sciences

Recent work has shown how closely the work of petrologists is allied to materials science. The stable silicate mineral in much of Earth's mantle is called Mg-perovskite; it is a remarkable coincidence that high-temperature superconducting substances recently discovered (for which the Nobel Prize in Physics was awarded), while differing chemically, also possess a perovskite structure (see CONDENSED MATTER PHYSICS).

A new range of ceramic substrates (backings onto which other materials can be deposited) widely used in the semiconductor industry is closely related in chemical composition and mineral family to substances well-known to petrologists from their geological studies. For instance, work on the solubility of gases in silicate melts is of great relevance to the formidable technical problem encountered in the glass industry of how to produce bubble-free glass.

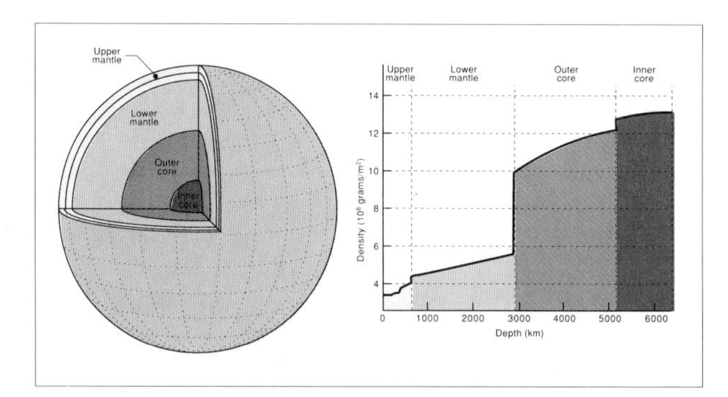

Right: The structure of the Earth and the density of the rocks within it. The research of petrologists examines how rocks behave in such conditions.

Pharmacology

The quality of life for Americans has been greatly enhanced by the availability of drugs which cure conditions that only half a century ago resulted either in death or prolonged disability. Nevertheless, some critics of the pharmaceutical industry are concerned about the toxic effects of drugs. Experimental pharmacologists are seeking to avoid or minimize toxic effects by finding drugs which are highly selective, acting only on specific cells, organs, or invading microorganisms. They also carry out extensive tests to confirm both the safety and the effectiveness of new drugs.

The developers of new drugs often achieve selectivity by designing molecules that are precisely shaped to fit into receptors on the surface of cells (see MEDICINAL CHEMISTRY). These receptors, composed of large, intricately folded proteins, ordinarily await the arrival of biological molecules such as hormones or the neurotransmitters which carry signals between nerve cells. By blocking the receptor, the drug can block the action of the molecule for which the receptor was intended; or, by mimicking the molecule, it can enhance the action. Other drugs are selective because they are shaped to fit into the active sites of enzymes which catalyze key biochemical reactions. Still others block minute channels which serve as gateways through cell membranes (see CELL BIOLOGY).

Drug toxicity

Long before a promising drug is first tested on humans, the pharmaceutical company will conduct toxicity tests on large numbers of animals over a period of months or years, especially for drugs which patients may be expected to use for long periods of time. The tests are carefully evaluated by statisticians to distinguish between genuine toxic effects and chance complications which have nothing to do with the drug.

The first tests of a new drug on human patients are intended to establish both the dose likely to produce a satisfactory response and also the severity of side effects occurring at higher dose levels. This will be followed by clinical studies on small numbers of patients to see if the drug is effective in treating the disease for which it is intended.

Once these preliminary tests have indicated that a new drug is comparatively safe and promises to be effective, carefully controlled clinical trials are carried out, usually comparing the new drug to others in common use. Quite often several hundred patients may need to be treated before doctors can be convinced that the new drug is really superior to those already available. As the apparent benefits of treatment might be merely tempo-

Above: A technician monitoring a micronizing device in the production of of respiratory drugs. Micronizing the active constituent of a drug or medicine means reducing its particle size to permit absorption in a particular part of the body, in this case the alveoli of the lungs.

rary, or superior only if compared with another drug for a limited period of time, long term follow-up of these patients is essential.

Licensing of pharmaceuticals

Because of a disaster involving over 100 deaths from a toxic solution of sulfanilamide in 1937, the United States has led the world in ensuring that medicines are as safe as they possibly can be. Thousands of children were born with severe deformities of their limbs after the sedative known as thalidomide was launched in Europe in 1959, but because of American caution the drug was never licensed in the United States. (However, due to the fact that the drug was illegally smuggled into the country, many American babies were severely damaged.) Since then, the American regulatory system has been copied in Europe and many other parts of the world.

All drugs sold in the United States must be licensed by the Food and Drug Administration (FDA). In order to receive a license, a new drug must pass a stringent series of standardized tests on animals and humans. Extensive documentation must be submitted by the manufacturer, detailing not only the clinical, pharmacological, and toxicological studies, but also the manufacturing process and the pharmaceutical properties of the final formulations in which the drug is administered. Impurities may creep in during the manufacturing

Left: Chemical analysis of new pharmaceutical compounds using nuclear magnetic resonance (NMR) spectrosopy. Here, a scientist is loading a sample tube into the spectrometer's cyromagnet. NMR chemical spectroscopy is used for determining the specific structure of novel chemical compounds, thus allowing chemists to judge how the compound would act in the body, helping them achieve selectivity. This photograph was taken at Nova Pharmaceutical Corporation in Baltimore.

process, or may even lurk in the fillers used to give a pill its color, shape, or flavor. The FDA insists that all side effects be thoroughly documented as well as featured in the promotional material provided to physicians.

Despite the close supervision exercised by the FDA and the pharmaceutical companies, one major problem remains. Any unanticipated hazard that occurs in fewer than, say, one in every 20,000 patients will probably not be noticed until 300-400,000 patients have received treatment.

The pharmaceutical industry is well aware of this. Consequently, all new drugs marketed in the 1990s will be more closely scrutinized than ever before through what has become known as "post-marketing surveillance." This involves direct contact between the pharmaceutical company's medical division and each prescriber, who is encouraged to keep careful watch on patients receiving the new drug. As a result, patients of the future will receive safer and better medication than ever before.

• FACT FILE •

- Merck Sharp & Dohme, the largest pharmaceutical company in the world, has recently developed a drug called Ivermectin™, which cures river blindness, the major cause of blindness in Africa. River blindness results from infection by a nematode worm known as *Onchocerca volvulus*. At least 17 million people are infected in Africa and Central America, hundreds of thousands of whom have lost their sight.

- Ivermectin is derived from a product which is secreted by the soil bacterium *Streptomyces avermitilis*. It prevents reproduction of the worm by mimicking and thereby augmenting the action of a neurotransmitter, gamma-aminobutyric acid, which inhibits the reproductive system of the female worm.

- Ivermectin is supplied free of charge to the World Health Organization by the manufacturers for use in Africa and Central America.

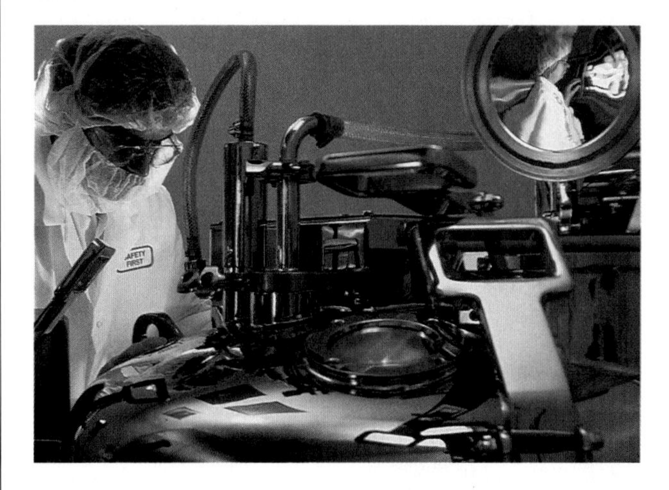

Above: A technician inspecting the contents of a reaction vessel during pilot scale production of a new pharmaceutical. Microprocessor control is used in this development-stage synthesis. The FDA will not license new drugs until it has received detailed information on the manufacturing process, as well as the results of exhaustive clinical, pharmacological and toxological studies, and data on the drug's pharmaceutical properties.

Physical chemistry

Physical chemistry is concerned with the physical properties and behavior of chemical substances – gases, liquids, solids, and their mixtures. It covers a broad range of subjects, all aiming to provide a physical basis for understanding chemical structure, equilibrium, and change. It is the task of physical chemists to explain how and why chemistry works.

There are several different divisions of physical chemistry. In spectroscopy, physical chemists discover the shapes and structures of molecules by studying how they interact with light and other forms of radiation. Many spectroscopic techniques are today used routinely to analyze chemical substances and mixtures. The interactions between molecules and radiation can be interpreted using molecular quantum mechanics, the fundamental theory of matter and radiation applied to molecules. Diffraction methods can also be used to determine the structures of molecules and crystals.

Chemical THERMODYNAMICS is used to explain the bulk properties of substances and their transformations from one state to another (such as gas to liquid). Electrochemistry is concerned with the properties, behavior, and reactions of molecules under the influence of electrical forces. Finally, in chemical KINETICS, measuring the speeds with which chemicals react together provides chemists with insights into how molecules combine and break apart.

Fast reactions

The most basic physical principles used by chemists have been established primarily by physicists and have not really changed since QUANTUM THEORY was introduced in the 1920s and 1930s. However, applying these physical principles to even the simplest of chemical systems often requires approximations or assumptions. Today, the chemist is guided in this difficult task by the results of experiments which enable the study of molecules at unprecedented levels of detail.

At the forefront of the new technological revolution in physical chemistry is the laser. In several very active areas of current research, lasers are being used to provide answers to fundamental questions concerning the structure and reactions of molecules.

Scientists at the California Institute of Technology in Los Angeles are using lasers to probe the very act of chemical reaction itself. The process of breaking a chemical bond had previously been thought to occur so quickly that it would be impossible to watch it happen. However, in one recent series of experiments, the Caltech scientists did just this. They monitored the breakup of sodium iodide molecules by using intense bursts of laser light each lasting only 60 femtoseconds (one femtosecond is a millionth of a billionth of a second). The scientists used a short pulse of ultraviolet light from a laser to excite the sodium iodide molecules. They then fired a sequence of 60-femtosecond pulses of visible light, one every 100 femtoseconds. The effect was somewhat like using a stroboscope to "freeze-frame" the rapid movements of a disco dancer. The short flashes of visible light caught the sodium iodide molecules with their chemical bonds stretched or compressed in different positions. The scientists could tell when the bonds had stretched and broken by monitoring the emission of light from free sodium atoms.

Above: Apparatus used at the California Institute of Technology to study the breaking of chemical bonds using 60-femtosecond pulses of laser light.
Right: Fleming Crim's team at the University of Wisconsin–Madison, who use lasers to control the rate of chemical reactions by stretching bonds.

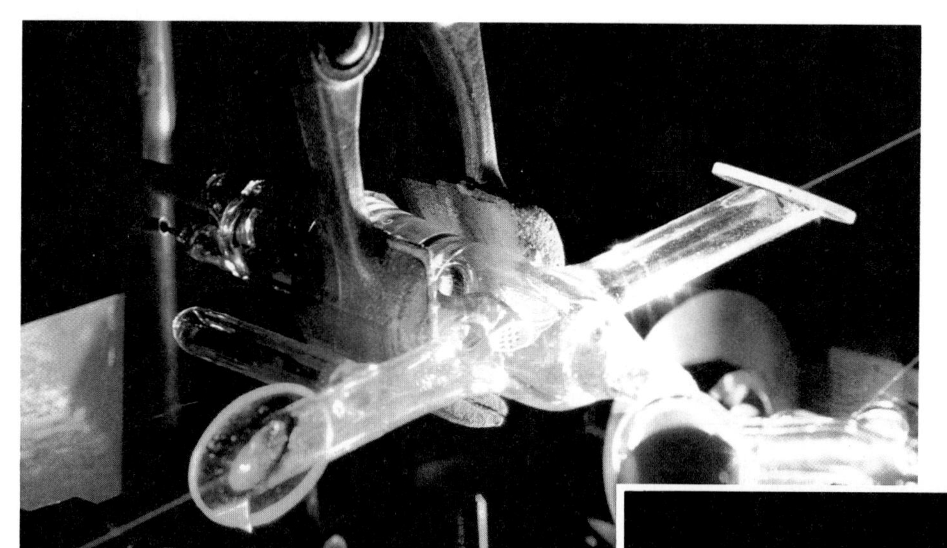

Left: The vibrations of molecules are detected by photoacoustic spectroscopy, in which a laser beam stimulates molecules to emit sound waves.

Below: Chemists are studying the properties of microtubes made of fullerene carbon molecules, as shown in this computer-generated structure.

Right: A series of images showing waves of chemical change in a shallow dish containing Belousov-Zhabotinsky reagent. The waves radiate from point sources at a rate of several millimeters a minute, demonstrating chaos like effects.

The reaction was all over in less than 10 millionths of a millionth of a second. The science fiction writer Isaac Asimov compared these experiments to taking a balloon only four billionths of an inch across (the size of an average molecule), and sticking a pin in it.

Applying theory

In the sodium iodide example, light was used to break a chemical bond between two atoms. This is the simplest kind of chemical reaction imaginable. However, physical chemists are also interested in reactions in which atoms or molecules come together, react, and then move apart. This kind of reaction may involve the formation of new bonds.

Chemists have long been able to interpret these more complicated types of reactions using simplistic theories. Applying quantum theory is too difficult, requiring calculations that not even the most powerful computer can perform in a reasonable time. Usually, theoreticians must first make assumptions to simplify the theory so that the calculations can be attempted.

But there are a few exceptions. The reaction between a hydrogen atom and a diatomic hydrogen molecule is the simplest reaction of this type, and quantum theory has been applied to it with some success. In this reaction, one hydrogen atom is exchanged for another: $H+H_2 \rightarrow H_2+H$. The hydrogen atom consists of only one proton and one electron, so the number of "fundamental" particles involved in the reaction is very low. This makes the application of quantum theory much easier.

Unfortunately, the factors that make the so-called hydrogen "exchange" reaction easy for the theoreticians also make it very difficult for experimentalists to study in the laboratory. Nevertheless, within the last ten years considerable progress has been made using lasers.

Scientists at the University of California at Irvine and at Stanford University near San Francisco have made detailed measurements on closely related reactions in which one of the hydrogen atoms is replaced by a deuterium isotope. This makes it easier to differentiate between the reactants and the products without making the calculations any more difficult.

The experimentalists have now so refined their techniques that they are challenging the theoreticians to come up with better calculations. There is generally very good agreement between theory and experiment, but some differences still have to be resolved. Nevertheless, the theoreticians are reassured that they are undoubtedly on the right track.

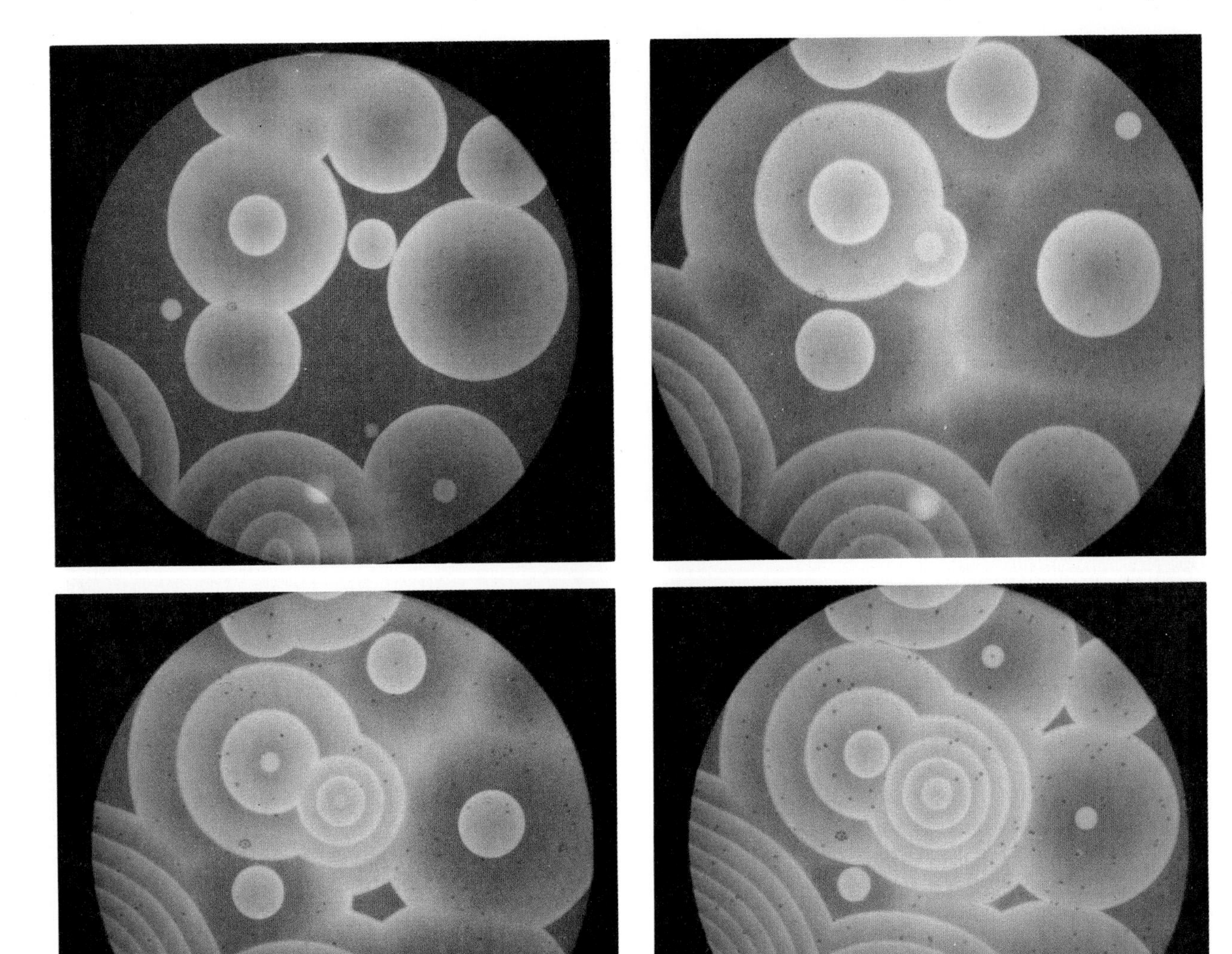

Bond-selective chemistry

Lasers are also being used in experiments to find out how much control chemists can exercise over the speeds and courses of chemical reactions. Industrial chemical processes control reactions by controlling bulk properties such as temperature or pressure and by using catalysts – substances which speed up reactions without themselves being changed chemically. Now, scientists at the University of Wisconsin at Madison and at Stanford University have shown that they can control reactions by selectively exciting individual chemical bonds.

However, the chemists demonstrated that there are exceptions to this general rule. They showed that they can control the course of the reaction between hydrogen atoms and partially deuterated water (HDO), by selectively stretching either its O-H or O-D bond. Stretching the O-H bond gave the products H_2 and OD, showing that the excited bond had broken preferentially in the reaction. Stretching the O-D bond gave HD and OH. This is the first example of "bond-selective" chemistry. Experiments in 1991 have revealed more examples, and chemists are eagerly looking for ways to apply bond-selective chemistry in practical systems.

Great balls of carbon

In 1985, scientists from Rice University in Houston, Texas, and the University of Sussex in England used a high power laser to make exotic molecules of pure carbon. They were looking to make molecules similar to ones that had been found in interstellar space, but instead they accidentally discovered a stable molecule made up of 60 carbon atoms. Scrambling for an explanation for

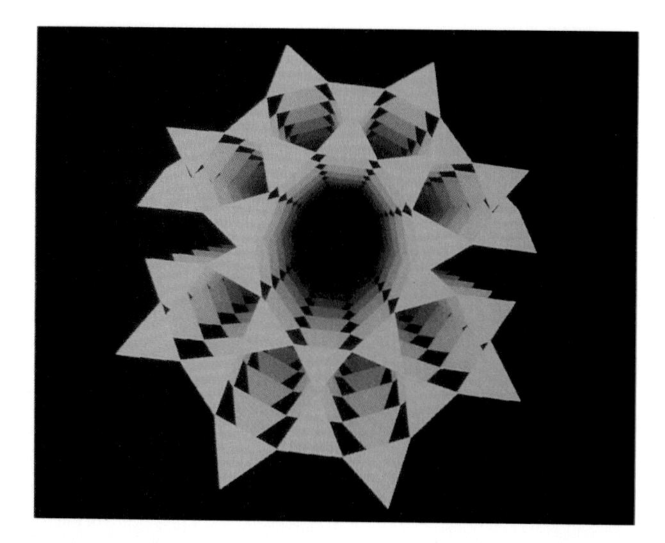

the molecule's stability, the scientists figured that it must have a perfectly spherical structure. They realized that a modern soccer ball is made up of 20 hexagons and 12 pentagons and has 60 vertices.

Chemists brought to bear all of the techniques of physical and chemical analysis in their studies of the structure of C_{60}, and provided overwhelming evidence that it is indeed shaped like a soccer ball. Other hollow cage molecules – collectively called fullerenes – have since been isolated and studied in the laboratory. Physical chemists all around the world are now investigating the properties and behavior of this new material, a third form of carbon after diamond and graphite. They are searching for practical applications as catalysts or lubricants (molecular "ball bearings"). A whole new era of "round" chemistry has begun.

Chemical chaos

The theoretical interpretation of the dynamics of unstable, non-linear systems – commonly called CHAOS THEORY – has captured the imaginations of scientists and non-scientists alike. Examples of chaos have been found almost everywhere, and chemistry is no exception.

Dynamical instabilities of the kind that characterize chaos can be found in any system in which positive feedback can occur – that is, where the results are fed back into the input, thus giving an even greater response. There are many examples of chemical reactions that produce products which can act as self-catalysts, making the reaction go faster. Examples of such "autocatalytic" reactions include combustion processes, reactions taking place on some catalyst surfaces and the "clock" reactions often used in high school chemistry classes to demonstrate the patterns of chemical change.

Scientists have studied these examples and have found many of the features that are known to be common to chaotic systems, such as "strange attractors". But there is considerable debate over just how this chaotic behavior arises. Some think that chaos might be intrinsic to certain chemical systems. Others are more inclined to think that the chaos comes from tiny imperfections in the way the experiments are set up and controlled. Either way, finding chaos in chemistry has come as something of a surprise for those who believed that reactions should always be predictable.

Left: Computer-graphics representation of the structure of unidirectional channels through the synthetic zeolite Theta-1. This can be prepared with a variable silicon content, thus enhancing its properties as a catalyst and molecular sieve.

• FACT FILE •

- At the end of the 1980s, the value of fuels, drugs, fabrics, foods, and other goods produced using catalysts was estimated to be in excess of $5 trillion.
- Many catalysts work by providing surfaces on which chemicals can come together, react, and separate, thereby increasing the speed of their reaction. Some catalysts are so effective that slowly reacting mixtures of chemicals can become violently reactive only millionths of a second after coming into contact with a catalyst surface.
- Molecular sieves form a special category of crystalline materials which provide catalyst surfaces on the insides of their structures. They contain "pores" through which only molecules of less than a certain size can pass. The sizes of the pores can be controlled, making the catalytic activity of molecular sieves very selective and versatile (see AEROSPACE MEDICINE)
- Chemists believe they can make molecular sieves so selective that they will begin to mimic the activity of enzymes. These are "natural" catalysts used by biological systems to speed up biochemical reactions. The enzymes are highly selective because they possess three-dimensional shapes which "fit" together with the reactants like a key fits a lock. If highly selective molecular sieve catalysts can be produced, they may transform the manufacture of very complicated molecules, such as drugs.

Physiology

The physiologist studies the activities of living cells, both individually and as part of a complete organism. Physiology thus includes the traditional subjects of the movement, nutrition, metabolism, excretion, reproduction, and behavior of living things. Investigations into the physiology of microorganisms belong to MICROBIOLOGY; plant physiology is part of BOTANY. As well as being a fundamental experimental science in itself, physiology has wide applications in human and VETERINARY MEDICINE, in agriculture, industry, and ENVIRONMENTAL SCIENCE.

Many physiologists study functions at the level of the molecule or of individual cells. These investigations have, for example, given us a new insight into how potassium and calcium pass through channels in the membranes of cells to cause the transmission of a nerve impulse, or bring about a muscle contraction. Much research is carried out on cells grown in culture. For instance, mouse pituitary gland cells have been genetically altered to produce human insulin. In early 1992 physiologists at the University of Texas Southwestern Medical Center successfully demonstrated that such cells will secrete stored insulin when glucose seeps into them from the medium surrounding them. This has brought closer the possibility of developing an artificial pancreas that could be implanted in diabetics.

Also in 1992, spurred on by the increasing dangers from infected blood (see HEMATOLOGY), scientists working in Colorado and England reported the development of a safe human blood substitute, prepared from modified human hemoglobin.

Neural diseases

Often it is necessary for physiologists to examine the whole animal, because a particular response may involve a number of tissues and organs. For example, motor neuron diseases result from the degeneration and death of nerve cells in the spinal cord and brain, leading to progressive muscle weakness. Frequently, the outcome is fatal because of respiratory paralysis. The first hope that a therapeutic strategy for these devastating diseases might be possible was reported in August 1992. Danish and German scientists influenced the course of the disease in affected mice with a growth-promoting factor that rescued the motor neurons from degeneration.

Everyone is now aware of the importance of transplants for the replacement of diseased or damaged organs. With the recent development of many new rejection-suppressing drugs, it is becoming possible to transplant animal organs (xenografts) into humans, thus overcoming the chronic shortage of donors. In June 1992 a baboon's liver was successfully transplanted into a 35-year-old man in Pennsylvania. Although he survived only two months, his death was due to infection, not rejection.

Left: Synthetic human hemoglobin, which can be used as a blood substitute. It was developed by American and British scientists using genetic engineering techniques and the bacterium *E. Coli*. The bottle on the left contains bacterial cells producing hemoglobin, which is red in color, while the one on the right consists of normal *E. coli* which have no hemoglobin production.

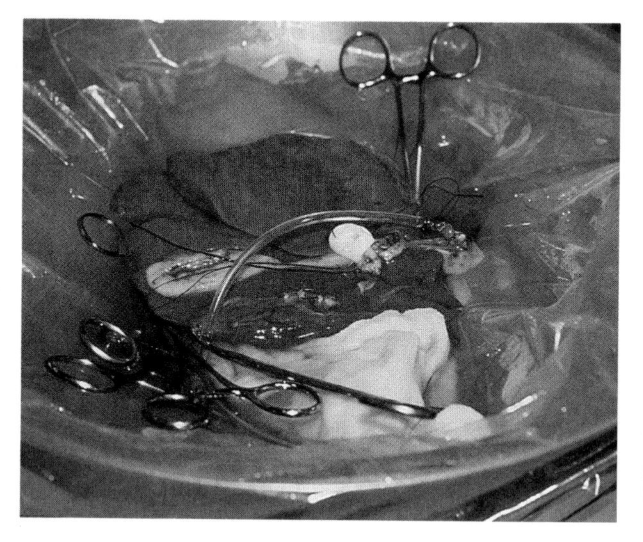

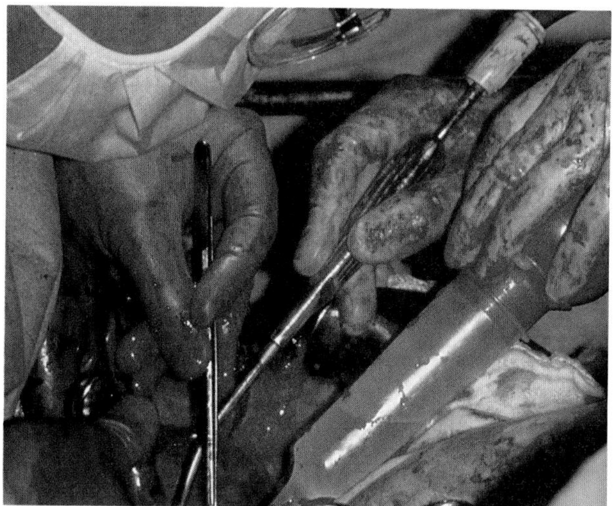

Above, top right and right: Surgeons at the University of Pittsburgh Medical School perform the first transplant of a baboon's liver into a human recipient.

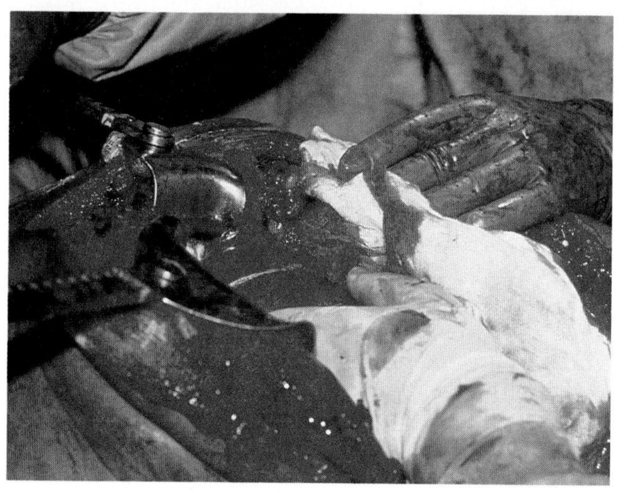

Reproductive research

Few areas of physiological research have had as great an impact on human behavior as that which led to a revolution in birth control – the development of the contraceptive pill. During the 1950s Doctors Pincus, Rock, and Change demonstrated at the Worcester Foundation in Massachusetts that ovulation could be suppressed with synthetic hormones. The contraceptive pill, licensed by the Food and Drug Administration in 1960, is currently used by over 60 million women worldwide. It has an extraordinarily low failure rate when used properly – less than two pregnancies per thousand users per year.

Other natural and synthetic hormonal preparations are now employed to treat infertility or to reduce the symptoms of the menopause. Others are used to increase productivity in farm animals.

Physiological research has produced other controversial results in the area of human sex and reproduction. In mid-1991 Simon le Vay, working at the Salk Institute in San Diego, reported that a particular group of cells in the human brain was twice as large in heterosexual men as in women or homosexual men. Le Vay's findings, which have aroused an enormous amount of controversy, suggest that sexual orientation may have a biological origin. However, a great many questions still remain unanswered – not least whether sexual orientation is primarily predetermined during fetal life, or is also influenced by formative factors in a child's upbringing.

Research, mainly on rodents, has established that the mammalian brain (like the reproductive system) is initially female, and remains so if not exposed to male hormones (androgens) during a limited critical time during development.

The human brain's sexual differentiation is believed to take place around mid pregnancy, when neuronal tissue in the male fetus responds to androgens secreted by the testes. This is when, it is claimed, the brain is programmed to exhibit male sexual behavior in adult life. After puberty that individual will not display the female cycles of reproductive hormone release.

During the 1980s Roger Gorski and his colleagues at the University of California at Los Angeles demonstrated the presence in the rat hypothalamus of a region known as the sexually dimorphic nucleus (SDN). This is apparently involved in controlling sexual behavior and the release of the reproductive hormones.

The sexually dimorphic nucleus is up to five times larger in the male rat than in the female. But its size can be altered during fetal development by altering hormone levels. Scientists working in Amsterdam have identified a similar structure in the human brain.

Planetary science

The Space Age has transformed our knowledge of planets other than our own. With every new space probe sent deep into the solar system, many questions have been solved but entirely new questions have been raised. The exploration of space is a long-term business: spacecraft such as Voyager 2, launched in 1977 and containing technology which in any other field would be considered obsolete, was still able to return remarkable pictures of Neptune in 1989.

In the 1990s, in addition to spacecraft such as Galileo, targeted at Jupiter, and Magellan in orbit around Venus, the Earth-orbiting Hubble Space Telescope (HST) (see ASTROPHYSICS) is proving itself capable of taking detailed planetary images. Even ground-based telescopes, suffering from being within Earth's turbulent atmosphere, which has bedevilled astronomers for centuries, are currently returning useful results.

Surprises at Neptune and Triton

The 1989 images of Neptune held a surprise. After the admittedly dull and featureless Uranus (imaged in 1986), Neptune turned out to have extremely active weather systems that are far more dynamic than on either Saturn or Uranus. Neptune has high, wispy white clouds and the Great Dark Spot, a giant atmospheric storm comparable in size to the Earth. Winds blow at around 1500 mph (2400 km/h), the strongest winds discovered to date on any planet. Voyager also discovered six new moons, in addition to the two already known, and found several rings, similar to those around Jupiter and Uranus.

Pluto and Charon

Pluto, discovered in 1930, is by far the smallest and usually most distant planet. For 20 years of its 248-year orbital period – between 1979 and 1999 – it comes closer to the Sun than Neptune. Nevertheless, its remoteness and small size have made it very difficult to study. Although no probes have been to Pluto, a cosmic coincidence has allowed astronomers to discover more about the planet. Between February 1985 and September 1990, Pluto and its moon Charon underwent a rare series of mutual eclipses, in which one passed in front of the other. These allowed astronomers to measure their diameters: 1444 miles (2323 km) for Pluto and just 753 miles (1212 km) for Charon.

Observations of Pluto's spectrum have confirmed that the planet has a surface layer of methane ice and polar ice-caps that may vary in size as it orbits the Sun. In June 1988, Pluto passed in front of a relatively bright star. Observations showed that Pluto has a very thin layered atmosphere of methane gas that extends at least 125 miles (200 km) above its surface.

The best picture of Pluto and Charon was taken in 1990 by the HST's Faint Object Camera. Precise measurements of such images enable their masses

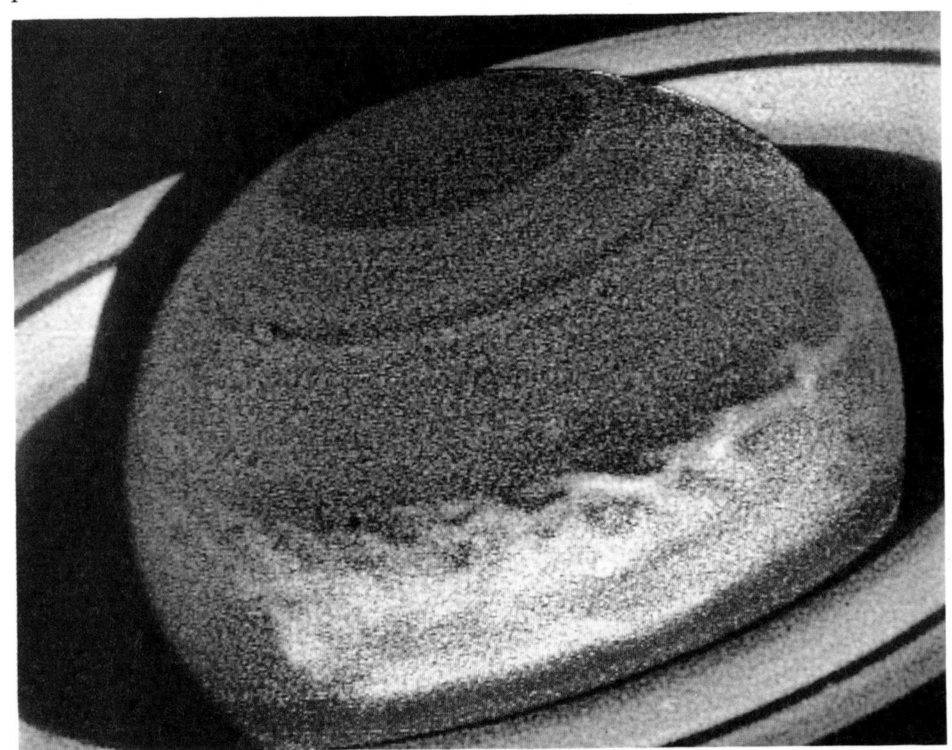

Left: A picture of Saturn's white spot, taken by the Hubble Space Telescope's planetary camera on November 9, 1990. The picture was taken in blue and infrared, as these colors allow atmospheric scientists to watch the motions of the clouds across the face of the planet. They also make it possible to study the vertical growth of these clouds.

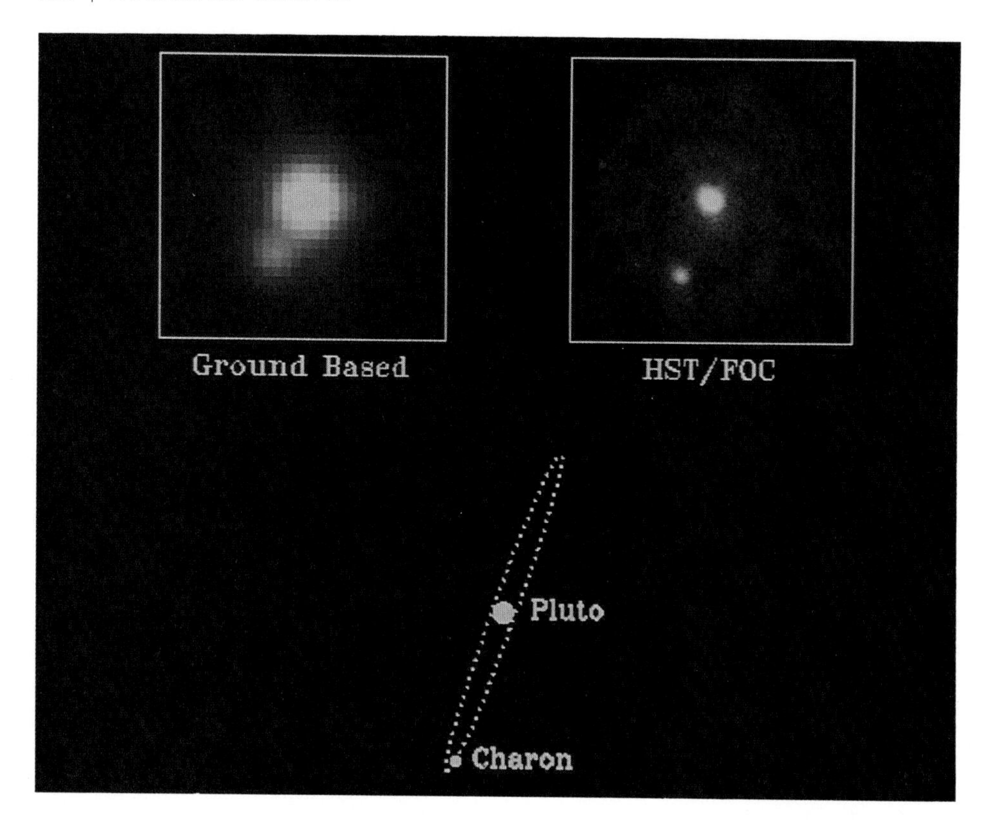

Left: This Hubble Space Telescope image of Pluto and Charon clearly resolves the separation between the two icy worlds. At the time of observation, Charon was near its maximum apparent angular separation of about 0.9 arc second. Pluto is at the center of the frame while Charon is the fainter object in the lower left. For comparison, the best ground-based image of Pluto and Charon ever taken to date (at the Canada-France-Hawaii telescope in Hawaii) is shown in the upper left.

and densities to be worked out. Pluto, with a density about twice that of water, probably has a rocky core surrounded by a mantle of ices. The combined mass of Pluto and Charon is only one-fifth that of the Earth's moon. Pluto and Charon may be large planetesimals, icy bodies left over from the formation of the planets.

New studies of Jupiter

The HST has observed fine detail in the clouds that cover Jupiter, including dark 'j-shaped' clouds along the equator caused by very strong winds, oval-shaped spots, and the Great Red Spot, a huge circulating storm system. HST observations made in ultraviolet light in February 1992 showed an aurora – equivalent to Earth's Northern Lights (see AERONOMY) – around the planet's north pole.

HST observations of the Jovian aurora were made simultaneously with the Jupiter flyby of the joint NASA/European Space Agency probe Ulysses. This spacecraft flew past Jupiter to be boosted onto a trajectory that will take it over the poles of the Sun in 1994 and 1995. Ulysses' instruments made important measurements of Jupiter's magnetosphere, the region of interaction between the planet's magnetic field, and the solar wind.

Radar mapping of Mercury

No spacecraft has visited Mercury since Mariner 10 in March 1975, which mapped about half the planet. In August 1991, radio astronomers mapped the unphotographed hemisphere of Mercury from Earth using radar. They found a large bright patch in the center of the disk which could have been caused by a huge impact with an asteroid in the distant past. A small bright patch at the north pole may be a polar icecap, consisting of ices of water, carbon dioxide, and other common gases. Although the surface of Mercury reaches 430° C, at the poles, the temperature could be as low as -150° C, so a polar icecap is possible.

Active volcanoes on Venus?

In August 1990, after a 15-month journey, the Magellan spacecraft went into orbit around Venus. Its arrival marked the United States' return to planetary exploration, after a gap of 11 years. Magellan's task was to map the surface accurately, using radar to penetrate the planet's constant, very dense cloud cover which hides the surface from view. Its only instrument was a synthetic aperture radar system, that mapped the surface of Venus, determined the height of surface features and measured natural thermal emissions from the planet. From its elliptical orbit that took it around Venus in 3 hours 9 minutes, Magellan's radar was capable of "seeing" surface features only 400 ft (360 m) across, ten times better than ever before. With the spacecraft passing nearly over both poles, around the very slowly turning planet, Magellan took 243 days to complete its first map covering 84 per cent of the surface.

Left: The Voyager 2 spacecraft was launched in 1977; in 1989, it returned remarkable pictures of the planet Neptune. The pictures revealed a planet which has extremely active weather systems, with winds blowing at around 1500 mph (2400 km/h). Neptune also has the Great Dark Spot, a giant atmospheric storm comparable in size to the Earth. Voyager discovered six new moons in addition to the two already known, and found several rings, similar to those around Jupiter and Uranus. Voyager investigated Jupiter, Saturn, and Uranus on its way to Neptune.

In early 1991 Magellan began a second 243-day mapping cycle to fill in the gaps in the first map and look for any changes occurring on the surface. During a third cycle, its motion was carefully monitored to find anomalies in the planet's gravitational field caused by regions of higher density rocks beneath the surface. The main aim of the mission was to find out if the processes shaping the surface of Venus are similar to those occurring on Earth. Large structures on Venus appear to be caused by the upwelling of hot molten rock, or lava, from far below the surface, rather than by plate tectonics, the process which produces the major land and undersea features on Earth.

Huge rolling plains cover 65 per cent of Venus, with lowlands accounting for 27 per cent and mountainous regions just 8 per cent. Venus is pockmarked by craters, many over 30 miles across. There are no small craters because the smaller rocky bodies colliding with the planet burn up in the dense atmosphere before hitting the ground. Large areas are covered by volcanic ash and there are lava flows over 100 miles (160 km) long.

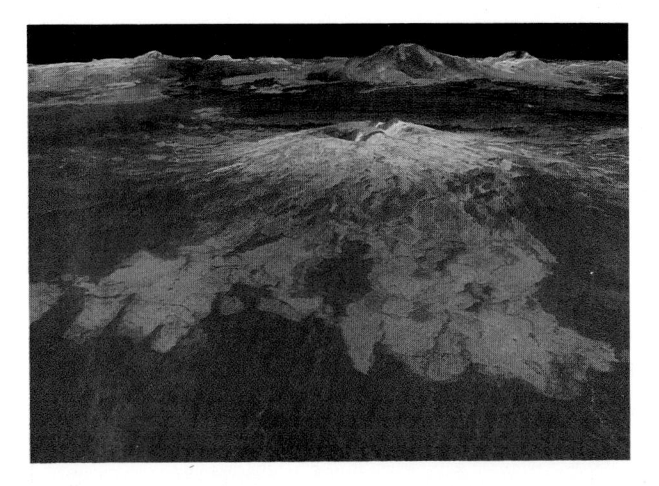

Magellan found that some volcanoes on Venus may still be active. The second highest peak, Maat Mons, which is five miles (8 km) high, seems to have been covered with fresh lava.

Further evidence for volcanic eruptions on Venus came from the Galileo spacecraft, making a flyby of the planet in February 1990, en route to its rendezvous with Jupiter in December 1995. Among its instruments were detectors which picked up intense, short-lived bursts of radio noise, possibly due to lightning flashes in the atmosphere of Venus. Such lightning flashes can occur in the cloud of ash spewed out by an erupting volcano.

The successes of Phobos 2

Mars was not visited by any spacecraft following the highly successful Vikings 1 and 2 missions in 1976, until Phobos 2, launched by the former USSR in July 1988. Although it did not achieve its objective of dropping two small probes on to the surface of Mars' larger moon Phobos, the Phobos 2 spacecraft acquired much useful data. One instrument produced a detailed, high contrast thermal map of Mars for the first time. Others measured the vertical structure, temperature, and composition of the atmosphere, and investigated the interaction between the solar wind and Mars' weak magnetic field.

Comets and asteroids

Asteroids are the debris of the solar system, comparatively small bodies orbiting between Mars and Jupiter. Comets have a very different appearance, with huge, glowing gaseous heads and, sometimes, gas and dust tails. But in recent years astronomers have found links between the two. These bodies may hold important clues to the origin of the solar system.

The first closeup pictures of any asteroid were taken by the Galileo spacecraft in October 1991,

Left: A computer generated three-dimensional perspective view of the surface of Venus, based on radar images taken by the Magellan spacecraft, showing Maat Mons in the background.

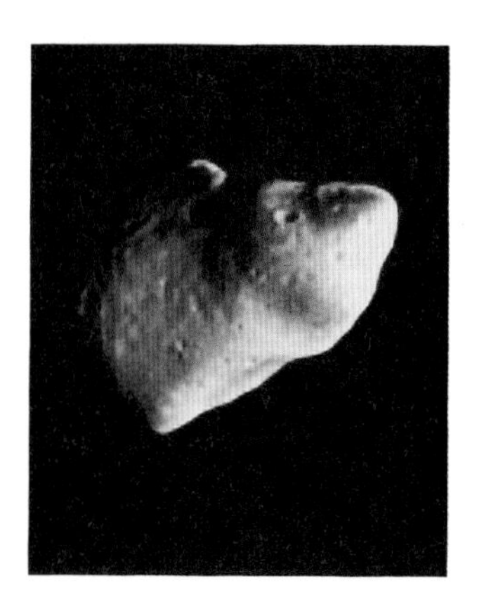

Right: The first pictures of an asteroid, Gaspra, were taken by the Galileo spacecraft in 1991. This view was reconstructed from individual images taken using three separate color filters.

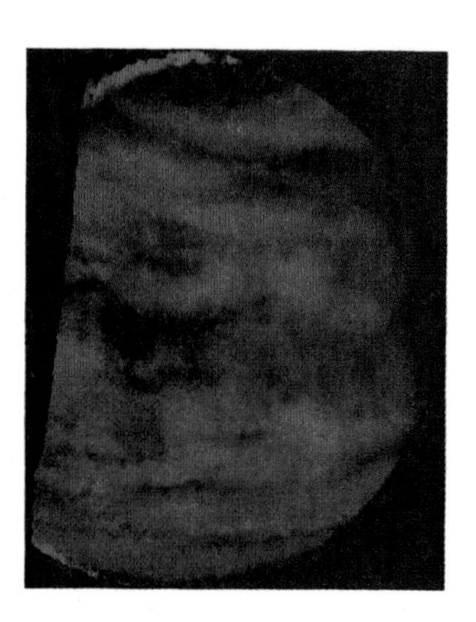

Right: The Galileo spacecraft, due to reach Jupiter in December 1995, used the gravity of the planet Venus to increase its speed. As it swung past Venus in 1990 it took this infrared view of the cloud-covered planet's night side, glowing from the heat radiating from the surface.

while en route to Jupiter. Gaspra appeared roughly wedge-shaped, with dimensions 12 x 8 x 7 miles (19 x 13 x 11 km), and very irregular. Its dark rocky surface was pitted with craters. There are surface fractures, and evidence that Gaspra may be part of a larger body that broke up after a catastrophic collision.

Great interest also surrounds Chiron, the unusual asteroidal object orbiting between Saturn and Uranus. The discovery in 1990 that it was surrounded by a cloud of gas and dust led to claims that Chiron is a giant comet. However, Chiron is very large for a comet, perhaps 120 miles (190 km) across. The cloud could be just the evaporation of icy deposits from the surface of a large asteroid as it passes its closest approach to the Sun.

Chiron may have something in common with 1992 QB1, which is the most distant object ever found in the Solar System, discovered in October 1992 beyond the orbits of Neptune and Pluto. It seems to be a very distant asteroid, but is, in fact, probably icy. Such objects as this may be neither comets nor asteroids but icy planetesimals like Pluto and Charon.

In July 1992, the European spacecraft Giotto, which took the closeup pictures of Halley's comet in 1986, encountered a second comet. Its target, comet Grigg-Skjellerup, was a small, rather old comet, orbiting the Sun in about five years, and ejecting about 1/1000th as much gas and dust as the very active and 'fresh' comet Halley. Although its camera was not working, Giotto detected a few impacts from dust particles, and measured the surprisingly complex interaction between the solar wind and the comet, which was more turbulent than expected.

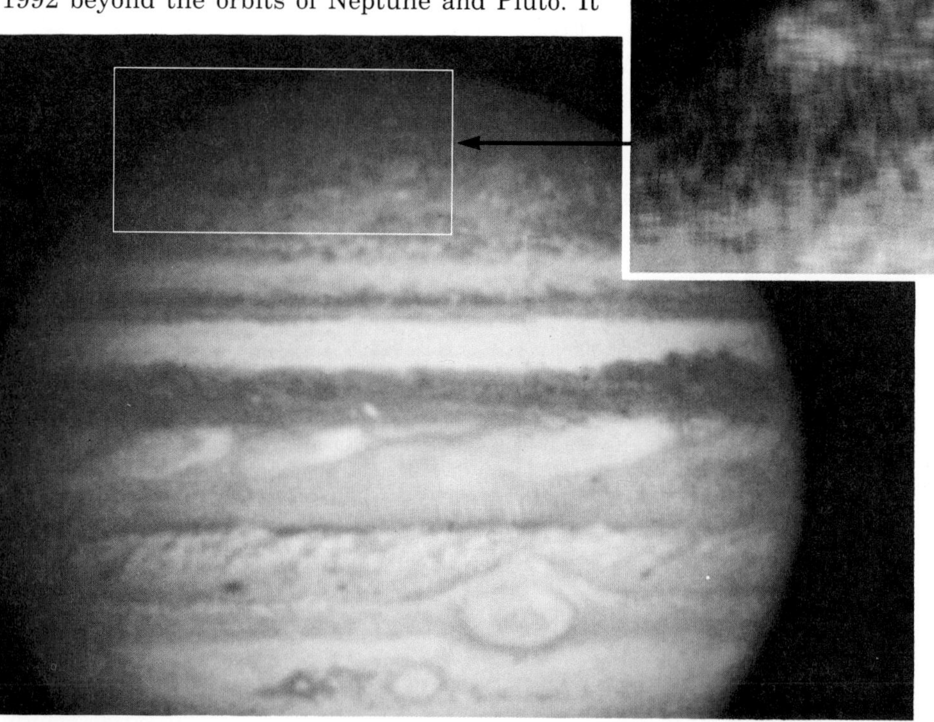

Left and above: These views of Jupiter combine images taken with the HST Planetary Camera (whole disk) and Faint Object Camera (inset) to show the location of an aurora in Jupiter's atmosphere. The observations were made at the same time as the space probe Ulysses flew past Jupiter in 1992.

Plasma physics

In medical circles, "plasma" refers to the colorless fluid that forms the substance of blood or milk. But to the physicist it is essentially a gas consisting not of complete molecules, but of equal numbers of negative electrons, positive ions, and possibly some neutral atoms and molecules. It is considered the fourth state of matter, after solid, liquid, and gas, and could hold the key to Earth's future energy resources.

Matter changes state as it is exposed to heat. At high temperatures, a gas becomes ionized – the electrons are no longer bound to the nucleus and are free to move independently. Since this plasma contains charged particles such as electrons and the positively charged nucleus ions, it can support an electric current and react to electric and magnetic fields applied to it. Plasma cannot be described as an ordinary gas which is electrically conducting; there is a fundamental difference between a neutral gas and a plasma, resulting from the very different nature of the interparticle forces. The dynamics of a gas are dominated by two-body, billiard ball-like collisions, where the forces are strong, but of short range. The forces between particles in a plasma, however, are comparatively weak and of long range.

Nature rarely produces plasma on the Earth's surface, lightning being the exception. However, plasma constitutes more than 99 per cent of the known universe. Interest in plasma and its properties stems from its importance in space physics and in the development of controlled nuclear fusion. This is the energy-producing process which takes place continuously in the Sun and stars. In the core of the Sun, at temperatures of 18 to 27 million° F (10 to 15 million° C), hydrogen is converted into helium, resulting in the creation of energy. For fusion energy on Earth the most suitable fusion reaction is the one between the nuclei of the two heavy isotopes of hydrogen, namely deuterium and tritium. But a temperature of over 180 million° F (100 million° C) is needed, at which temperature the isotopes are in the plasma state.

Aiming for breakeven

Today, scientists are mainly concerned with the containment and control of such high-temperature plasmas, to get more energy out of the system than is put in – what is called energy breakeven. Two main schemes have emerged as candidates for future power reactors using fusion energy: inertial confinement and magnetic confinement. In a magnetic field the charged particles readily spiral

Above: A view through the inspection window of a magnetic containment nuclear fusion device. The blue haze is a hydrogen isotope which is superheated until it splits into nuclei and electrons, creating plasma. If this plasma can be further heated, nuclear fusion occurs.

Below: The spheromak S-1 nuclear fusion experiment at Princeton, N.J. The spheromak is designed to study magnetic containment fusion reactions.

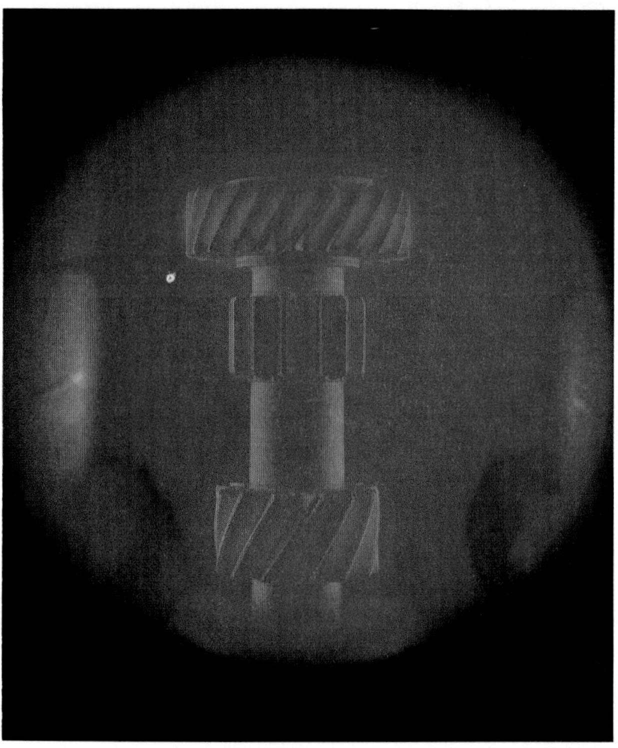

Above: A plasma polymerization unit, which coats microprocessor chips to improve their electrical conductivity.
Right: A transmission gear undergoing a hardening process in a plasma chamber. Ions from the plasma dissolve onto the steel, forming a new, harder alloy on the surface. This photograph, taken through the inspection window of the chamber, shows the part fluorescing as the excited plasma ions recombine with electrons in the steel and give off energy.

along the field lines but diffuse only very slowly across them. The particles behave as if they were tied to the magnetic field. The most promising magnetic confinement systems are toroidal (doughnut-shaped) and, of these, the most advanced is the tokamak, which confines the plasma better than previous devices. In a tokamak, plasma is heated in a toroidal vessel, isolated from the walls by magnetic fields. In the early 1990s, important experiments were made using the world's largest tokamaks, the Tokamak Fusion Test Reactor in the U.S. and the Joint European Torus in England. In these fusion demonstration experiments, scientists confined a deuterium-tritium plasma hotter than 180 million° F (100 million° C) to produce more than a megawatt of fusion power.

In inertial confinement fusion, a small pellet of deuterium-tritium fuel is irradiated by high-energy laser or particle beams to create an implosion, producing the high density and temperatures needed for fusion. This is what happens inside hydrogen bombs, where the required energy to implode the pellet comes from a fission explosion. Less violent power production requires small millimeter-sized pellets to be ignited every second. Scientists at Lawrence Livermore National Laboratory in the U.S. are confident that laser pulses of 10 million joules in energy will be sufficient to produce energy breakeven.

Scientists are finding that plasmas can solve many technological problems. These include plasma etching processes in the semiconductor industry. Ion beams, produced in pulsing plasma discharges, etch silicon chips. Plasma deposition is commonly used to coat materials; for example, diamond coating can be achieved using high temperature hydrocarbon plasma discharges to produce very hard scratch-resistant surfaces. Plasma torches and high-temperature arcs are being investigated for their use in destroying harmful chemicals (see CHEMICAL TECHNOLOGY).

Surfing particles

Very recently, scientists working at the University of California at Los Angeles have been able to produce the world's largest accelerating electric field of 700 million volts per meter, known as the plasma beat wave accelerator. In this, two laser beams of slightly different frequencies are injected into a plasma. The interaction between the lasers and the plasma produces a space charge wave or plasma wave capable of trapping and accelerating the plasma particles, which "surf" on the wave at velocities near the speed of light.

Conventional accelerator technology, used, for example, in accelerators at Fermilab near Chicago, is limited to about 20 million volts per meter. To produce high-energy particles these accelerators have to be very large – the Superconducting Supercollider will be over 50 miles (80 km) long. Such research into plasma accelerators may one day produce much smaller versions with many applications from producing radioactive isotopes and X-rays, to tunable electromagnetic sources.

Psychiatry

Recent years have seen the greatest advances in psychiatry since Freud. They have consisted of new diagnostic categories, new drugs, developments in NEUROLOGY, and new non-drug treatments. There has also been a welcome trend towards seeing people holistically, rather than viewing mind and body separately, and drawing distinctions between mental and physical illness.

In 1987 the American Psychiatric Association published a revision of the third edition of their *Diagnostic and Statistical Manual*. Known as DSM-III-R, this has become the single most important reference manual for psychiatrists around the world. DSM-III was translated into ten of the world's major languages, including Chinese and Japanese. By 1992, 600,000 copies of DSM-III-R had been sold.

Many "new" disorders, previously unrecognized or underdiagnosed, are being brought to medical attention. *Bulimia nervosa*, for example, consists of having regular overeating binges at least twice a week, counteracted by exercising, vomiting, or taking purgatives in an attempt to maintain "normal" weight.

Post-traumatic stress disorder is the development of characteristic symptoms following a psychologically distressing event outside the normal range of human experience. This includes being a hostage, rape, torture, war, death camps, or being in a major fire. Some of these, such as being tortured, frequently produce PTSD; others, such as being in a car accident, do so only occasionally. The trauma is re-experienced in various ways such as flashbacks, dreams, and dissociative states. The patient may become generally numb or try to avoid stimuli associated with the event, and may suffer from insomnia, irritability, wariness, and difficulties in concentrating.

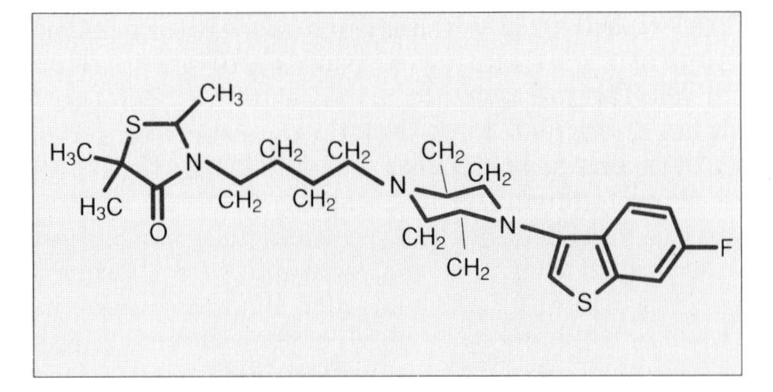

Above: U.S. chemists have produced this design for a drug, codenamed HP 236, to combat schizophrenia without the side effects of existing drugs. It is undergoing clinical testing.

Above: Thomas Sutherland (on the left) was released from years of captivity in Lebanon in 1991. In common with all the other released hostages, he was treated for post-traumatic stress disorder which often follows a psychologically distressing event outside the normal range of human experience.

Somatoform disorder is becoming increasingly common. It consists of multiple physical symptoms and complaints, without any apparent physical basis, in apparently healthy people who may be generally disabled by their symptoms. It is equally common in men and women. *Chronic fatigue syndrome* has become increasingly prevalent since the mid 1980s. Psychiatrists complain that patients suffering from somatoform disorder and chronic fatigue refuse psychiatric help because to them, this suggests that their illness is "all in the mind" – a prejudice that draws on the fallacious distinction between mind and body.

Schizophrenia, however, is decreasing in incidence. This seems to be a real phenomenon, and not just a changing fashion in diagnosis. Hysteria – neurological symptoms without neurological cause, often after trauma – has decreased considerably over several decades.

New drug treatments

Advances in drug therapy have improved the quality of life for many patients. In the 1970s depression was treated by a class of drug called

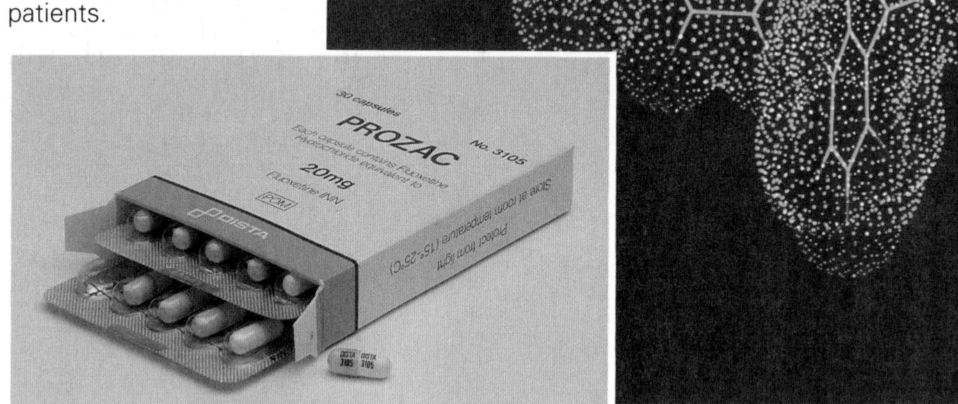

Right and below: The molecular structure of the antidepressant fluoxetine (Prozac). Drug therapy can greatly improve life for many psychiatric patients.

monoamine oxidase inhibitors (MAOIs). These interacted with some other drugs and a variety of foods, including cheese and yeast extract, causing, in high doses, blackouts. In the 1980s MAOIs were replaced by tricyclic antidepressants, which caused dry mouth and other minor side effects but did not interact with foods. Recent research has shown that they are also useful for panic disorder and obsessive-compulsive behavior. Since the late 1980s, new antidepressants have been developed that prevent further uptake of a neurotransmitter, serotonin, in the brain. These include fluoxetine (Prozac™), flupenthizol (Fluanxol™, Depixol™), and fluvoxamine (Faverin™).

Clozapine is a new drug that relieves the symptoms of schizophrenia in many patients who do not respond to other drugs or cannot tolerate them. It can cause destruction of white blood cells and for that reason is only available from hospitals, whose staff must carry out regular blood tests. Like all new drugs, its long-term effects, both good and adverse, are relatively unknown.

An important advance in non-drug treatment has been the development of cognitive behavior therapy. It is a form of self-help given under the supervision of psychiatrists and psychologists. Its popularity is due to its relative cheapness, long-term effectiveness, and speed. It combines behavioral retraining with a form of reinterpreting thoughts. For example, people suffering from chronic fatigue typically avoid exercise because it makes them feel worse. For this reason their physical fitness may decrease severely, so that any effort is followed by distressing symptoms; thus they feel that effort makes them feel worse and they may stay in bed. With the aid of a therapist and the friendly supervision of a family member, they can be shown that much of their fatigue is due to lack of exercise. A small effort brings symptoms back; but if this effort is repeated daily the person soon becomes able to tolerate and then enjoy it, and to see that the fatigue was caused by lack of fitness. In this way, an infinite number of small gains can be made until the patient regains health.

• FACT FILE •

- Two apparently unrelated problems have recently been found to be linked. People with obsessive-compulsive disorder (OCD) may wash their hands dozens of times a day to get rid of imagined dirt. Dogs suffering from acral-lick dermatitis (ALD) constantly lick, scratch, or bite their paws or flanks.

- In 1992, psychiatrist Dr. Judith Rapoport of the U.S. National Institute of Mental Health in Bethesda, MD found that the antidepressive drugs that reduce OCD in people also reduce ALD in canines. This discovery offers a quick method of screening drugs for an anti-OCD effect, and a good way of easing life for many pet dogs. Rapoport's team has started a brain bank for dogs that displayed ALD during their lives.

Quantum mechanics

In the 1920s and 1930s, a series of crises in physics led to a revolutionary new theory of matter and radiation – quantum theory. In the sub-atomic world of "fundamental" particles, long-cherished physical concepts were swept aside and replaced by new concepts that many physicists (including Einstein) found bizarre and disturbing. Today, physicists recognize that quantum theory is rife with paradoxes and contradictions. But it is also one of the most successful scientific theories ever devised. Physicists are constantly devising new ways to test the theory's predictions to see if the world really is as strange as the theory suggests.

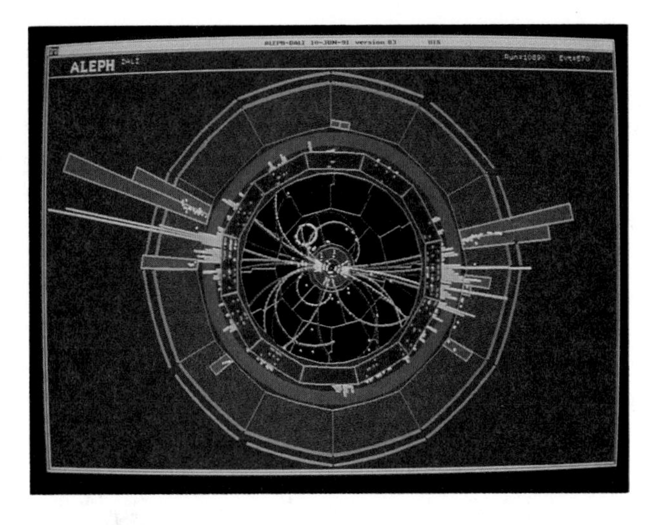

Above: Collisions observed in particle-physics experiments obey quantum laws rather than those of standard Newtonian physics.

Interfering particles

Does light consist of waves or particles? Isaac Newton decided on particles, but at the beginning of the 19th century, experiments demonstrating light interference effects seemed to point conclusively to a wave interpretation. Interference arises when the peaks and troughs of two or more wave disturbances coincide in space (constructive interference) or cancel each other out (destructive interference). Thomas Young's celebrated two-slit interference experiment, which produces a pattern of alternating light and dark bands, is most easily understood if light is assumed to be made up of waves.

All this was overturned in the quantum revolution. Now light is understood to consist both of waves and particles, with wave-like behavior revealed in one kind of experiment, and particle-like behavior revealed in another. In a bold move, the French physicist Louis de Broglie suggested in 1923 that matter itself might show similar wave-particle duality.

Experiments carried out in the last 70 years have confirmed this startling hypothesis. In 1989, a group of physicists in Japan performed the classic two-slit interference experiment with a beam of electrons. With only 100 electrons detected as tiny spots on a photographic plate, the spots appear random and there is no obvious pattern. However, by the time 70,000 electrons have been detected, a clear pattern of alternating "light" and "dark" bands is seen.

Interference effects have now been observed with whole atoms. Groups of physicists in America and Germany have recently announced results of experiments showing interference effects in beams of helium and sodium atoms. Apart from providing solid evidence for the wave-like properties of matter, scientists at Stanford University in California are also using their apparatus to measure the effects of gravitational acceleration on atoms. Perfecting these techniques could open up more challenging tests of fundamental physical theories.

Spooky action at a distance

Taken a stage further, wave-particle duality has profound implications for the way we understand physical reality. There is no logical difficulty in having a wave disturbance "spread out" through

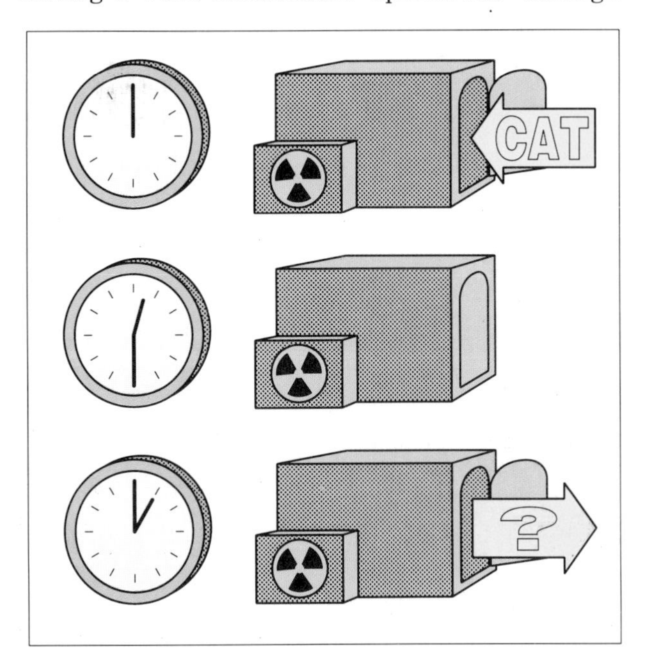

Right: The puzzle of Schrödinger's cat. A cat is placed in a box equipped with a radioactively triggered poison for a time during which there is a 50-50 chance of it dying. While it seems absurd that the cat might be both alive and dead during the experiment, this is what quantum theory predicts.

space, but a particle like an electron or an atom is detected as a tiny, self-contained bit of matter. Interference effects are explained in terms of spread-out waves, so what happens when an atom is detected in an interference experiment? What was a spread-out wave must collapse to become a tiny particle, generating a localized spot on a photographic plate.

To Albert Einstein, this collapse implied that matter is subject to strange, ghostly influences over long distances, in what he called "spooky action at a distance". He did not believe this was physically reasonable and, having laid the foundations of the quantum revolution, he became one of the theory's most strident critics.

The kind of spooky action at a distance suggested by quantum theory has since been debated at great length by physicists and philosophers, but in recent years it has been possible to test this idea in the laboratory. Making use of new developments in lasers and quantum optics, physicists in America, Germany, France, and elsewhere have put the theory to several very stringent tests. The results are still hotly debated, but it is generally accepted that quantum theory passes with flying colors. Wave-particle duality and spooky influences on matter over long distances remain to puzzle the next generation. Further experiments are being planned.

Schrödinger's cat revisited

The Austrian physicist Erwin Schrödinger described a hypothetical experiment in which quantum theory would predict that a cat can be suspended between states of life and death. Such an ambiguous either/or situation is accepted for objects like photons, electrons, or atoms, but is apparently absurd when extrapolated to cats.

Today, physicists are actually trying to carry out the kind of experiment that Schrödinger described, using devices called superconducting quantum interference devices (SQUIDs). The SQUIDs are ring-shaped and about a centimeter or so in diameter. Large numbers of electrons can be made to flow in one direction or the other around the ring when it is in its superconducting state.

The physicists are trying to observe interference between two SQUID states in which the electrons go around the ring in opposite directions. As with Schrödinger's cat, such interference goes against common sense for large objects.

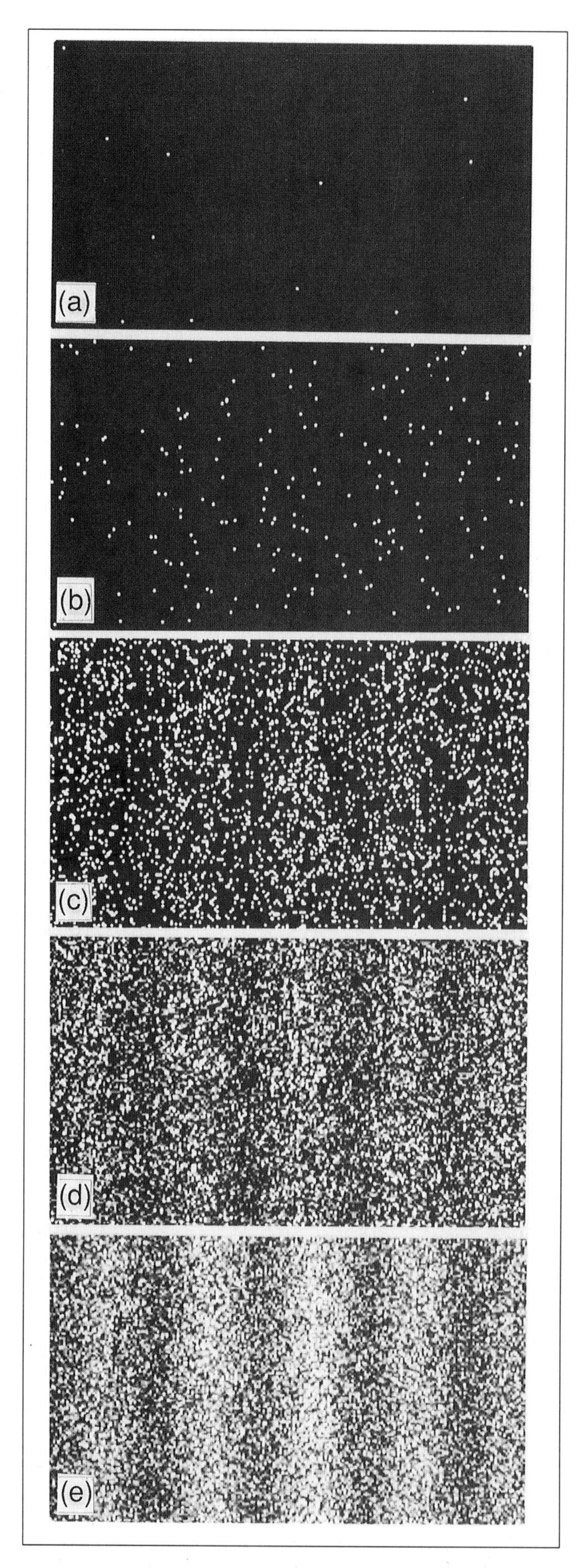

Right: Results of an electron-interference experiment. With small numbers of electrons, events are seemingly random. But with many thousands, classic interference patterns build up. Yet how do individual electrons "know" which path to take?

Radiation medicine

Radiation medicine divides into two separate areas: radiological imaging and radiotherapy. In radiological imaging, which traditionally meant X-rays, several new imaging techniques, such as ultrasound, CT scans, and MRI (see RADIOLOGY and ANATOMY AND SURGERY) have revolutionized the diagnosis and treatment of many diseases. The new techniques are much safer than X-rays, and provide much clearer images of structures inside the body, or images that could not be obtained at all with X-rays.

The availability of these new techniques has assisted doctors working in the second branch of radiation medicine, radiotherapy. They use radiation to treat disease – mostly cancer. In many cases, radiotherapy, often in conjunction with surgery or chemotherapy (anti-cancer drugs), can cure cancers completely.

One problem in radiotherapy is in delivering a dose of radiation to the tumor that is sufficient to kill it, while avoiding damaging the surrounding normal tissues, such as muscle, skin, bone, or intestine. CT and MRI scanning have helped radiotherapists to determine the precise position of the tumor, so that they can target the X-ray beam very accurately onto it, while shielding normal tissues. Further scans make it possible to assess how the tumor is responding.

Other new techniques have also helped to make radiotherapy more effective. In order to give patients more radiation without inducing unacceptable side effects, the radiation must be *fractionated* – that is, given in small, frequent doses. Traditionally, this has meant receiving one dose of radiation a day, five days a week for about six weeks. Recent research has shown, however, that radiotherapy is more effective if patients receive two or three smaller doses of radiation a day, seven days a week. This method, called *hyperfractionation*, also makes it possible to reduce the period over which radiotherapy is given.

Accurate targeting

The source of the radiation for much radiotherapy has traditionally been a machine containing radioactive cobalt. Over the past 20 years, a more powerful and accurate radiotherapy machine called a linear accelerator has allowed further advances in the treatment of certain cancers. Both types of machine can be rotated around the target site, to deliver concentrated beams of radiation to the tumor from different directions without affecting the tissue around the tumor. The increased precision of the linear accelerator beam makes it more suitable for treatment of brain tumors in children, as well as pelvic and lung tumors.

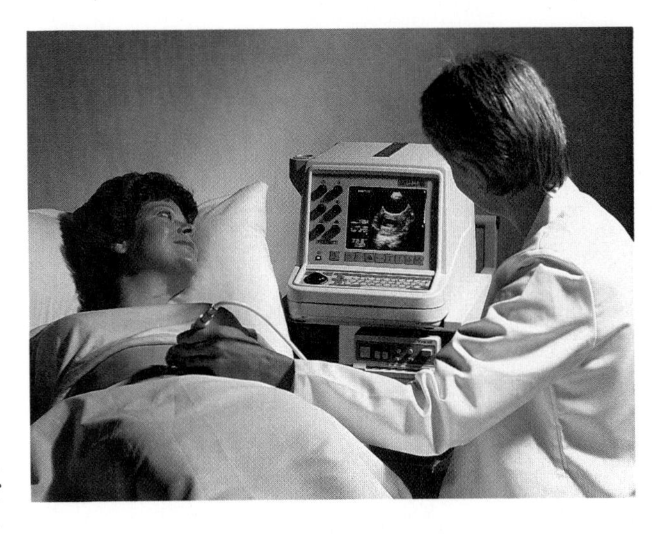

Above: Radiation medicine includes ultrasound scans as well as traditional X-ray methods. Ultrasound is used in many medical fields, from obstetrics to cardiology and kidney transplants.

In the past, the shape of the radiation beam was determined by the shape of the aperture of the cobalt machine or linear accelerator. A new device, called a multi-leaf collimator, makes it possible to shape the radiation beam so that it matches more closely the shape of the tumor. Such collimators contribute to another new technique called conformational therapy, which has also been successfully used in conjunction with linear accelerators.

Before beginning conformational therapy, the patient has a series of CT scans to determine the three-dimensional shape and size of the tumor. During the therapy, a moving arc of radiation is directed at the tumor, its speed calculated to deliver the correct dose to each part of the tumor, from dif-

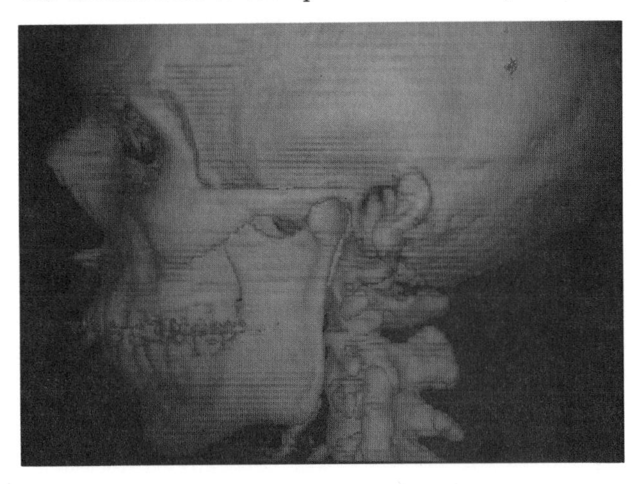

Above: From a series of CT scans, three-dimensional reconstructions of parts of the subject's body can be produced using a computer.

Left: Interventional radiology is used to guide the placement of objects within a person's body. This is the delivery system for small coils used to block abnormal arteries or those feeding a tumor.

ferent angles, according to its thickness. The collimator, linear accelerator, and the machine which moves the beam are all under computer control.

There has been renewed interest in radioactive implants as a way of delivering radiation directly to a tumor. Some women with breast cancer have implants of iridium wires into the breast. Further external radiotherapy is sometimes needed with this treatment. Radioactive implants can also help in the treatment of gynecological cancers and tumors that develop in readily accessible areas such as the tongue.

Monoclonal antibodies (see BIOTECHNOLOGY) that "seek and destroy" tumor cells also hold out hope for more effective radiotherapy. In principle, an antibody that binds to a specific tumor protein should be able to seek out rogue cells wherever they have spread in the body. The antibodies can be linked to poisons (see IMMUNOLOGY). Some researchers have linked them to mildly radioactive chemicals that show up on a body scan, in order to indicate where the cancer has spread. But it is also possible to combine the antibodies with highly radioactive particles, in the hope that they will kill the cells that they bind to. This approach is already being tried in the treatment of childhood leukemia and bowel cancer.

Radiology by wire

Interventional radiology is a recent offshoot of radiological imaging, which takes imaging one step further, from diagnosis to treatment. Radiologists can now insert fine wires and instruments deep into the body, guided by the view on an ultrasound or CT scan. Surgery that would have once warranted an incision in the skin now leaves only a small puncture mark. As a result, patients can be treated more quickly, often without the need for general anesthetic.

One example of interventional radiology is balloon angioplasty, which makes it possible to open up blocked or narrowed blood vessels. The surgeon feeds a guide wire into the blood vessel and then, over the wire, a specialized catheter. This has a balloon on its end that can be inflated in the narrowed part of the blood vessel, removing the blockage, which is normally formed by a fatty material called atheroma. Carried out on the main artery that supplies the leg, this procedure can restore a good blood supply to the whole limb.

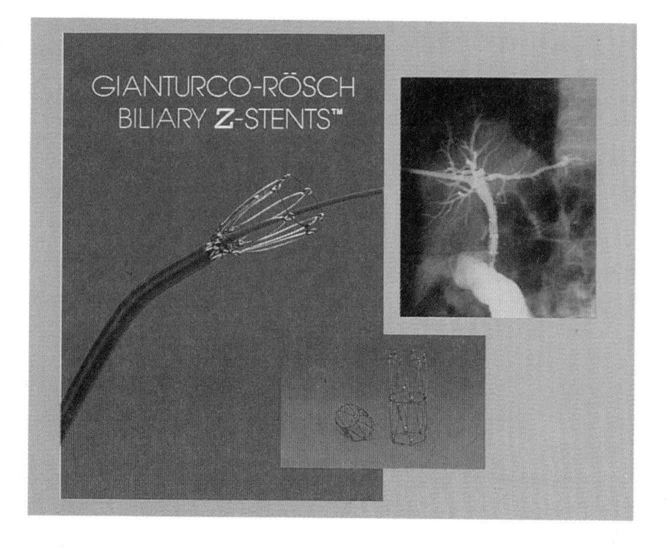

Above: Obstructions within the bile duct, usually caused by cancer, can be relieved by placing these stents using interventional radiology.

Radio astronomy

The evening of November 15th, 1988 was a sad one for U.S. astronomers. One of the nation's biggest radio telescopes, the venerable but aged 300-foot (91 m) dish at Green Bank in West Virginia, collapsed into a heap of twisted steel. Fortunately for radio astronomers, the National Radio Astronomy Observatory is now constructing a replacement 328-foot (100 m) dish that will rank alongside Germany's 100-meter one as the world's largest fully steerable radio telescope.

Welcome though the telescope will be, it is likely to be the last of the giant dishes to be built. A radio telescope collects radio waves from celestial bodies, just as an optical telescope uses light. The larger the collecting dish, the more sensitive it is to faint signals and the better the resolving power – the ability to discern fine details. In the quest for ever greater resolving power, radio astronomers are shifting their attention from giant dishes to arrays of telescopes, spread over large distances, which work as a single telescope of enormous diameter and high resolution.

The best known is the Very Large Array in the New Mexico desert, spread over an area up to 22 miles (36 km) across. Similar arrays are being operated in Britain, the Netherlands, Australia, and India, and telescopes across the world are regularly linked up to form arrays the size of Earth.

Active galaxies and black holes

The new high-resolution arrays have allowed astronomers to make detailed pictures of some of the most enigmatic objects in the universe: the so-called "active galaxies". Ever since the early days of radio astronomy it has been known that some galaxies are pouring vast amounts of energy out of a tiny region in their cores. These objects go by many names – quasars, QSOs, Seyfert galaxies, N galaxies, BL Lac objects, blazars – but astronomers now think that the same process is at work in all of them.

Above: Part of an array of radiotelescopes in Britain known as MERLIN (Multi-Element Radio-Linked Interferometer Network). The large dish receives signals from space, which are then transmitted by the small microwave antenna on the mast at left to a control center 42 miles (67 km) away. Together with other dishes, this simulates a single dish 136 miles (218 km) across.
Below: The MERLIN array covers a large part of England. All the dishes operate simultaneously with their outputs combined at Jodrell Bank.

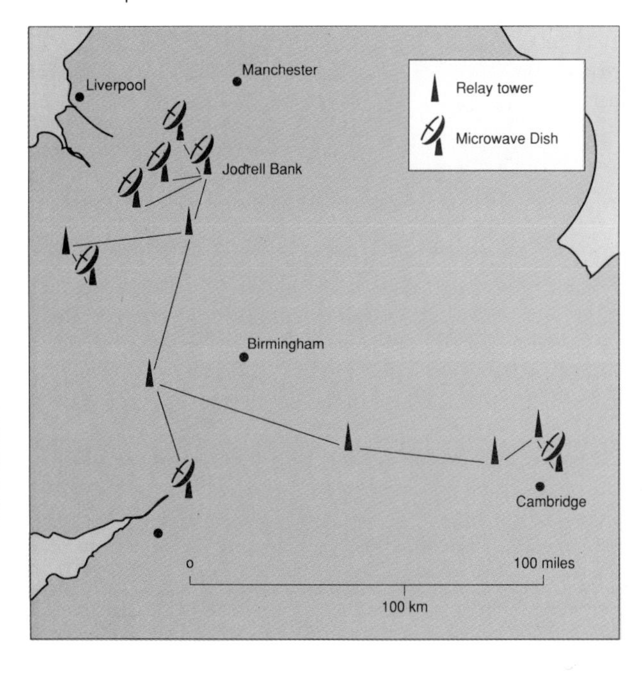

Above: In New Mexico, 27 dish antennae make up the Very Large Array. The dishes can be moved to fill in gaps in the spacings as the data build up.

According to this view, the power source at the heart of the galaxy is a black hole, a region of space where gravity is so strong that not even light can escape. The hole is likely to have been created by the crashing together of stars and gas soon after the galaxy was formed.

Although the hole itself cannot be seen, its effects on its surroundings are dramatic. Gas and stars falling towards the hole are swept into a swirling disk around it, before being dragged inward like water going down a plug hole. Some of the gas is then blasted out again in the form of two opposing jets, which shoot far out beyond the galaxy. Radio astronomers now have many fine images of these gigantic cosmic gushers but theorists are still struggling to understand them.

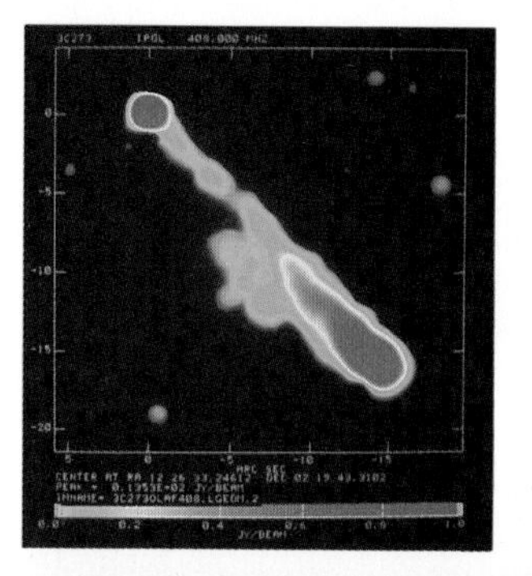

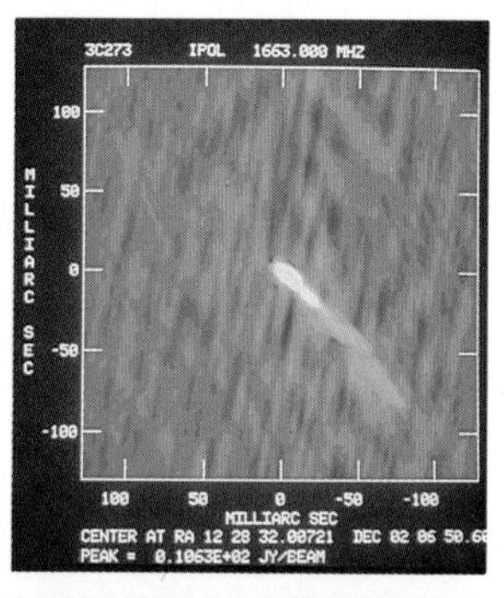

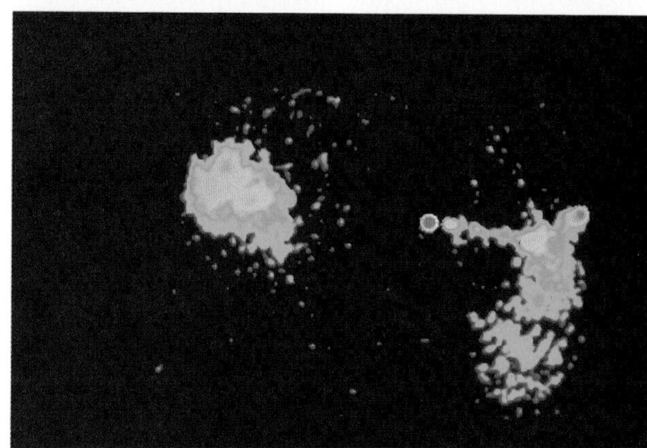

Top left: MERLIN image of the quasar 3C273 – one of the closest of these active galaxies. The red spot is the quasar itself, which has a jet extending from its center.
Top right: Detail of the center of 3C273, made by combining MERLIN with similar arrays in the U.S. and Europe to give an effective dish size of 6000 miles (10,000 km). The image is 1/100 the scale of the basic MERLIN image.
Above: The distant quasar 3C179 is shown in this image which combines observations made using MERLIN with those made by the Very Large Array in New Mexico. This allows finer details to be revealed than using one array alone.

Recycled pulsars

One field of radio astronomy for which big dishes are essential is the study of pulsars. Pulsars are neutron stars which are the remnants of stars, which ended their lives in supernova explosions (see ASTROPHYSICS). These highly magnetic objects, just a few miles across, rotate rapidly and emit a beam of radio waves that seems to pulse as it passes over the Earth, much like the beam from a distant lighthouse. Over a period of a few million years they radiate away their rotational energy and fade out.

In the last few years, the story has taken another twist with the discovery of pulsars in globular clusters. These clusters only contain ancient stars and any pulsars formed there should have long since disappeared. The explanation seems to be that these are also recycled pulsars, but they arise from very old neutron stars created by supernova activity early in the life of the cluster, that have been captured into orbits around ordinary stars and then spun back to life.

Dozens of recycled pulsars are now known, mainly in globular clusters. In 1991 a British-Australian team announced the discovery of no less than 11 superfast pulsars in one cluster, named 47 Tucanae, all of them with pulse rates of less than six milliseconds. Why this cluster should be so favored remains a mystery.

In the summer of 1991 a team of radio astronomers from Manchester University in England announced that they had discovered a planet circling a pulsar. By carefully timing the pulses they found that the star was being pulled back and forth by an unseen companion about 10 times the mass of the Earth. The discovery made the headlines because it appeared to be the first definite news of a planet beyond the solar system.

Astronomers around the world rushed to observe other pulsars. Early in 1992 an American team announced that they had observed a pulsar called PSR 1257+12 with two planets in orbit around it. It suddenly seemed that pulsar planets might be commonplace.

But within days the astronomical community was thrown into confusion. Professor Andrew Lyne, whose Manchester group had discovered the first planet, told a meeting of the American Astronomical Society that he had made a mistake. The "planet" was nothing more than an error in the program used to analyze the data. When the error was corrected the planet disappeared.

The astronomers who discovered the second planets hastily checked to see that they had not also fallen into this trap. But they had not. It appears that the two companions to PSR 1257+12 really are the first planets to be found outside the solar system.

Seismology

Seismologists study earthquakes. They are interested in the earthquakes themselves to find out what happens in the ground when they occur, and why they happen at the places they do. They also study, with engineers, the effects of earthquakes on structures and landscape and use earthquake waves that pass right through the Earth to explore its deep interior. In the future, they may be able, if not to predict earthquakes, at least to minimize their effects.

Earthquakes occur when slow movements deep in the Earth cause a sudden break in the rocks near the surface, usually a few miles down. If this break reaches the surface it is seen as a geologic fault. Earthquakes can occur almost anywhere, but most cluster along certain well-defined zones, which mark the boundary of so-called "plates" in the Earth's outer layers. Worldwide, up to 3000 earthquakes are detected each month, but most are far too small to be felt and fortunately only a few each year are big enough to cause serious damage.

The break at the fault sends out vibrations through the ground which are recorded by seismographs and affect people and structures. In the last few decades there has been a revolution in earthquake recording. New sensitive instruments at remote sites can be linked together by radio or satellite to form huge arrays, much more powerful than each one alone. Instead of wiggly lines written on paper, the signals are stored in large computers, which give fine details of how the ground actually breaks, as well as how big the earthquake is and its precise location. The farther away you are from an earthquake the less you will be shaken, but when you see pictures of very serious damage, this is usually the result of poor construction or building on soft ground. Poor ground can increase shaking many times; this caused buildings to collapse in the bayside Marina district of San Francisco 50 miles (80 km) from the center of the 1989 Californian (Loma Prieta) earthquake.

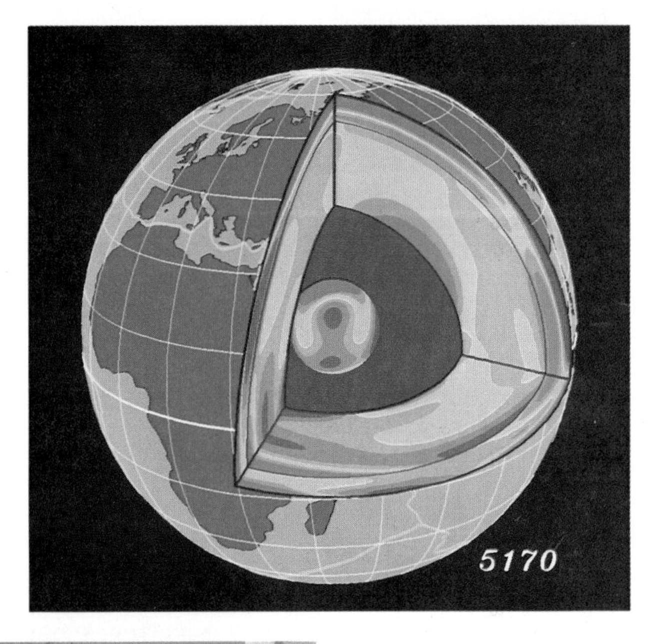

Above: Cross section of the Earth's interior, color-coded to show the rate at which earthquake waves travel: faster in the blue zones, slower in the red.
Left: The Lomo Prieta earthquake of October, 1989 caused considerable damage in the Marina district of San Francisco. The loose soil of the area behaved like a dense liquid, causing the collapse of this three-story building. At the time of the 1906 earthquake, this area was a lagoon, which was then filled with the rubble from buildings destroyed in that event.

Left: A solar-powered earthquake-monitoring station which transmits a continuous record of seismic activity to a central collecting station.

Right: Part of the University of California at Berkeley's network of seismographs, in a disused mine at Jamestown, CA. This has detectors to record short-period vibrations – about 1 second.

Earthquake prediction has always seemed an exciting idea, but scientists are finding it unexpectedly hard. For instance, no immediate prediction was given before the Loma Prieta earthquake, although such an event has long been considered likely in that area. Many people are now questioning if it is all that useful to predict exactly when an earthquake will occur, and point out the economic and social disruption that would follow "false alarms" or vague predictions.

Instead, seismologists are concentrating on finding a "seismic hazard" which gives the longterm likelihood of shaking at different places, and helps engineers and planners to reduce the "seismic risk" by proper standards of construction and siting buildings away from dangerous ground. This has been approved by the United Nations, which, following a suggestion by Dr. Frank Press, President of the U.S. National Academy of Sciences, has designated the 1990s as the International Decade for Natural Disaster Reduction.

Exploring the Earth

The locations where earthquakes happen reveal the Earth's weak parts, sometimes extending up to 450 miles (720 km) beneath the surface. Tracing the paths of earthquake waves from these sources to recording stations all over the world helps to build up an X-ray-like picture of the Earth's inner structure. The main divisions of the Earth have been known since the early part of this century. The rocky outer crust is about 20 miles (33 km) thick, and covers the mantle which extends about halfway to the Earth's center (1800 miles or 2900 km). The mantle is solid and it is only below this in the core that the Earth becomes liquid. At the very center there is a small solid inner core.

Up to now scientists had assumed that at any particular depth the Earth is the same everywhere, but the recent advances in highly detailed recording and supercomputers for analysis allow them to look simultaneously at millions of individual readings of different earthquakes at different recording stations all over the world to build up a three-dimensional picture or "tomographic image" of the whole Earth. These allow the mapping of small differences from average structures, such as wavy bumps on the surface of the core, a few miles high, and small variations in the speed of earthquake waves beneath different parts of the Earth. This new detail may help us to understand the slow movements deep in the Earth which, as well as giving clues as to the Earth's geologic history, could help explain the underlying cause of earthquakes.

Kanamori magnitudes

People are used to thinking of earthquake size on the Richter scale of magnitude, but this is now being replaced by a new concept of seismic moment, which gives a Kanamori magnitude, named after the scientist who developed it.

Richter first introduced his scale in 1935 to measure how much energy an earthquake releases at its source, but seismologists later realized that it does not give a high enough reading for the very biggest events. Seismic moment, like magnitude, can be worked out from instrumental records, but it can also be found more simply by measuring the size and movement of the fault that causes the earthquake.

Both Richter and Kanamori magnitudes are logarithmic scales, with each step of one on the scale meaning a change of ten times in ground shaking or about 30 times in energy release. The biggest earthquakes, such as those in Chile in 1960 and Alaska in 1964, have magnitudes of more than 9, and the smallest recorded can go as low as –2 on the logarithmic scale.

Space astronomy

Most of the information that reaches the Earth from astronomical objects in space is in the form of electromagnetic radiation, ranging from the shortest wavelengths of gamma rays, through X-rays, and ultraviolet, visible light, infrared, microwaves, and finally to the longest wavelengths, radio waves. Much of this radiation, however, is blocked by our atmosphere before it reaches ground level. It is therefore hardly surprising that astronomers have tried to observe from above the atmosphere, usually from satellites. It is this field, which has become important only within the past two decades, which is known as space astronomy.

Only the very highest energies of gamma rays can penetrate the Earth's atmosphere. They originate from the most energetic and chaotic objects and events in the universe, such as supernova explosions, quasars, which are the nuclei of very distant active galaxies, and neutron stars and pulsars, the spinning superdense remnants of stars that have exploded (see RADIO ASTRONOMY). Gamma rays may also reveal black holes, which are collapsed massive stars. As matter is sucked into a black hole it radiates gamma ray photons.

In 1988, the Earth-orbiting Solar Maximum Mission satellite was used to observe gamma rays coming from SN1987A, the brightest supernova to be seen since 1604 (see ASTROPHYSICS). The astronomers found gamma ray spectral lines resulting from the decay of the short-lived radioactive element cobalt-56. These observations confirmed the theory that heavy chemical elements are both made and dispersed by such massive stellar explosions.

The latest gamma ray satellite, the Compton Observatory, launched in 1991, is the first spacecraft not only to study gamma rays with a broad range of energies, but also to reveal exactly from which direction they came. It has looked at gamma rays from point sources, such as neutron stars and distant galaxies, together with the diffuse emission originating in our own galaxy and beyond.

Many distinctly separate gamma ray sources have been identified, including two supernova remnants: the Crab Nebula and the Vela pulsar. Another, called Geminga, is one of the strongest gamma ray sources known, but for many years there was no other trace of its existence. It shows up at the highest energy gamma rays but is invisible at lower energies. However, it has now been identified as a neutron star several hundreds of light years distant.

The Compton Observatory has also recorded a gamma ray glow inexplicably concentrated towards the center of our galaxy. Then there are the mysterious energetic random gamma ray

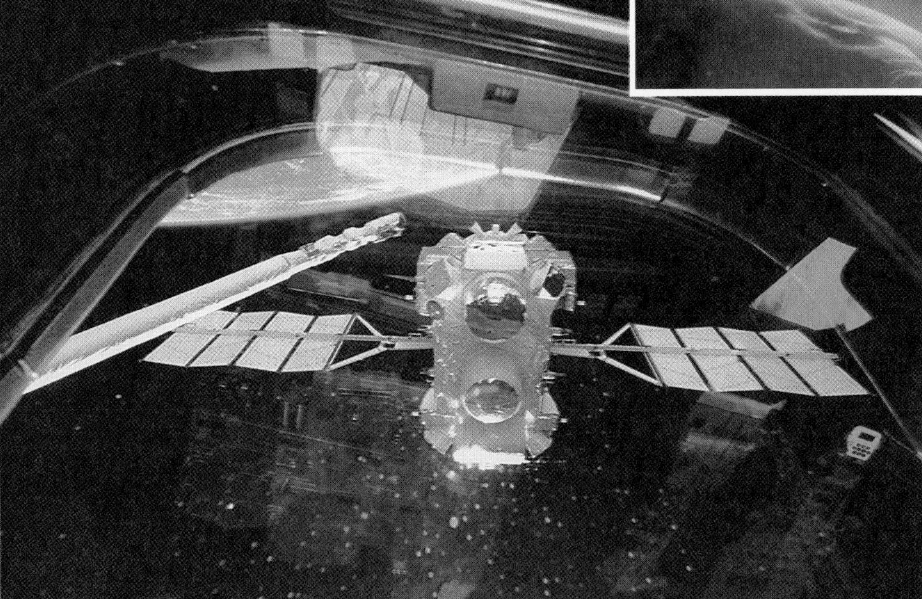

Left: NASA's Compton Observatory, for observing gamma rays, rises from the cargo bay of space shuttle Atlantis in 1991.
Above: Artist's impression of the German satellite Rosat in orbit, which observes in both X-rays and the extreme ultraviolet wavelengths.

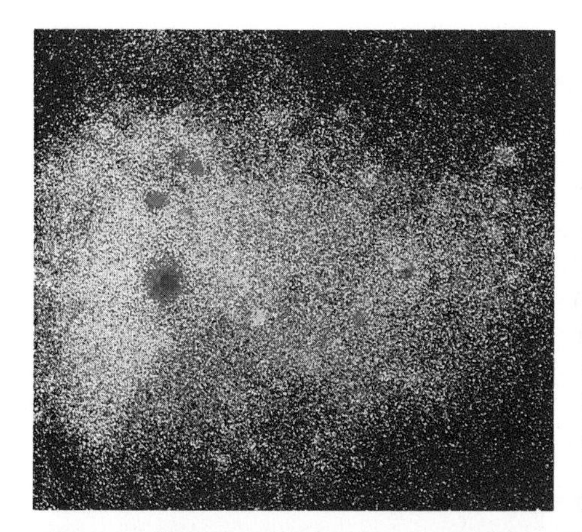

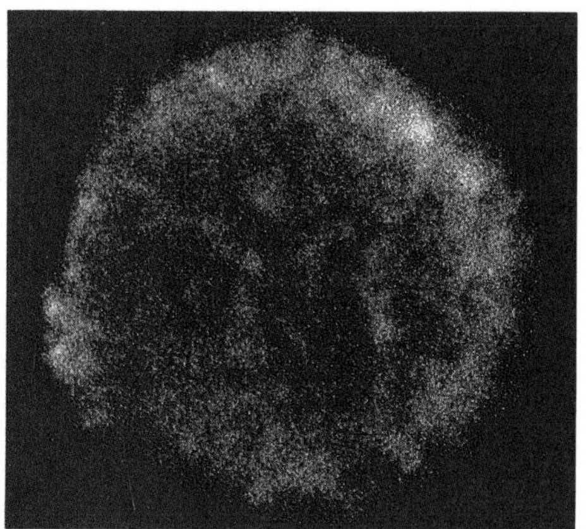

Left: Two ROSAT images. Far left, an X-ray view of the Large Magellanic Cloud, a small neighboring galaxy, shows an overall glow from hot gas rather than individual stars. Left, the shell left by a supernova in our own galaxy which was seen to explode in 1572 and is still a major X-ray source.

Above: Space and ground false-color views of the galaxy M81. The space view at top was taken in ultraviolet light by the Astro-1 payload aboard a space shuttle, while that above was taken in red light at Kitt Peak National Observatory in Arizona.

bursts which appear to be spread almost uniformly across the sky, suggesting that they are not part of our galaxy. Equally puzzling, there are no really faint bursts, implying the existence of some boundary beyond which no bursts can be observed. Only when a more detailed map of the bursts is available will astronomers be able to solve the puzzle.

X-rays from the stars

Two satellites have recently been studying X-rays from space. ROSAT was launched in 1990 by the European Space Agency, while the Anglo-Japanese spacecraft Ginga was in operation from 1987 to 1992.

ROSAT has made the first ever complete survey of the sky in the little-explored extreme ultraviolet (EUV) region lying between ultraviolet and X-ray wavelengths. Its two telescopes were then pointed at interesting individual sources for detailed observations. The main instrument aboard Ginga was the largest X-ray detector to be launched into space. Simultaneous observations using both satellites enabled the X-ray spectra of many objects to be studied over a very wide energy range. Ginga measured faint spectral features relating to the chemical composition of distant stars and galaxies.

ROSAT has made X-ray studies of active galactic nuclei or AGNs, including the special varieties of active galaxies known as quasars and Seyfert galaxies. It has confirmed that some quasars have spectral features which resemble those of the less luminous Seyfert galaxies, suggesting that the two are more similar than they appear. Many of the spectral features observed in these objects are thought to originate from X-rays reprocessed in cold material close to massive black holes at the centers of these galaxies. When this cold material is sucked into the black hole it provides the "fuel" for the huge energy output observed. Within our own galaxy, ROSAT has studied such objects as binary star systems containing a white dwarf. It also showed that a large part of the X-ray back-

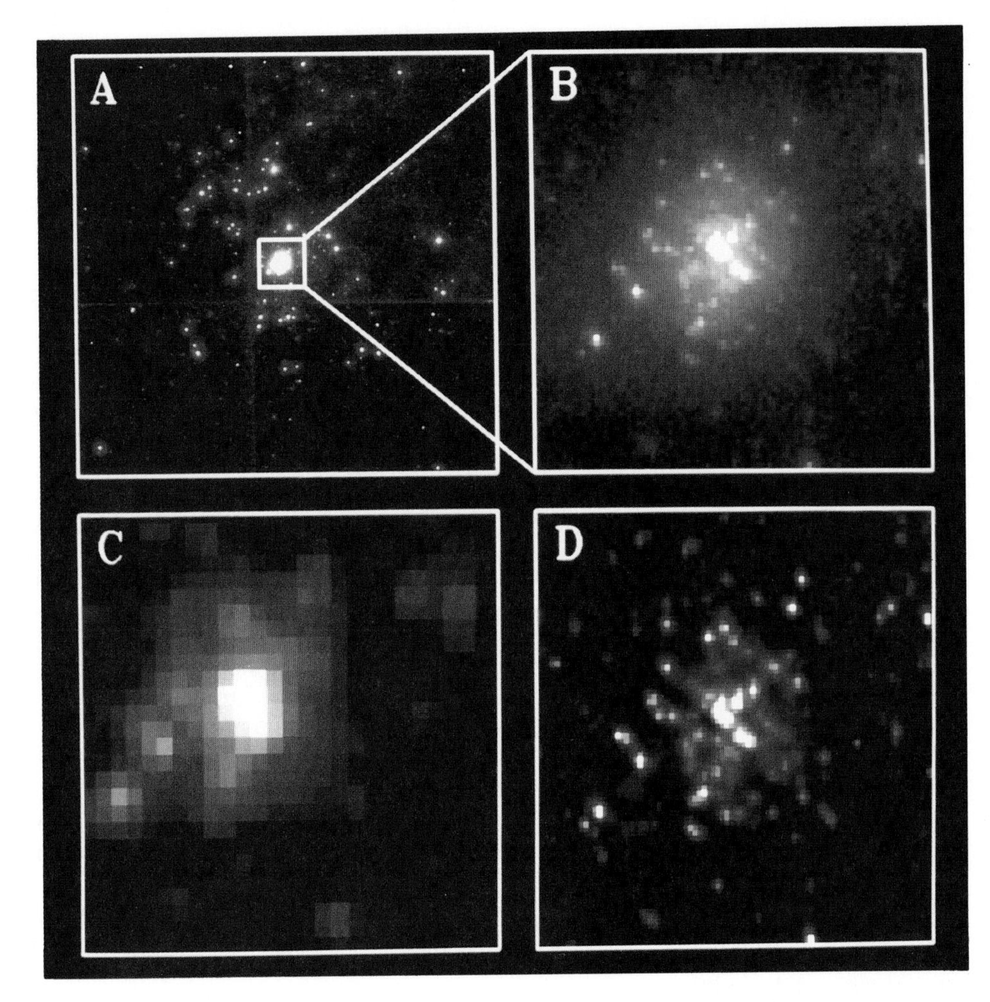

Left: A cluster of tightly packed stars within the Large Magellanic Cloud, photographed using the Hubble Space Telescope's Wide Field/Planetary Camera. Panel A shows the original image, while B is an enlarged portion of the cluster before computer processing. C shows the same area photographed by a telescope in Chile, while D shows the result of "cleaning-up" image B to remove the spurious halos caused by HST's faulty optics.

ground at low energies comes from distant quasars. The origin of the higher energy X-rays which contribute most energy to the cosmic X-ray background radiation remains uncertain.

Ultraviolet astronomy is also of great importance. Most ultraviolet sources are unusually hot but otherwise normal stars which have strong gas flows. These celestial searchlights also illuminate nearby gas, yielding information on the chemical elements in the gas. Even in the case of other galaxies, where the stars themselves cannot be distinguished individually, ultraviolet observations reveal the presence of these hot stars. Variations in the ultraviolet spectrum of the active galaxy NGC 4151, for example, led to an estimate of 1,000 million solar masses for the massive black hole believed to lie in the nucleus of the galaxy.

The most successful ultraviolet satellite has been IUE, the International Ultraviolet Explorer. It was launched in 1978 with an expected lifetime of two to three years, but was still operating in 1992, and has provided material for more research papers than any other spacecraft in the history of space research. Ultraviolet studies were also carried out by astronomers using the Astro-1 payload carried into orbit by the space shuttle Columbia in December 1990. Before Astro-1 no detailed ultraviolet photographs of any object apart from the Sun had been obtained.

The Astro-1 payload carried two telescopes for studying the spectra of quasars and active galactic nuclei, and for imaging stars and galaxies, with a photometer sensitive to polarized radiation. The highest energy objects such as active galaxies were also studied by a fourth instrument, an X-ray telescope. The sensitive ultraviolet telescope obtained images of very hot stars and gas, including the hottest stars in the globular cluster Omega Centauri and shock waves in the Cygnus Loop, a ring of hot gas and debris expanding from the site of a supernova explosion. The polarimeter detected clouds of hot gas and dust, whose ultraviolet light was polarized, bursting out from the surface of the red giant star Betelgeuse.

Interesting results also came from NASA's Extreme Ultraviolet Explorer (EUVE) satellite, launched in June, 1992. During its six-month survey of the entire sky, it recorded the radiation emitted by the multi-million degree outer atmosphere of a star much like our Sun, and the hot

Left: The HST Faint Object camera was used for this ultraviolet image of the jet of material which emanates from the nucleus of the galaxy M87. The jet may be powered by a massive black hole.

surfaces of white dwarf stars. An explosive outburst of EUV radiation was also observed from a close pair of stars as very hot stellar material, pulled from the outer layers of a normal star, fell on to the surface of its white dwarf companion. The EUVE also caught flares, similar to those which occur on our own Sun, on two very dim red dwarf stars, and the first EUV-emitting object outside our own galaxy.

The Hubble Telescope

The much-maligned Hubble Space Telescope (HST) provides unmatched capability for observations in the ultraviolet because its main mirror is very clean, and ultraviolet reflectivity is good. The telescope can also make excellent spectroscopic observations in both visible and ultraviolet light. The Wide-Field/Planetary Camera has been used to study bright, high-contrast objects, such as the planets and nearby star clusters and galaxies. It has revealed new detail in the compact cores of galaxies. Bright clouds of gas in the active galaxy NGC 1068 provide evidence that a black hole with a mass of 100 million suns lies at its center. An even larger black hole with a mass of 3 billion suns may lie at the heart of the giant galaxy M87.

The HST's Faint Object Camera has imaged high-energy jets in distant galaxies, resolved close, rich star clusters into separate stars, and probed the core of a nearby exploding star. Hubble's two spectrographs have achieved excellent results on brighter sources, particularly in the ultraviolet part of the spectrum. Finally, the Fine Guidance Sensors, although designed primarily for precise pointing of the HST, may also be used for ASTROMETRY, complementing those of the European satellite Hipparcos.

At wavelengths longer than visible red light is the infrared region. The most successful infrared satellite to date has been the Infrared Astronomical Satellite (IRAS). Although its mission lasted only ten months in 1983, it mapped the whole sky, and catalogued 245,000 infrared sources, more than 100 times the number known before the launch. Analysis of the vast quantity of information sent back by IRAS still continues to yield surprises.

IRAS has found that some nearby stars, such as the brilliant Vega and Fomalhaut, are associated with cool material which may indicate the presence of planets or a forming planetary system. With one such star, Beta Pictoris, the material was subsequently photographed at optical wavelengths. IRAS also sent back new data about objects such as the hidden stars inside the famous Orion Nebula; these stars are young and extremely luminous, but it is not possible to see them optically due to the intervening nebula material.

These results show the vital importance of conducting astronomical observations from space. New spacecraft are currently being planned, and should be in orbit well before the end of the century; they will range over the entire electromagnetic spectrum and will add immeasurably to our knowledge of space.

• FACT FILE •

- Operating from an orbit 380 miles (610 km) above ground level, the HST has perfect skies all the time. When launched, it was confidently expected to outperform any Earth-based telescope, even though its 94 in (2.4 m) diameter mirror is much smaller than those of many ground-based telescopes.

- During construction of the HST's main mirror, a mistake was made in testing which misled those making it into believing that it was correctly shaped, when in fact it is too shallow by an amount equal to 1/50 the thickness of a human hair. This was not discovered until after the telescope was in orbit.

- NASA plans to add special corrective lenses to the HST, or replace some of its onboard cameras with new instruments that contain corrective lenses – a job that will be carried out by visiting space shuttle astronauts in 1994.

Sports medicine

Sports medicine is a wide-ranging discipline. Sports physicians are involved in the treatment, coaching, and counselling of athletes, and in the rehabilitation of athletes who have undergone surgery or suffered illness. One recent development has been the supervision of disabled athletes, whose participation in all branches of sport has increased dramatically over the past decade. Another, affecting the population as a whole, has been the general increased emphasis on keeping healthy through exercise.

Most serious athletes today regularly visit a human performance laboratory. Here, electrical monitors and gas exchange systems can be attached to the athlete's body while he or she works out on, for example, a treadmill or cycle ergometer. These monitor the performance of the athlete's heart, lungs, and BIOCHEMISTRY. Underlying disorders can be detected by measuring such parameters as the blood plasma's acidity, and the levels of blood lactate, urea, and hormones, as well as hemoglobin concentration.

Benefits and dangers of exercise

Sports physicians can advise patients who are undertaking exercise. Regular exercise can slow down the development of illnesses such as arteriosclerosis and alleviate the effects of others, such as chronic bronchitis, diabetes, and hypertension. It can also counteract some of the age-related changes in the body. But elderly people and patients with any medical condition should train only under medical supervision. For example, squash involves very heavy exertion which is obviously dangerous for patients with an impaired heart or blood circulation. Diabetic athletes need to avoid exercise if they have not eaten for several hours, in case their blood sugar level should fall dangerously during exercise. Glucose-rich food or drink should always be available for them.

Healthy eating can greatly enhance performance. A properly balanced food intake limits fatigue, both in training and during competition. Athletes need to be made aware of, for instance, the importance of eating large amounts of carbohydrates in the days preceding endurance events such as the marathon. They are even encouraged to have pasta parties beforehand. Eating and drinking carbohydrates during prolonged exercise will also aid performance.

The sports physician must pay special attention to the food eaten by younger athletes. During adolescence, when they are rapidly growing and developing, they require most nutrients, especially calcium, in much greater amounts in relation to body size. Female athletes might need to include iron-rich food in their diet; several studies have shown that up to 80 per cent of female runners may be anemic or suffer from iron deficiency.

Because human beings vary greatly in their

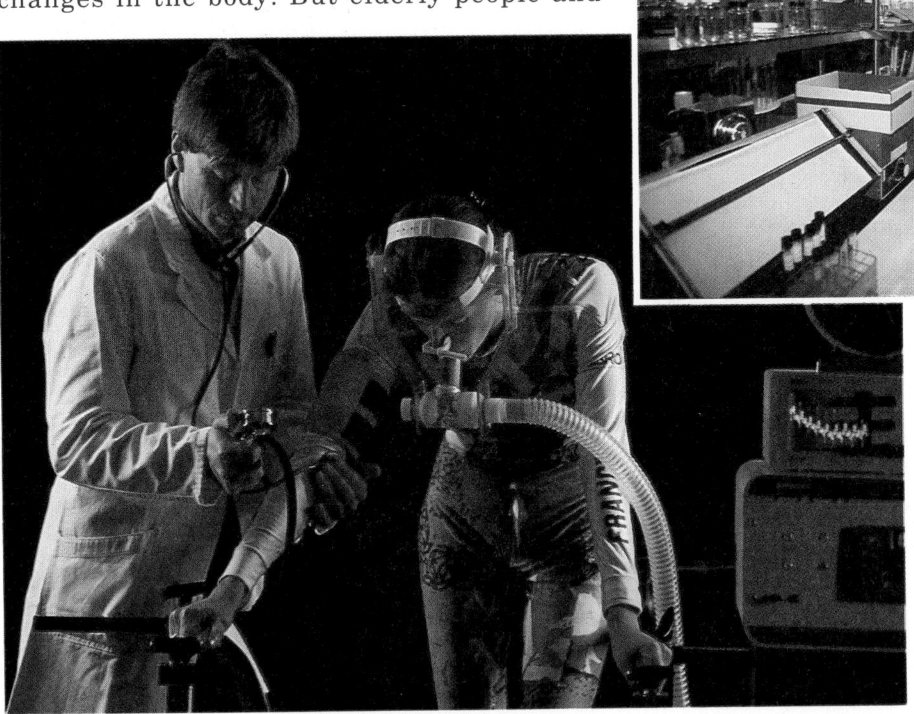

Above: The Drug Testing Center at the Barcelona Olympics in July, 1992 played an important role in the Games.
Left: Testing an athlete's fitness on a VO2Max machine which measures the amount of oxygen used in a given period. The doctor measures her pulse rate as she walks on a treadmill.

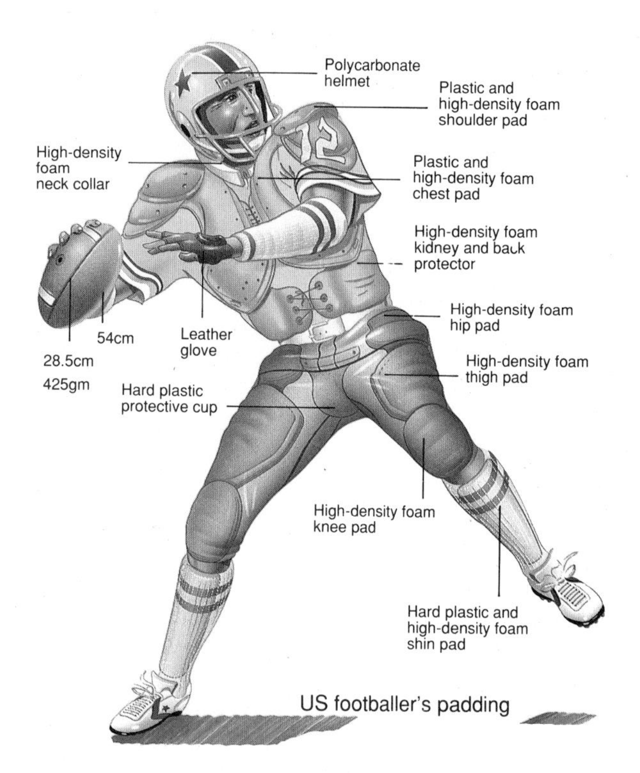

Left: Football players have led the way in body padding, now being recognized as vital to health even in less physical sports.

physique, some sports are far more suited to one person than to another. Sophisticated anthropometric instruments are now available to measure very accurately such variables as height, weight, girth, muscle size, body fat, and bone mass. Using the data obtained, coaches can choose the training to suit the individual.

Sports psychologists help by training athletes in emotional control, self-esteem, and interpersonal skills. Because people with different temperaments do not react in the same manner to stress, athletes are given questionnaires so that the most suitable counselling can be given. Sports psychologists can therefore help athletes enjoy training, display the right amounts of aggression and concentration, and cope adequately with failure – and with success.

"Staleness" – overtraining – is a recognized cause of reduced achievement, particularly in elite athletes. It shows up as a leveling off, or even a fall in performance because of a failure to tolerate or adapt to the training load. A physician can prevent this by carefully controlling the stress imposed by exercise and by varying the training to limit fatigue.

Until the 1970s, very few girls and women took part in vigorous competitive sports, or even in regular exercise programs. As the number of female athletes grew, it soon became clear that this could lead to a variety of reproductive disorders. For example, hormonal imbalance can cause a delay in puberty for up to three years, as well as irregularities in the menstrual cycle. In some instances the disturbances are severe enough to cause infertility and bone loss. Menstrual disorders may afflict as many as 50 per cent of endurance runners, but in most instances simply exercising less will help.

Drug testing

In 1988 at the Seoul Olympics, Canadian Ben Johnson ran the fastest 100 meters ever seen. But it was the steroid Stanolozol™ that had enabled him to perform this feat. To try to detect such abuse, the International Amateur Athletics Federation in 1990 introduced widespread out-of-competition drug testing.

As the number of athletes testing positive for drugs has risen, there has been a falling away from the performances achieved in the early 1980s, especially in field events and certain women's track races. This may indicate that those earlier standards owed something to drug abuse that is now being deterred.

The banned substances include stimulants such as caffeine in concentrated form and analgesics such as codeine. Even a few cups of strong coffee before an event may put an athlete over the limit. It is therefore essential for athletes to consult a physician familiar with the substances on the IOC's banned list before accepting a prescription.

This necessity was emphasized at the 1992 Barcelona Olympics when several athletes were prevented from taking part after testing positive for Clenbuterol™. This drug has muscle-building properties but is also sometimes prescribed for the relief of asthma.

Right: Computers can help analyze the movement of an athlete – here a discus thrower – to improve performance and avoid medical problems.

Statistics

There are many sorts of statistics, from lists of baseball scores which enthusiasts of the game find fascinating, to scientific data. Statistics is also the science of collecting, presenting, and using data in various ways. Sometimes the mathematics of probability are used to work out what the basic data mean. This is why statistical science is a branch of applied mathematics.

In recent years, computers have revolutionized statistical practice. The statistical tool kit includes novel and powerful techniques which are now applied to problems previously untouched by statistical thinking. Computer packages can supply awesome statistical firepower.

Statistics in criminology

A good example of the way statistics deals with the new methods of data acquisition comes from forensic science. An early use was the introduction of fingerprint identification in the 1890s. Statistics showed that no two people had the same fingerprint patterns. A century passed before another such technique was discovered when, in 1984, a British scientist, Alec Jeffries, found that individuals can be uniquely identified by measuring the lengths of certain stretches of their chromosomes, or DNA sequences. This technique, called DNA fingerprinting, has been refined so that all that is needed are microscopic quantities of body tissue or fluid.

DNA fingerprinting can clear a suspect by showing unambiguously that the person could not be responsible for any traces of semen or blood left at the scene of a crime.

If, however, a sample from the suspect does match one found at the scene of a crime, the chance that it did not come from the suspect (or a blood relative) is less than one in a billion. This calculation relies on a statistical analysis of DNA profiles. Not surprisingly, the suspect is highly likely to be found guilty if the samples match, but the evidence rests on statistics rather than absolute proof.

The statistical issues are complex. They involve assumptions about genetics, about the measurement errors of DNA fingerprinting techniques, and about the population group from which the criminal is supposed to have come. A recent U.S. National Academy of Sciences report on the controversy may, however, have found the right balance, thereby assisting parties to agree on a standard and acceptable way of presenting the statistical analysis and conclusions in court.

Statistics in chemistry

A major task in ANALYTICAL CHEMISTRY is to determine the concentration of a particular substance in samples of raw material. Traditional methods usually mean first removing some other constituents, whose presence would upset the analysis. In some cases the only way is to extract the actual constituent from a sample, which can be a costly process.

Cheap and effective alternatives are now available. A good example is near infrared (NIR) spectroscopy, in which the sample is exposed to a large number of infrared wavelengths, and the

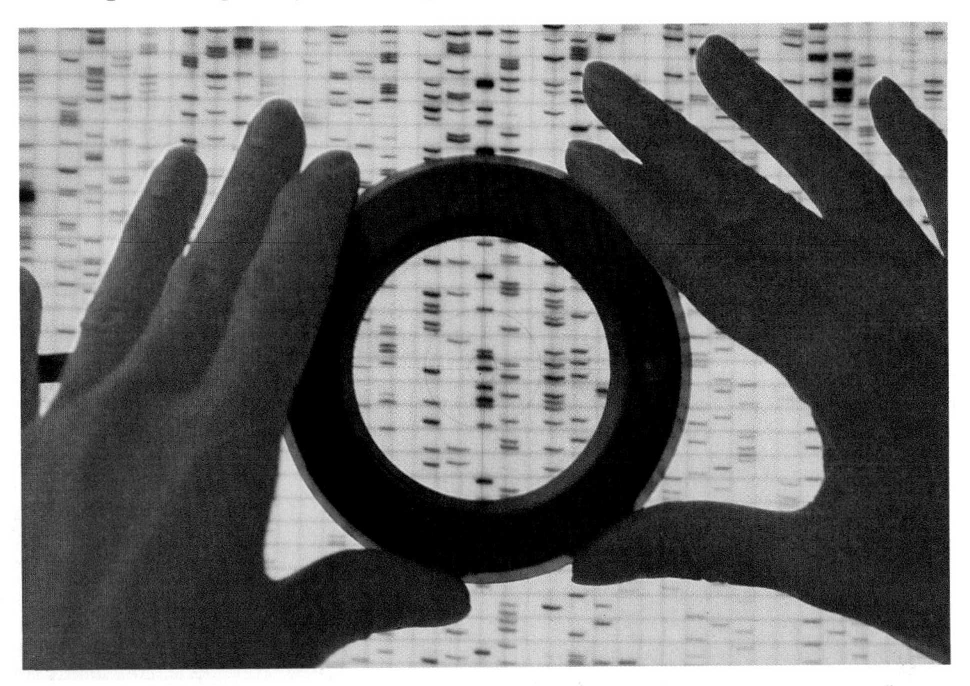

Left: A circular computer "scanner" used to read sections of DNA sequencing autoradiograms for subsequent computer analysis. DNA fingerprints require statistical analysis to address such issues as possible errors in the DNA fingerprinting technique before they can be used as evidence of a suspect's guilt or innocence.

amount of radiation reflected at each wavelength is recorded. It is a remarkable fact that, for many raw materials, this spectrum contains all the information needed to determine the required concentration with adequate precision and without any preliminary processing of the sample. The information can be extracted by routine statistical methods involving comparisons with samples of known concentrations.

The NIR method has been successfully applied to controlling the protein content of flour. The method is even running in "real time", allowing the protein percentage to be automatically controlled by the addition of gluten, the protein obtained from wheat.

Estimating a risk

In the field of medicine, statistics is used to provide a cost-effective way of deciding whether a patient needs special attention. For example, much effort has gone into detecting Down's syndrome – a serious genetic abnormality – as early as possible. In 1988, a team of clinicians and statisticians at St. Bartholemew's Hospital in London, England, found a way of estimating the probability of the abnormality occurring in any particular mother.

The mother gives a blood sample which is analyzed to determine the concentrations of three specific biochemicals. These concentrations tend to be higher when the abnormality is present.

A statistical analysis of available data led the researchers to develop a formula for estimating from the results of these tests the probability of abnormality occurring in the child. Mothers estimated as being at high risk are about 15 times as likely to have a child suffering from the abnormality. These mothers can then be given an amniocentesis (see OBSTETRICS AND GYNECOLOGY) for a definite verdict.

The Big Bang

Another significant use of statistical analysis occurred in 1992, when a satellite called COBE made front-page news all over the world after it had provided important evidence about the origin of the universe. While the results are accepted by the scientific community as genuine, it was not widely realized that the much-publicized pictures from the satellite showed no more than electronic "noise" from the detectors on board the spacecraft.

The maps of the background radiation, detected at microwave wavelengths, showed clear ripples scattered across the skies. These were hailed as evidence of early structures in the universe soon after the Big Bang (see COSMOLOGY). But in fact each individual map showed features that were at the same level as the instrumental noise. No two maps showed the same features.

The researchers used statistical analysis on the locations of the ripples and found a positive correlation between features on different maps. In other words, there was better agreement between the apparently random scattering of features than could be explained by chance. The real evidence comes not from the maps, but from statistics.

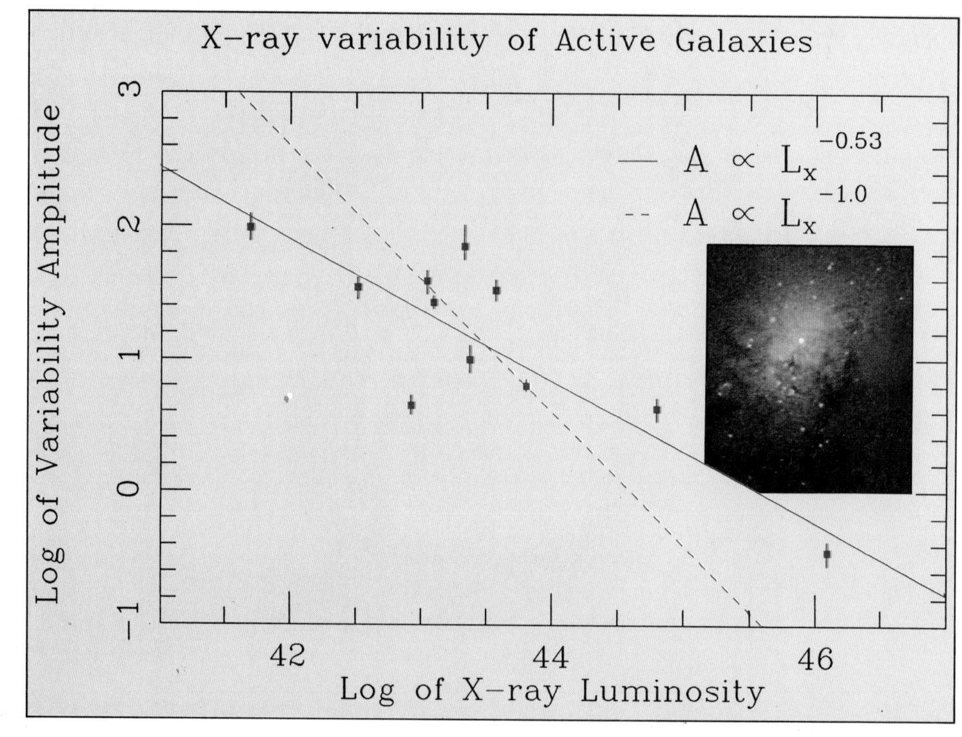

Right and inset: Scientists use statistical methods to help interpret data. In a study of active X-ray galaxies (inset) published in 1993, it was shown that brighter galaxies vary in output more than the fainter ones. But a regression analysis on the 12 data points showed that the best fit comes from a line which varies with the square root of the brightness, rather than just brightness – that is, the brighter galaxies vary less than expected. Vertical lines on each point show statistical error of each.

Telecommunications

One of the most remarkable examples of modern technology is available in virtually every home. While the basic technology of the telephone is over a century old, the potential of the phone network has never been greater, and is increasing every year. As well as giving the ability to contact people in over 200 countries within seconds, telephone lines now provide channels for transferring information from office to office or home to home with the use of fax machines and electronic mail. In the 1990s, simple videophones, which show a color image of the person at the other end of the phone, are being marketed. Though the image is low-quality and jerky, phone companies are hoping that the system will become widespread by the next century.

TV and telephone networks can put people in touch with each other much more cheaply and efficiently than travel. Furthermore, the passage of an electronic signal has very little environmental impact. But as the networks expand, engineers are facing the problems of providing enough capacity for all the requirements.

Because of the great expense of laying new cables and the increasing demand for telephone lines, engineers have continually tried to develop ways of using a single cable for many telephone calls at the same time. This is called multiplexing. Instead of sending the complete telephone signal along the cable, the varying electrical signals which carry the information are *digitized*, that is the strength of the signal is measured many thousands of times per second and converted into binary numbers consisting of ones and zeroes. These numbers can be transmitted along the cable very rapidly and the original signal reconstructed at the other end from the strings of numbers received. As the cable is only used for a very short period every few thousandths of a second to transmit information for each telephone call, the information relating to many thousands of different calls can be interleaved and sent along the cable one after the other.

Right: A cross-section of an undersea optical fiber cable. The optic cables – which are resin-coated for protection and color-coded for easy identification – are arranged around a central kingwire. A double-layer copper tube surrounded by strengthening steel wires carries the power feed current. A sandwich of aluminum tape and polythene insulates the components, preventing the electric field from radiating out into the sea and attracting sharks. Finally, a dense, polythene shield, which is resistant to shark bites, waterproofs the cable.

Fiber optics

Recently, cables consisting of bundles of optical fibers have been laid in preference to the ones consisting of copper wires. Optical fiber cables have many times the capacity of copper ones, being able to carry many thousands of multiplexed telephone calls at the same time. The combination of optical

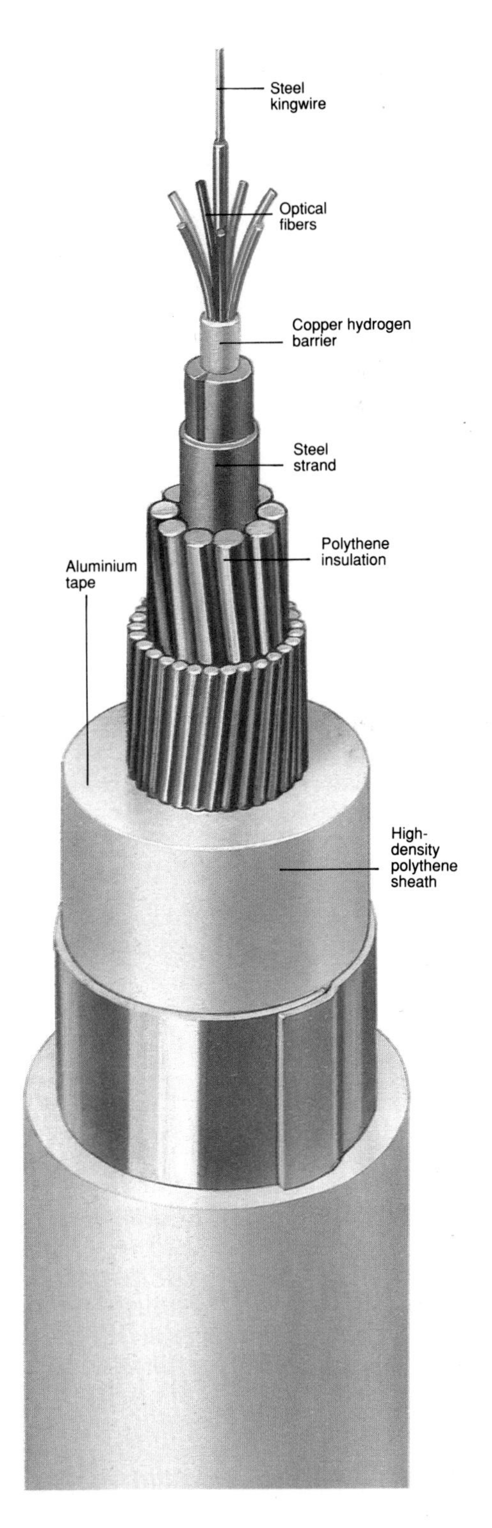

fibers and laser light has increased the capacity of telecommunication networks many times over.

The first transatlantic telephone cable to use optical fibers, TAT-8, has linked the United States with the U.K. and France since 1988. The cable is 4,114 miles (6,620 km) long with 130 opto-electronic repeaters to boost the signal at intervals of about 30 miles (50 km) all along the cable. It carries television, telephone, and data, and is expected to have a lifetime of 25 years. It can handle 37,500 simultaneous telephone conversations.

While optical fibers increase capacity between main centers, most telephones outside big cities are linked to the network by copper cables which may have been in place for decades. Therefore, efforts are being made to increase the capacity of existing cables. This can be done by compressing signals by removing redundant or unchanging information. Even in a complex musical passage, for instance, the sound at one instant is very similar to that at the next. By registering only the changes in a digital signal, much less space is needed. In this way, the information-carrying ability of a telephone line can be expanded enormously. At the moment, a phone line can carry a data signal at up to 19,200 bits per second (bps) before compression. Using a transmission system called Integrated Service Digital Networks (ISDN), an ordinary home phone line could provide two 64,000 bps channels for data or voice plus an additional 16,000 bps channel for data or control signals. While this is a fraction of the 45 megabits per second offered by optical fibers, ISDN could provide such facilities as real-time video conferencing without the need for expensive high-capacity lines.

The use of ISDN could become widespread by the end of the 1990s, but another system, called ADSL, for asymmetric digital subscriber line, is under trial by telephone companies. This could offer a massive 1.5 megabytes of capacity over existing copper wires, enough for high-definition TV, but in one direction only – to the subscriber. For home use, however, this could provide unlimited access to entertainment simply by dialing an electronic library.

The question remains to what extent domestic subscribers need to exchange information. As postal services deteriorate, fax has become standard in offices, though less so in the average home. Predictions that electronic mail will transform communications have yet to be realized. While networks such as CompuServe have made e-mail simple to operate for both office and domestic use, they are usually taken up by people or businesses who already use computers for other purposes.

The potential of electronic information on the ordinary home or office has yet to be realized in the U.S. But in France, millions of phone subscribers use a system called Minitel. A purpose-designed terminal plugged into a phone line gives instant access to a wide range of information services, from directory enquiries to train bookings, though it does not provide full e-mail facilities. The success of the system was the result of an initial free distribution of the terminals to anyone who wanted one. Now people are buying the terminals.

Transmission telecommunications

Modern telecommunications networks rely on cable or microwave transmissions over land,

Left: The Mercury, one of the world's most modern cable laying vessels.

Right: A satellite dish used by a household in the Amazon region of Brazil to receive television signals.

between relay towers in line of sight to one another, and on *geostationary satellites* for links across continental distances. When the first geostationary satellites, which have orbits that keep them constantly over one point on the Earth's surface, were launched, they seemed to offer the ideal method of providing long-distance telecommunications. Now, however, there is increasing competition for suitable locations for the satellites. In busy areas, such as over the Atlantic Ocean, satellites are almost literally jostling for position with one another.

The power transmitted by a communications satellite is dissipated when it is directed towards the Earth with a wide beam. The size of the area covered by the beam is called the "footprint" of the satellite's antenna. Increasingly, satellite antennae are able to concentrate the signal on the ground within a specific target area, placing the maximum power exactly where it is needed. These are called "spot beams" and they allow the ground antennae to be much smaller. The greater the power of the signal transmitted by the satellite, the smaller the antenna needed to receive it. Large ground stations used for worldwide communications may have dish antennae up to 100 ft (30 m) in diameter. However, home subscribers to satellite TV are often restricted by local laws to antennae only about 24 in (60 cm) across. These have poor abilities to point at individual satellites and may increasingly suffer from interference as the orbits get more crowded.

Frequency allocation

The allocation of frequency bands is carefully controlled by the International Telecommunications Union which holds regular World Administrative Radio Conferences to allocate not only the frequencies but also the orbital slots for new satellites. At present, satellites operate within the so-called C or Ku bands, depending on the frequencies they use for transmitting and receiving signals. In a C-band satellite system, signals are sent within a 500 MHz bandwidth, on a carrier frequency of 6 GHz for the upward journey and 4 MHz back down to Earth. This change in the central frequency prevents the incoming communication signals from interfering with the outgoing ones.

Until recently, bandwidth limitations restricted the number of signals which could be carried. A bandwidth of 40 kHz was needed to carry the human voice (80 kHz for a two-way telephone circuit). Within the allowed 500 MHz bandwidth, each transmitter or transponder on the satellite could carry 1000 voice channels (500 two-way telephone circuits) or one TV program, since a television picture requires one voice channel for every line on the TV screen. A complete C-band satellite with 12 transponders would be limited to carrying 12 TV programs or 6000 simultaneous conversations, or some mixture of the two.

The shortage of available bandwidth has forced engineers to try new techniques to squeeze more signals into the same space. Using similar digitizing techniques to those used for land signals, engineers can now transmit at up to 100 million bps over a single transponder. Modern satellites have up to 50 transponders so the total capacity is extremely high. The demand for capacity on satellites is so great that engineers are moving up to even higher transmission frequencies; experi-

Above: An image seen by Cable News Network viewers during the Gulf War of the portable satellite communications unit used by the network's TV crew in Baghdad.

ments are already taking place in the Ka band between 26.5 and 40 GHz and even at 60 GHz. However, at such high frequencies there are problems because the signal is affected by heavy rain or snow showers and even clouds over the receiving station.

Satellite delays

Perhaps the most familiar drawback of satellite communications is the delay introduced by the time the signal takes to make the 50,000 mile (80,000 km) round trip from the ground up to the satellite and back down again. This amounts to about 0.3 seconds in each direction, and, together with technical mismatches between different phone systems, it complicated two-way conversations in the early days of telecommunications. Today, engineers have cleverly introduced circuits which compensate for this delay, and on a well-adjusted circuit it is often difficult to know whether one is speaking via a satellite link or not.

The bulk of commercial traffic uses the Intelsat satellites, operated by a consortium of nations. In 1982, the latest generation of Intelsat satellites was born – the Intelsat 6 family. Each of these satellites carries 120,000 telephone circuits and three TV channels, operated with the new advanced digital modulation techniques. Each Intelsat 6 satellite requires 2,600 watts of electrical power, and has 48 transponders operating in the C band (6/4 GHz) and the higher K band at 14/11 GHz. Their planned operational lifetime is approximately 14 years. Construction of the first of the next generation of satellites – Intelsat 7 – began in November 1991. Today, Intelsat is facing increasing competition from other operators of communications satellites in various countries all over the world.

• FACT FILE •

- In the future, even mobile phones may use satellites. There are plans for a network, called Iridium, of 77 satellites, in comparatively low orbits at 490 miles (780 km) altitude. These will divide the ground into cells, just as land-based cellular phones do.

- Analogue land cellular phone networks are already overloaded, and new frequencies are needed to provide extra capacity. Digital systems which will improve the capacity of existing frequencies are already being tested, such as for an all-Europe system known as GSM. Iridium will use similar technology.

- A satellite system would overcome the "dead zones" that are common in any land-based system, and would also link into national phone systems giving access from anywhere in the world. At an estimated cost of $3 per minute, Iridium would be more expensive to use than conventional cellular phones, but the manufacturer, Motorola, is proposing that the units would also include circuits to use the cheaper land-based services where available. The system could be in use by 1997.

Left: The capture of the Intelsat 6 satellite by the space shuttle Endeavour in 1992. The satellite was subsequently mated with a booster and redeployed.

Tropical medicine

Each year, more than 1000 people return to the U.S. with an unexpected passenger aboard: the malaria parasite. Perhaps they forgot to take their anti-malaria pills, or encountered drug-resistant strains of the parasite. Either way, they experience a tropical disease easy for people in developed countries to forget, even though it afflicts 270 million people worldwide at any one time.

Malaria is top of the league in the table of tropical diseases. About 2.1 billion people – half the world's population – in 103 countries are at risk of contracting it. There are an estimated 110 million new cases each year. Between 1 and 2 million people die each year from the disease.

The malaria parasite is transmitted by the bite of infected female mosquitoes. Controlling the disease is especially difficult because of the parasite's ability to develop resistance to the drugs used. As a result, the World Health Organization is searching for new drugs to treat the disease. Research is also under way into development of vaccines to control malaria, by preventing infection, by reducing the severity of the symptoms, or by reducing transmission of the parasite (see PARASITOLOGY).

Flies and snails

Almost half a billion people around the world are at this minute suffering from a tropical disease, usually caused by parasites spread by flies and snails. Measures to control them are therefore often based on controlling these organisms – using insecticides, for example, or draining watery areas where they live and breed.

Underdeveloped countries find it difficult to invest in such measures, however. Many tropical diseases are poorly controlled because the people affected by them live in developing countries where governments spend an average of only $4 per person per year on health care.

Schistosomiasis, for example, is curable. It is spread by a parasite present in freshwater snails, which become infected when the water where they live is contaminated by human excrement. The parasite damages the urinary system or the intestines, sometimes with fatal results. It can be cured by a drug costing less than $1 per person. But poor sanitation means that people are frequently reinfected.

There have been some success stories, however. Leprosy is no longer the dread disfiguring disease it once was. It is now curable with a combination of three drugs. The number of registered cases fell from 5.8 million in 1987 to 3.9 million in 1989. More than 2.6 million people with leprosy are receiving the new treatment and, of them, 850,000 have already been cured.

Onchocerciasis, also known as river blindness, is another tropical disease that is beginning to be controlled in many affected countries. It is caused

Right: Patients in rural Ethiopia receiving multidrug therapy (MDT) from a mobile MDT unit. The therapy – a combination of three drugs – led to a drop of over 50 per cent in the incidence of leprosy in Ethiopia from 1983 to 1989.

Left: World distribution of malaria, 1990.

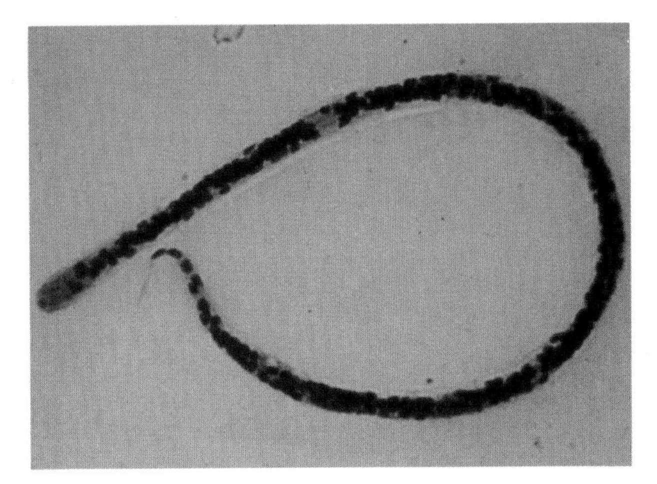

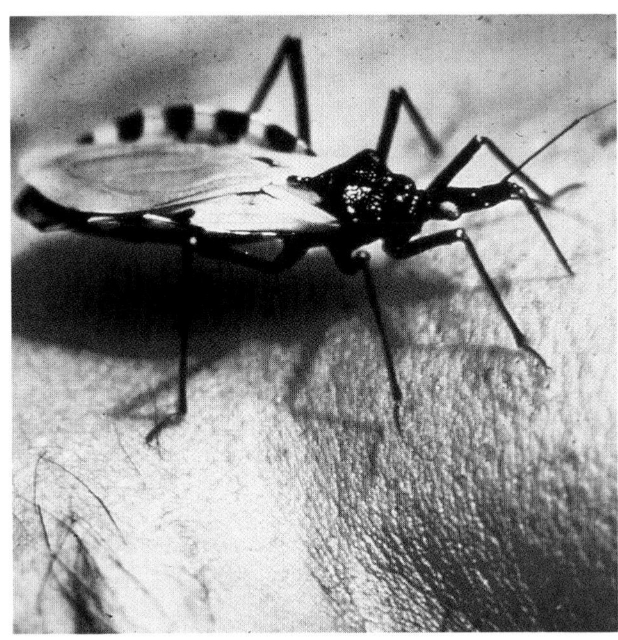

Above: The onchocerca volvulus, the parasite which causes river blindness.
Right: A triatomine bug feeding on human skin. The bug transmits the parasites which cause Chagas disease.

by a parasitic worm that lives for up to 14 years in the human body. The adult female worms produce millions of microscopic larvae which spread within the body, causing itching and eventually, if not successfully treated, blindness. The parasite is spread by the blackfly.

Control programs focus on destroying the fly's larvae by spraying breeding sites in fast-flowing rivers with insecticides. In addition, a drug called Ivermectin™, which is being made available free by the U.S. pharmaceutical company Merck & Co, can prevent infected people from going blind.

An international program to eliminate onchocerciasis from much of West Africa has already managed to protect more than 30 million people from the disease. More than 1.5 million people who were once seriously infected have been cured. By the end of the century, the program estimates that it will have prevented about 300,000 cases of blindness.

Chagas disease

In South America, health departments began mounting a campaign during the 1990s to eradicate a disease that cripples millions of people and kills tens of thousands every year. Chagas disease is spread by bugs resembling large bedbugs. They hide in cracks and crevices in poor quality houses. At night, they emerge to suck blood from their sleeping victims.

Many of the bugs are infected with the parasite that causes Chagas disease. As the bug feeds, it defecates onto the person's skin. When the person scratches the bite, the parasite is rubbed into the wound and enters the blood stream. Many people die during the fever that follows infection; those who survive become chronically infected, developing abnormalities of the heart and intestines that can eventually kill them.

The campaign to eradicate Chagas disease in South America depends on spraying more than eight million homes with an insecticide to kill the bugs. Communities will monitor houses to check that no bugs survive. The cost of the 10-year campaign is thought to be between $180 million and $370 million, but it will allow huge savings on the health care costs of treating the disease.

Guinea-worm disease

One tropical disease that the World Health Organization hopes can be eradicated before the end of the century is dracunculiasis, or guinea-worm disease. This is caused by a parasitic worm which spends part of its life cycle in humans and part in a copepod, or water flea, called cyclops, which enters the body when people drink water containing the infected fleas. The ulceration, pain, and swelling that result usually prevent sufferers from going to school or working.

About 140 million people are still at risk of guinea-worm infection in India, Pakistan, and subSaharan Africa. But while there used to be 10 million cases of infection a year during the 1980s, the number of cases had dropped to under three million a year at the beginning of the 1990s.

This drop in the number of sufferers has been achieved by educating people to filter water for drinking, and by installing piped water supplies and concrete-lined wells. Dracunculiasis may gain a place in history as the second disease in the world to be wiped out. The first was smallpox, which was eradicated in 1979.

Urology

The science of urology deals with the urinary organs and their diseases. One of the most significant recent advances in urology is the development of laparoscopic or "keyhole" surgery, a technique that has had repercussions throughout the whole of surgery (see ANATOMY AND SURGERY).

Laparoscopic surgery avoids the need for a major incision through skin and muscle. Instead, two or three small puncture wounds ("keyholes") are made in the skin, through which the surgeon passes fine tubes bearing surgical instruments. The manipulation that goes on inside the body can be seen with the help of small telescopes called endoscopes. Fiber optics allow light to pass along these, illuminating the field of view. The image can be displayed on television monitors in the operating theater. Sometimes such surgery is carried out while the surgeon watches the maneuver on an ultrasound or CAT scan.

New treatment for kidney problems

Formation of stones (renal calculi) in the kidney or bladder is one of the most common urological complaints. The stone or stones may cause few symptoms, although when a kidney stone enters the ureter, it causes severe pain.

Several other new techniques, in addition to laparoscopic surgery, have improved the treatment of kidney stones. One of these, called *extracorporeal shock-wave lithotripsy*, involves directing high-frequency shock waves at the stone, through the patient's skin. This causes the stone to disintegrate into small pieces which can be passed out in the urine.

Larger fragments that remain after lithotripsy (and small stones in general) can be removed by the surgeon passing fine tubes into the kidney through a small puncture wound, carrying instruments that crush the stone and suck the pieces out. Sometimes a laser is passed down the tube into the kidney, to shatter the stone to fine dust or sand.

Knowledge about why stones form, and what they are made of, has helped doctors to advise patients how to reduce their risks of developing further stones. This may be possible with the help of drugs and/or dietary restrictions, to avoid high intakes of the minerals that are to blame.

People who develop kidney failure in the 1990s have a very different prospect in front of them from those who suffered this condition even in the early 1980s. Many of them now can have their dialysis using a new technique called continuous ambulatory peritoneal dialysis (CAPD), which eliminates the need for several trips to hospital each week.

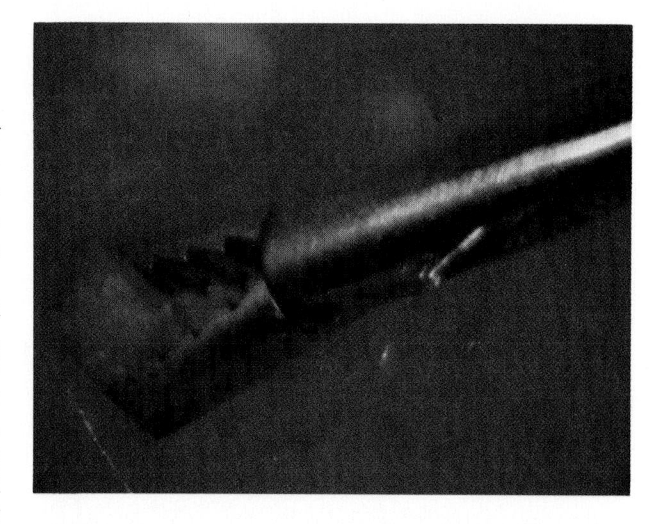

Above: Endoscopic view of a kidney stone clamped in the jaws of a second endoscope, prior to being withdrawn from the body. The incision needed for this operation is comparatively tiny.

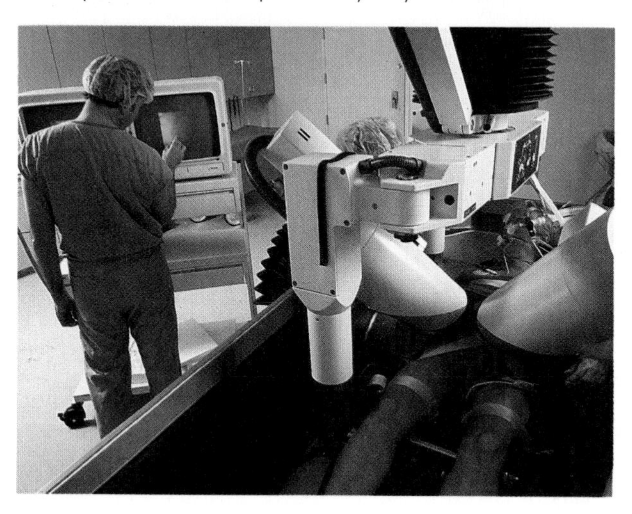

Above: Lithiotripsy uses ultrasound to break up kidney stones. The patient is immersed in a water bath while the two sound sources focus blasts of ultrasound on to the stones. A surgeon monitors progress using a scanner.

In a conventional kidney machine, the patient's blood circulates along many feet of tubing, which are bathed by fluid. Impurities in the blood, such as urea, diffuse across the tubing, which is made of a semipermeable membrane, into the surrounding fluid. The cleaned blood is then reinfused into the patient's veins.

Someone who is going to have CAPD first has a tube inserted into his or her abdomen, connecting the peritoneal cavity to the outside. The patient runs about 4 pints (two liters) of dialysis fluid into the cavity. Impurities such as urea diffuse out of the numerous blood vessels in the membranes pre-

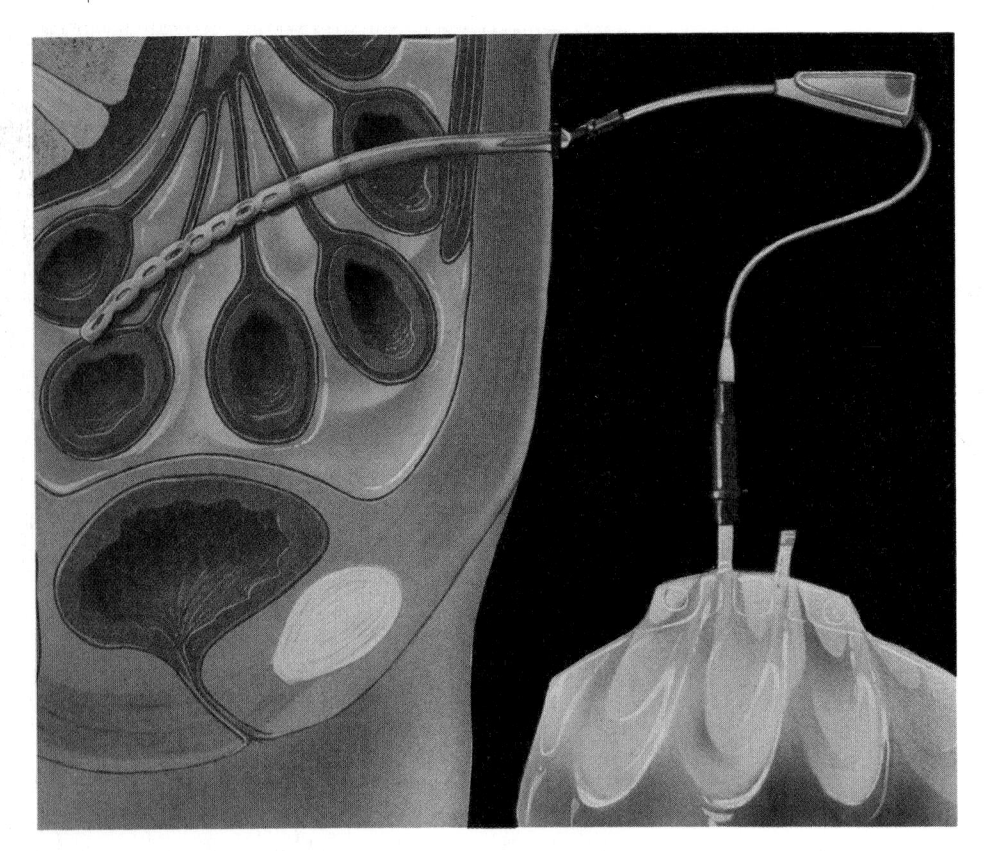

Left: Artwork of a cross-section through the abdomen showing the plastic catheter used for CAPD. This infuses dialysis fluid from the plastic bag directly into the peritoneal cavity.

sent in the abdomen, and into the fluid. A few hours later, the patient drains the fluid off and throws it away. The process is repeated three to four times in every 24 hours. During the treatment, the patient can carry on with normal activities at home and work.

Prostate operations

A common urological problem that affects men is enlargement of the prostate gland, a condition called *benign prostatic hypertrophy*. The prostate gland encircles the urethra, so when it enlarges, the bladder cannot empty properly. Urine may back up in the ureters to the kidneys, eventually causing kidney damage.

This condition can be tackled with an operation called transurethral resection of the prostate. The surgeon passes a fine tube through the urethra, allowing removal of the part of the gland that is causing the blockage. The operation is best done by skilled hands, otherwise the patient risks suffering side effects such as incontinence, hemorrhage and impotence.

Because of the risk of adverse effects from surgery, doctors have tried to find other ways of reducing the enlargement of the prostate. Unfortunately, there has been little success in developing drugs that have this effect.

New surgical techniques hold out greater promise. One approach has been to insert a probe into the rectum (one wall of which lies next to the prostate) and direct microwaves at the enlarged gland. Alternatively, a laser that can cut away at the gland, a few cells at a time, from within the urethra, may make it possible to improve the accuracy of transurethral resection.

Advances are also being made in the early detection of prostate cancer. Ultrasound screening of the prostate, by inserting a probe into the rectum, may soon be able to give early warning of this dangerous disease.

Innovative surgical techniques have also helped people born with abnormalities of the urinary tract. Some of these used to be fatal, while others resulted in life-long urinary incontinence. It is now possible, for example, to reconstruct the bladder with a piece of the patient's colon. If the bladder sphincter does not work, it may be possible to insert a mechanical sphincter. Another option is to transfer the patient's appendix so that it forms a conduit between the inside of the bladder and the outside of the abdominal wall. The patient can be taught to insert a catheter into the bladder via the tube formed, to drain the bladder.

Lasers have been helpful in treating bladder cancer, but for those patients who need to have the bladder removed, it is possible to bring the ureters to the surface of the abdomen, with the help of part of the patient's ileum (part of the small intestine), so that urine drains into a collecting bag.

Veterinary medicine

Veterinarians care for many kinds of animals, from the smallest pet to the largest zoo specimen. Veterinary professionals are now trained to standards similar to those of medical doctors. Many of the techniques of veterinary medicine and surgery developed from those used on humans. However, in recent years there has been a tremendous growth in specialized applications for specific animals. For example, vaccines for the prevention of distemper in dogs and infectious peritonitis in cats, and effective medicines for parasitic worms in cattle have brought dramatic improvements to the health and welfare of the animals concerned.

Keeping racehorses fit

The veterinary profession was first involved with horses because they were of vital importance as a means of transportation. Horses still occupy much veterinary attention, but mostly as sporting animals. The slightest ailment can affect a horse's performance, and therefore its racing or show-jumping potential. Thus the equine veterinarian will have the very latest diagnostic equipment and state-of-the-art operating and hospital facilities, with biometric equipment to monitor the performance of the equine athlete.

Genetic fingerprinting techniques enable each horse and its parentage to be precisely identified from a single blood sample (see FORENSIC MEDICINE). Any attempt to make a false claim for the breeding history of a horse, or to pass off one horse as another, can therefore be easily spotted.

New developments

The role of veterinarians is constantly developing. Increasingly, they are called on to deal with problems caused by cats that mess in the house, or by dogs behaving aggressively to people or to other dogs. "Pet psychiatry" has now become a recognized veterinary specialty. Psychological techniques are applied to train out undesirable behavior patterns. Recently, Queen Elizabeth II, who keeps corgis, consulted a specialist in canine psychology to deal with bad behavior in some of her dogs.

Dogs and cats can suffer metabolic disorders, obesity, or diabetes, just like humans. Specially formulated diets have been devised to control many such disorders, thus restoring health or prolonging the active life of a loved pet.

Study of some animal disease can be valuable in seeking cures for human conditions. When in the 1980s cats unaccountably started to die in Californian kennels, it was discovered that a virus very similar to the human HIV virus, responsible for AIDS, was the cause. This virus, called FIV, had its own similarities to one studied in Scotland in the 1960s, for which a successful vaccine was developed. Veterinary scientists at Glasgow University, Scotland, led by Prof. William Jarrett, are currently collaborating with colleagues at sev-

Left: The vet's traditional role in caring for farm animals is now augmented by modern techniques: ultrasound scanning of a ewe to check for twins.

Left: The therapeutic value of keeping pets is now established: pet keepers live longer and are happier. Homeless people, as here, and prisoners are among those to benefit.

eral centers in the U.S. in studies aimed at possible development of an effective vaccine against AIDS. Vaccines for the new virus are being developed which are reported to be very encouraging in their effects on cats. Therefore studies of the disease in cats may eventually provide clues to controlling HIV infections in humans. Similar work on wart viruses in cattle is being applied to human tumors with the hope of an eventual cure for cervical cancer.

While the source of the human AIDS virus remains a matter for controversy, it was found in 1992 that the members of the cat family which suffer from FIV diverged from other cats some two million years ago on the evolutionary tree. The implication is that at least one immunodeficiency virus has been around for a very long time.

Veterinary work in zoos has acquired a new dimension with many wild animals in danger of extinction. Much work in zoos is now devoted to preserving stocks of endangered species. Efforts to breed the panda from specimens in the world's zoos are an example of international cooperation in this field.

Not all advances in veterinary science have been universally welcomed. Treatment of animals with the growth hormone, somatotrophin, can greatly enhance growth rates or, in cattle, increase milk yields, without a corresponding increase in feed intakes. Although the hormone is available commercially, considerable controversy surrounds its use. Welfarists oppose it, claiming it can create a health risk for the cow. Growth-promoting substances that economically improve meat quality are also available, but some, based on anabolic steroids, are banned in certain countries.

• FACT FILE •

- Monitoring the health and welfare of a group of animals, such as a herd of cows, can now be carried out automatically. An electronic device, consisting of a microchip connected to sensors and a radio transmitter, enables parameters such as blood pressure (a stress indicator) and temperature (an indicator of infection) to be recorded without having to handle the animals.

- The multifunctional microchip measures about 0.16 inch by 1.18 inch (4 mm by 30 mm). It is inserted painlessly under the skin at the base of the ear and remains there during the animal's life. Data transmitted from each animal are picked up by an antenna and displayed on a computer screen or printed out. A code transmitted with the data identifies the animal from which it was obtained.

- The device is being tested in the European Community, where it is expected to offer benefits in the health and welfare of animals, particularly when they are being shipped over long distances.

- A smaller, simpler device, carrying only an identifying code and without a transmitter, is becoming widely used in dogs. It is inserted permanently under the skin. Any stray animal equipped in this way can be identified by reading the code with a special scanner. The owner can then be traced and notified that the dog is awaiting collection.

Zoology

Zoology is the branch of biological sciences concerned with the study of animals, ranging from single-celled protozoa, such as amoebas, to the blue whale, which can measure more than 100 ft (30 m) in length and weigh over 150 tons.

Over a million different kinds of animals have been named, but there are many that remain unidentified, particularly in the tropical rain forest. Unfortunately, many of these will be made extinct by forest clearance before they are discovered.

Communication and behavior

In recent years there has been extensive research into the behavior and ecology of many species of animals; this has greatly increased our understanding of their lives and needs. We are beginning to find out how animals communicate with each other. Elephants use low frequency sounds called infrasound; although we are unable to hear these sounds, they are audible to other elephants over very long distances. At the other end of the sound range, mice and bats use high frequency sounds known as ultrasound for communication and, in the case of bats, for echo location to detect their prey.

Whales and dolphins produce a wide range of calls to communicate with other members of their species. Humpback whales "sing", and their songs can be heard at least 20 miles (32 km) away, probably helping to bring whales together for mating. Studies of sperm whales have shown that each individual has a distinctive "voice".

Male frogs croak to attract mates, with the sound frequency varying between species and even between areas, so that if female American cricket frogs are taken from South Dakota to New Jersey, they ignore the local males because they do not recognize their calls.

Not surprisingly, it is the groups of mammals most closely related to humans which show the highest forms of social behavior and communication. Although the grunts of East African vervet monkeys all sound the same to us, those grunts contain information, often about events of interest to the other monkeys, such as the approach of another group.

There have been several studies of communication by chimpanzees. At the Language Research Center at Georgia State University chimps have been taught to "talk" to humans using sets of symbols to which they can point. They can indicate objects and actions, but whether this is similar to language as used by humans is still under debate.

Chimps also show very advanced behavior in other ways. There is evidence from the Ivory Coast that chimps may actively teach their infants, for example, by showing them the correct way to crack open palm nuts. Chimps also use tools for such tasks as extracting ants from their nest, which they do with a stick. It now appears that they may treat themselves when ill by eating plants that contain antibiotics. When a chimp dies, a closely related individual will clearly experience grief, though there is no evidence of sympathy from unrelated chimps in the group.

Above: The U.S. government has established the Bitter Creek refuge to provide for the protection of the Californian condor.

Mysteries of migration

Many animals, particularly some birds and insects, may undertake periodic migrations over huge distances, showing great feats of speed and endurance. Tiny ruby-throated hummingbirds, for example, migrate 620 miles (1000 km) across the Gulf of Mexico, many completing the journey in 20 hours of nonstop flight.

One of the most spectacular mass migrations in the animal kingdom is that undertaken by the monarch butterfly. In the fall the butterflies fly southward from southern Canada and northern

U.S. to their winter sites in California and Mexico, before returning northward in the spring. By marking thousands of butterflies with tiny harmless tags it was found that some individuals flew as far as 1800 miles (2900 km).

It is still not known precisely how these animals find their way back to the same areas each year. Many migrating animals use the sun as a compass for orientation, using it to maintain a particular direction. They make use of an internal clock which compensates for the movements of the sun during the day and keeps them on course. Birds can also use the stars for orientation. It is also possible that birds and butterflies can detect and use the earth's magnetic field, perhaps with magnetic material contained in their bodies.

Many birds show evidence of an ability to navigate; they can reach a distant place even if displaced from their original route. This means that they must know the position of their home site, rather than just its general direction, and have some type of internal map of the route imprinted on their memory.

Conservation

Knowledge of the behavior and dietary, territorial, and other needs of animals provides essential background to their conservation. It has been realized that an animal cannot be conserved unless a suitable habitat is preserved for it to live in.

To aid these background studies on animals' lives there is increasing use of new scientific techniques. One of these is the use of radios and radar to monitor animal movements. Radio transmitters are fitted onto collars while animals are temporarily immobilized, then the signals are tracked by VHF radio or even by satellites. Radios that weigh only $^{1}/_{40}$ oz (0.75 g) can now be fitted to small animals and birds. Other techniques include genetic fingerprinting (see FORENSIC SCIENCE) to assess the genetic background of populations, and computer modeling to predict changes in populations and suggest key measures for protecting them.

Radio tracking is being used to study mountain lions (cougars) and black bears in the U.S. Numbers of mountain lions have been greatly reduced by shooting and habitat destruction, and they have become confined to a few wild recolonized former haunts. Tracking studies in Idaho and New Mexico have shown that they are very territorial, with the size of their territory determined by the available food supply, so limiting the numbers that can live in a given area. The studies also showed that they did not significantly reduce the size of herds of deer and elk because most of their prey is either very young or very old, rather than of breeding age.

Elephant herds in parts of Africa present a complex conservation problem. As many as ten million elephants roamed Africa 500 years ago, but by the

end of the 1970s numbers had fallen to well below one and a half million; over the next 10 years about half of these died, many from poachers' bullets. A ban on the trade in ivory has reduced the threat from poachers to some extent, but elephants are still menaced by human population pressure and loss of habitat across much of their range. In some game reserves their numbers are too large for the available land area and they may damage their own habitat. Elephants are shot in some reserves in southern Africa to reduce populations, but zoologists now realize that elephants grieve over their dead and remember such disturbing events, so it is vital to find more humane ways of population control. They are investigating the possibilities of using birth control as an alternative to culling.

Although many animal species remain threatened with extinction, more and better scientific studies have resulted in success stories with some of them. One of the most spectacular comebacks has been that of the Californian condor. By 1986 it had declined so drastically that only three birds were left in the wild. By 1991, however, thanks to a successful breeding program, the population had risen to 52.

The condors' decline was originally due to the reduction in numbers of bison, their main food source. Later, many were poisoned by pellets of lead shot or pesticides in the animal carcasses on which they feed. In 1987 the last three wild birds were captured and placed with 24 others already in captivity in southern California. As breeding techniques have improved, so the captive flock has flourished. One problem with these hand reared birds is that they are liable to bond with their human rearer rather than with other condors, so to prevent this their keepers wear glove puppets carrying models of the heads of adult condors. Also, the newly released birds have to learn how to scavenge in the wild, so before two were released in January 1992, 13 Andean condors were freed in the same area. The Californian condors could learn how to survive from these related birds.

The spectacular whooping crane is at the center of a remarkable effort by U.S. and Canadian conservationists, which has raised its population from an all-time low of 21 wild birds in 1944 to 200 birds in wild and captive flocks by the late 1980s.

Above: This chimpanzee has been taught to communicate with human beings by touching symbols on a keyboard.

Left: Elephant bulls in Kenya. Scientists are investigating the possibility of using birth control as an alternative to culling herds which have become too large for their habitats.

Right: The "song" of the humpback whale can be heard by other whales at least 20 miles (32 km) away. It probably helps to bring males and females together for mating.

Above: The codling moth caterpillars cause substantial amounts of damage to apples and other fruit each year by burrowing into them, leaving holes such as this one. Researchers are attempting to devise methods of controlling the moth.

The measures that have contributed to this success have included the careful management of the small population of wild cranes which annually migrates the 1860 miles (3000 km) from Canada's Northwest Territories to the Gulf Coast of Texas, the rearing of cranes in captivity, and the establishment of an additional wild population using sandhill cranes as foster parents.

Captive breeding is an increasingly important tool in the conservation of endangered species, and scientific advances are increasing the survival chances of more and more animals. In these breeding programs it is important to maintain a diverse gene pool, so it is essential to know the genetic structure of the captive population.

Above: A drugged and tagged seven-month-old mountain lion in Yellowstone National Park. Radio collars help keep track of the animal's movements.

New scientific techniques in BIOCHEMISTRY and GENETICS are aiding this research. Genetic fingerprinting here enables an animal's parentage to be identified and the degree of genetic diversity in a particular population to be determined. Artificial insemination and transfer of embryos are other techniques that may be used.

A further example of success with captive breeding was that of the first aye-aye born in captivity outside its native Madagascar, which was being reared at the Duke University Primate Center in North Carolina in 1991. This curious animal is one of the most endangered species of lemur. It has a very long middle finger, looking rather like that of the film character E.T., which it uses to locate and extract animal larvae (its favorite food) from timber. However, all the efforts of captive breeding will be in vain unless suitable areas of habitat, into which the bred animals can eventually be released, are preserved.

Insects

The largest group of animals are the insects, with over 700,000 different kinds already named and many more still to be identified. Some insects are pests but scientists are increasingly looking to control them without resorting to insecticides which may pollute the environment.

Insects use scents to attract mates, to mark trails to good food sources, and to warn their companions of danger. Female moths attract male moths over very long distances by emitting a scent which only elicits a response from males of that particular species. The males have very sensitive detectors on their antennae that can react to a single molecule of the scent, called a sex pheromone. Chemists have identified the structure of some pheromones and are able to synthesize them, leading to a novel method of pest control.

The caterpillars of the codling moth burrow into apples, pears, and walnuts. Researchers in California are attempting to control this pest by preventing the moths from mating. They do this by flooding the air with the artificial pheromone of the moth, so that the male moths can no longer find the females by following distinct trails of the scent in the air.

In Africa, desert locusts form voracious swarms which consume an amount of vegetation equal to their own body weight every day. A swarm covering 386 square miles (1000 km square) will eat about 80,000 tons of foliage a day. Satellites are now being used to give early warning of the buildup of swarms so that rapid action can be taken against them.

Acoustics

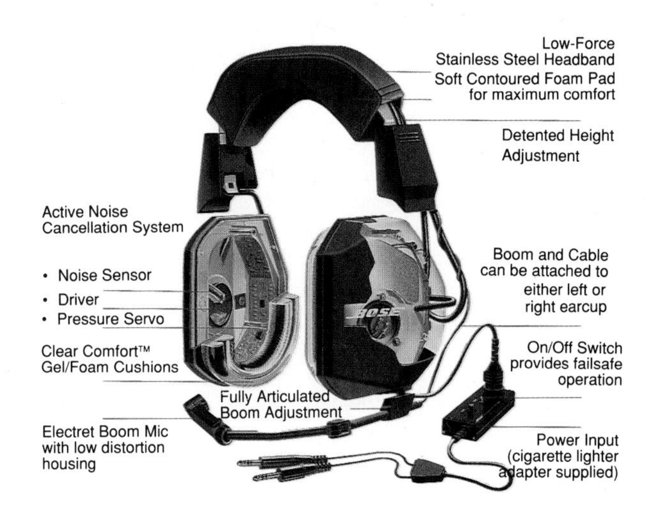

Above: Noise-reducing aviation headset. Regular external noise is sensed and cancelled out rather than muffled, giving a more comfortable unit.

Acoustics is the science of sound. It deals with how sound is generated, how it is transmitted through the air, and how it is heard. It is of use in a wide range of fields, from architecture to medicine.

For many years it has been the dream of acoustical engineers to cancel out unwanted sound by actually creating the exact opposite sound wave, thus creating destructive interference. In the past, such methods have been unsuccessful because sound waves are highly complex, arriving at the ear by many different routes. In 1992 a set of headphones for aviation use was brought out which uses electronics to cancel out low-frequency noise while allowing through, for example, the sound of the intercom.

Acoustics has also been used to develop a refrigerator that does not use CFCs – the gases that have been linked with the destruction of the Earth's ozone layer (see ENVIRONMENTAL SCIENCE). Sound waves in safe inert gases are used to create the cycles of compression and expansion which produce cooling. The advantage of using this system is that since it does not use a conventional pump in the compressor, the refrigerant gas need not be compatible with the pump's lubricant, so CFCs need not be used. The fridge is also 40 per cent more efficient than a normal one. This would mean a huge saving in Americans' electricity bills. A prototype has already been tested on the Space Shuttle.

In another advance, new silicon chips for TV sets are speeded up using acoustics. The electrons in the microchips "surf" along the crests of sound waves sent through the silicon.

Aeronomy

Aeronomy is the study of processes in the Earth's upper atmosphere, combining aspects of astronomy and METEOROLOGY. The atmosphere's tenuous upper limit may be considered to lie at about 60 miles (100 km) altitude, where the number of particles is a millionth of that at sea level. Even so, it can have dramatic effects – the outer atmosphere expands at times of increased sunspot activity, causing drag on low-orbiting satellites and sometimes bringing them to Earth prematurely.

The Sun ceaselessly bombards the upper atmosphere with both sunlight and high-speed subatomic particles (the solar wind). Aurorae – the northern (or southern) lights – are produced by energetic particles originating in the Sun, shot into the high atmosphere around the poles from the radiation belts that girdle the Earth. The eruption of Mt Pinatubo in 1991, and possibly Mt Mayon in 1993, could affect Earth's upper atmosphere considerably. Aeronomists have seen a great increase in numbers of noctilucent clouds in recent years. These are whitish clouds, at a height of 51 miles (82 km), visible only in midsummer at high latitudes. They may indicate significant changes in the atmosphere caused either by eruptions or by pollution.

Above: Aurora photographed from shuttle Discovery. Auroral study was one of the tasks of this mission, which took place in April–May 1991.

Analytical chemistry

How much caffeine is there in a cup of coffee? How much lead in leaded gasoline? What is the concentration of chlorofluorocarbons in the atmosphere over Antarctica?

Any question that asks how much of a chemical substance is present in a mixture is answered using the methods of analytical chemistry. All rely on separating and identifying substances in mixtures varying in complexity from the air we breathe to crude oil.

The methods of analytical chemistry are derived largely from the physical properties and behavior of chemicals, and are developed by physical chemists. These methods include chromatography, spectroscopic techniques, and the measurement of electrically charged ions and their fragments in mass spectrometry.

Although the instrumentation required for chemical analysis can often be very sophisticated, this does not necessarily mean it is confined to the laboratory. British Petroleum recently developed a new method for oil exploration in which the presence of a thin layer of crude oil is detected on the surface of the sea. The apparatus uses an instrument to measure light emitted from the oil after it has been illuminated with light from a laser, and can be installed for use aboard an aircraft.

Anesthetics

In recent times the science of anesthetics has taken much of the pain – and fear – out of surgery. Since the 1980s, halothane and related compounds have been used as general anesthetics which render the patient unconscious for major surgery. These are administered as gases which are inhaled by the patient.

Intravenous injections of the depressant drugs, such as barbiturates, are also used as a short-term general anesthetic. Injections of compounds of the drug cocaine – notably Novocain – are used as local anesthetics. These numb a part of the body so that dental work or minor surgery can be performed without unnecessary suffering.

All anesthetic compounds have side effects. The kidneys, particularly, are susceptible to damage. A new way to minimize the danger is to block the transmission of pain up the spinal cord with tiny localized injections, rather than swamping the whole system with anesthetic compounds. Pain can also be reduced by cooling parts of the body.

One advance is to allow a patient to control the flow of anesthetic to help dull post-operative pain. This has the advantages that lower quantities are often needed, and the patient need not fear a sudden increase in pain with no one to help.

Astrometry

Astrometry is the measurement of the positions and motions of celestial objects. Its applications range from navigation and timekeeping to establishing the size of the universe. Some astrometric observations use a specialized telescope known as a transit instrument, which records the positions of stars as they pass through the field of view. More common is the measurement of photographic plates taken by ordinary telescopes to provide positions of objects from distant galaxies to newly discovered comets.

An important role of astrometry is finding the distances of stars from their parallax, the change in the star's position when viewed from opposite sides of the Earth's orbit.

Astrometry also provides the only way of "weighing" stars, since the size of a double star's orbit depends on the components' masses. A recent application of astrometry is the detection of slight wobbles in the positions of stars, amounting to only a few thousandths of a second of arc, which can reveal the presence of unseen planets orbiting them.

In 1989 a satellite called Hipparcos was put into orbit. By 1995 it will have established parallaxes and motions for over 100,000 stars far more precisely than is possible from the ground, considerably improving our distance scale for the universe.

Above: The Carlberg Automatic Transit Circle is a fully automated system which can measure positions of hundreds of stars each night.

Cytology

The study of the cells that are the fundamental unit of all living things is called cytology

Living cells can be studied by phase contrast microscopy – where special illumination of the subject is used – or by utilizing special dyes to stain structures within the cell. These highlight particular details scientists want to study. Fluorescent dyes and radioactive tagging are also used to observe the interaction of specific proteins or antibodies. Electron microscopes that can reveal details down to the size of a molecule, laser techniques, and high speed centrifuges are also being used to study the tiny chemical messengers that perform the crucial functions inside cells. Clinically, cytology is used to classify cells to determine an individual's blood group or identify antibodies.

In the 1990s, research cytologists are trying to unravel the deepest secret of them all – why cells die. At the end of their lifespan, healthy cells suddenly seem to self-destruct. Fathoming this mystery could help reveal the mechanisms behind AIDS, cancer, aging, and even death itself.

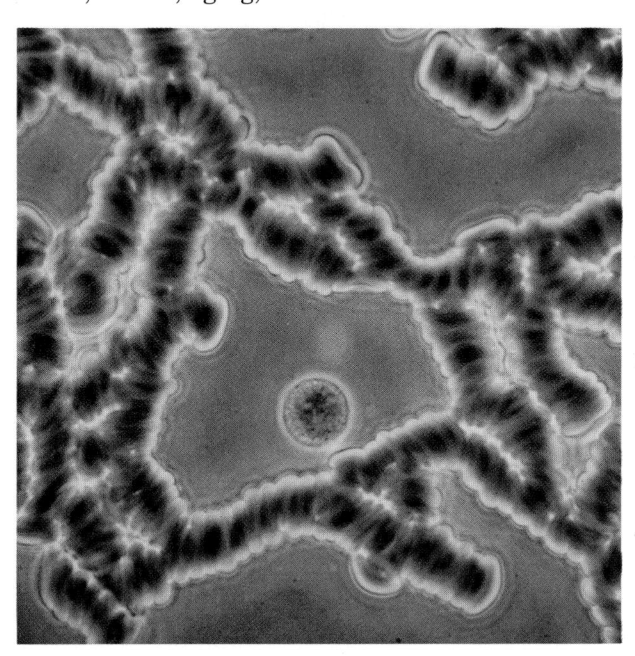

Above: Phase contrast micrograph of human red blood cells clumped together with a granulocyte – a type of white cell – trapped between them.

Dendrochronology

An archaeologist wishing to discover the precise date of a site may well turn to dendrochronology – the science of determining dates from the annual growth rings visible in timber. As trees grow their trunks and branches increase in diameter by putting on a new layer around their circumference each year. Because the rings vary in width from year to year it is possible to identify sequences from specific years.

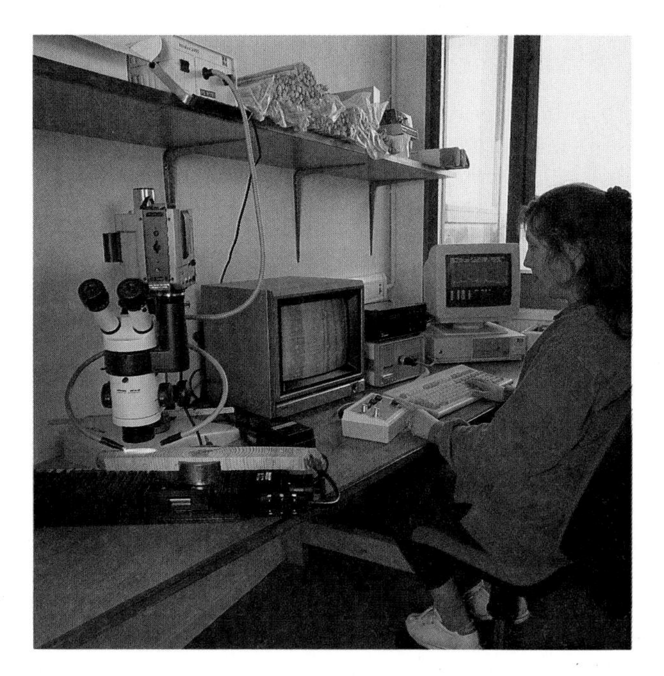

Above: Tree-ring analysis is carried out using a microscope with TV camera attached. A computer provides instant readout of the measurements.

Although individual trees do not survive more than a few hundred years at the most, some – notably the bristlecone pine – live for over 4000 years. The long sequences from these have been invaluable in tying together the series from less long-lived trees.

Modern science has taken this method to extremes of precision. Experts have linked ring sequences from many parts of the world, using logs preserved in such places as Irish bogs and Swiss lake shores, where towns were built on stilts in prehistory. Advances in computer analysis have made it possible to discover the precise date, to within a year, when a piece of wood maybe thousands of years old was felled.

The width of the rings themselves indicates the conditions under which the tree grew. Long periods of minimal annual growth in ancient European timber have been linked with a nuclear-winterlike spell thought to have been caused by a massive Icelandic volcanic eruption, which could explain the desertion of settlements at that time.

In addition, tree-ring measurement is important in FORESTRY, where it can help quantify the effects of human interference and the environment on tree growth in plantations.

Dermatology

Dermatology is the branch of medicine that specializes in the diagnosis and treatment of diseases of the skin. There are a huge number of skin diseases and dermatology is a broad and complex discipline. The most common disease of the skin is dermatitis.

Viruses also cause skin problems including shingles and herpes. Bacteria cause boils. Anthrax is caught from infected animals. Molds and fungi cause problems such as ringworm and athlete's foot. Psoriasis, the flaking of scaly patches which affects around three per cent of the population, is inherited.

Acne is the result of numerous factors, including heredity, hormones, bacteria, climatic changes and emotional stress. Its cause is often difficult to pin down as there are over 50 different types of acne.

Both cold and heat can also cause dermatological problems. Exposure to cold causes chilblains and frostbite. Heat exposure causes sunburn. Ultraviolet light from the sun can cause a further dermatological problem – skin cancer. The latest challenge facing dermatologists is the growing incidence of skin cancer, caused by the depletion of the ozone layer.

Exobiology

Exobiology describes the scientific investigation of the possibilities for life elsewhere in the universe. Many think it likely that, given the large probable number of habitable planets in our galaxy, life must have arisen more than once. As yet, however, conclusive evidence for life elsewhere has not been forthcoming.

The vast distances between stars rule out any possibility of direct investigation of other planetary systems. Using the Hubble Space Telescope, astronomers hope to be able to at least positively confirm the existence of planets around other stars (see ASTROMETRY).

The best chances of detecting life beyond Earth currently lie with SETI, the search for extraterrestrial intelligence. The emergence of technological civilization on Earth saw a great output of communications based on radio waves. The most hopeful forms of SETI research aim to detect similar characteristic signals from planets around other stars.

A major SETI program initiated in 1992 is using large radio telescopes to systematically survey large numbers of stars in detail over a wide range of radio frequencies. While skeptics see this work as having limited chances of success, such intensive study may provide useful astronomical data.

Above: In October 1992, NASA announced a major search for extraterrestrial radio signals using this giant radiotelescope in Puerto Rico.

Fluid mechanics

The movement of weather systems, fish swimming through water, the flight of birds, the flow of air through a jet engine or blood through the heart, and the eruption of a volcano are all the province of fluid mechanics, the science of liquids and gases.

Fluid statics – sometimes known as hydrostatics – is the study of fluids at rest. It looks at the way pressure and forces are transmitted through fluids and provides the theoretical basis for hydraulics. It also examines how fluids react to being heated and cooled.

The other branch of the science, fluid dynamics, examines how fluids flow. In fluid dynamics, liquids and gas are treated together as they flow in much the same way.

The smooth – or laminar – flow of fluids is relatively easy to describe in mathematical terms. However, scientists run into serious difficulties when the flow suddenly becomes turbulent. The transition is rapid and, in many ways, unpredictable. But new insights into the nature of turbulent flow are now being developed using CHAOS THEORY, which shows how simple mathematical rules can, under some circumstances, generate complex, chaotic results.

Despite its heavily mathematical roots, fluid dynamics is not simply a theoretical science. It has wide practical applications ranging from the design of turbines to the development of artificial heart values.

Geochronology

Above: ISOLAB, an advanced mass spectrometer used at Cambridge University, U.K., to determine the proportions of elements in rock samples.

Geochronology is the study of the history of the Earth, built up from the interpretation of fossils and rock layers. The science began in the early 19th century with the systematic study of the layers of sedimentary rocks that were exposed at cliff faces or during excavations. These rocks were laid down at the bottom of ancient seas. The layers nearer the surface overlay those deeper down, so they must have been deposited later.

Different rock layers contained different fossils, showing a broad development from the simplest creatures at deeper levels to the more complex creatures known today nearer the surface. Scientists then tried to work out the age of the rock layers, based on estimates of the accumulation of salt in the sea, rates of deposition, erosion, and the development of life. The breakthrough came in the 1930s when radiometric dating was discovered.

Various naturally occuring radioactive elements in rocks decay to form lead. The rate of decay of the radioactive elements can be accurately determined in the laboratory, so comparing the amount of radioactive elements and the amount of lead in a rock sample can be used to work out how old it is.

Other products of radioactive decay are now used to date rocks. However, some scientists question the basis of radiometric dating, pointing out various anomalies. The radiometric dating of the atmosphere, for example, would indicate that it is younger than the fossils of some air-breathing creatures.

Geodesy

The science of the shape and size of the Earth and its gravitational field is known as geodesy. This knowledge is vital when constructing roads, bridges and dams, or making maps and fixing international boundaries. The task of actual map-making, however, is known as land surveying and cartography.

The traditional technique of triangulations is still widely used in surveying and navigation. It is based on the principle that, in a triangle, if two angles and the length of one side are known, the length of the other two sides can be calculated.

Until recently the points of the triangle had to be visible from one another so that surveying instruments could be used. Now, however, geodesy has been taken over by the satellite and high-speed computer. The position of each point is measured using the Global Positioning System (GPS) – a network of satellites that transmit exact details of their positions, enabling the location of a portable ground station to be found relative to the satellites. The accuracy of this system is measured to a few parts per million of the distances involved. So the relative positions of two points, say, a mile apart can be found to within a few millionths of a mile – about 1/10 inch.

Geodesy also extends the study of the precise orbit of the Earth, the movement of the poles, and variations in gravity across the surface of the Earth. Its principles are also used in the study of the surfaces of other planets.

Above: Geodetic Surveyor, a precision surveying system using GPS, runs on camcorder batteries and measures positions with high accuracy.

Geomorphology

Geomorphology is the study of landforms and the processes by which they are formed. A number of recent technological advances have been of direct benefit to geomorphologists. Improvements in laboratory equipment enable detailed chemical analyses of the weathering processes by which rocks break down and soils are formed. New age-determination techniques have enabled geomorphologists to build up detailed models of landform evolution during the Quaternary period (the last 1.8 million years), during which most present-day landforms developed.

Digital data loggers are sophisticated recording machines which can be connected up to field monitoring equipment such as stream flow monitors or automatic weather stations, enabling data to be collected all the time without someone being there to write it down. Studies at sub-microscopic scales are possible using scanning electron microscopes. At the other end of the scale, satellite imagery enables large scale landform evolution to be studied and changes monitored over time.

A branch of geomorphology is concerned with hazard monitoring, prediction, and mitigation. Disasters are often the result of ill-advised development in areas prone to a particular natural process, such as farming on the flanks of an active volcano or building on a river's floodplain. Geomorphologists are able to advise on such developments, thereby minimizing the risk of disasters.

Glaciology

Glaciology is the study of glaciers, which are formed on the landmasses that extend into the polar regions and high up in mountains.

The temperature of the ice in polar glaciers is always well below freezing, except for a small surface layer whose temperature rises to freezing point in the summer. In temperate glaciers, such as those in southern Alaska, the main body of the glacier remains at freezing point while only the surface layer drops below freezing in winter. Other glaciers have layers of subfreezing ice between layers that are at freezing point.

Mountain, or alpine, glaciers tend to be small and flow down valleys like slow-moving rivers. Polar glaciers are much larger. They form the Antarctic icecap and huge icesheets, though valley glaciers may spread out from the edge.

Glaciers are built up in layers which mark each winter's snowfall and each summer's thaw. By drilling into a glacier, it is possible to build up a picture of what the weather was like year by year, for thousands of years gone by.

Air bubbles are trapped in the ice as the glacier forms. Scientists are analyzing this air in their investigation of the greenhouse effect, to see if increasing levels of carbon dioxide correlate with warmer weather.

Above: Aerial view of one of the giant glaciers in Antarctica, the Liv Glacier in the Queen Maud range of the Transantarctic Mountains.

Hydraulics

Hydraulics is a practical application of fluid mechanics. It puts the scientific study of liquids in motion to practical use.

The power of flowing water has been exploited by humankind since the invention of the water wheel to grind flour. This same principle, that running water can turn a turbine, is now used to generate hydroelectric power.

The laws of hydraulics developed in the 17th and 18th centuries have now found numerous mechanical applications. Automobiles utilize them in hydraulic transmission, hydraulic steering, and hydraulic brakes. And when an automobile is obsolete, it is compacted into a block of steel by a hydraulic car crusher.

Airplanes use hydraulics to move their control surfaces. Modern machine and agricultural tools are controlled and operated hydraulically. Missiles and space rockets also utilize the principles of hydraulics. Even the humble bicycle is being brought into the hydraulic age with the development of hydraulic brakes that are lighter and more effective than cable-operated ones.

Hydrology

Hydrology is the study of water and its relationship with the environment. Within the discipline of hydrology, there are several subdisciplines. Hydrography is concerned with the mapping of lakes, seas, and oceans. Hydrometeorology is the study of water and water vapor as it is carried through the air. Hydrometry is the measurement of rainfall and water runoff.

Increasingly, these subdisciplines are being combined to give proper management of water resources, although floods, drought, and famine brought about by lack of proper irrigation still plague the world.

It is not just the Third World that suffers. Water shortage has become a major problem in the U.S., particularly in the American southwest. Farmers have found their crops shriveling as the cities of Tucson, Phoenix, and Los Angeles drain their supplies.

The Central Arizona Project is now diverting water from the Colorado River to the farm lands. Farmers are installing storage tanks to catch rainwater. A huge new desalination plant is being built at Santa Barbara in California. But for the long-term solution, hydrologists are turning to satellite studies and computer simulations to help manage the scarce water resources of the world.

Jet technology

Since the introduction of the jet in the 1940s, aero-engine designers have concentrated on increasing the thrust, reducing the fuel consumption and limiting the noise of their creations.

In the 1990s emphasis has shifted to reducing engine emissions, although debate continues over the exact extent to which aircraft contribute to the depletion of the Earth's ozone layer. Efforts concentrate on improving how the fuel is burned, to cut production of smoke, unburned hydrocarbons, carbon monoxide and, most importantly, ozone-destroying oxides of nitrogen.

Fuel consumption continues to be a concern but reductions are increasingly hard won, as current engines extract almost all the energy available from the fuel they burn. Instead designers plan to use that energy more efficiently, by building ultra-high-bypass turbofan engines.

In a turbofan only part of the air which enters the engine is mixed with fuel and burned. The rest passes through the fan, which provides most of the thrust. Typically the bypass ratio is 5:1. In ultra-high-bypass turbofans the ratio is 15:1 and, for the same thrust, fuel consumption is cut by 20 per cent. Propfans, which combine the characteristics of propellers and turbofans, have bypass ratios around 40:1 and burn 40 per cent less fuel than today's turbofans.

Kinetics

When light shines on the retina, it is absorbed by special light-sensitive cells. A series of chemical changes takes place which eventually generate an impulse which passes down the optic nerve to the brain. All this seems to happen in less than the blink of an eye, but how long does the process of vision actually take? The science of chemical reactions such as this is kinetics.

The first step in the chemistry of vision is a rapid chemical reaction in which the light-absorbing molecule changes its geometry. American scientists recently studied the kinetics of this reaction and discovered that in certain types of cell, the reaction is complete within 200 millionths of a billionth of a second.

Modern technology has pushed back the frontiers of chemical kinetics. By using spectroscopy to identify and monitor reagents, products and unstable intermediate molecules, the chemistry of complex reactions can be unscrambled.

Chemists all around the world are currently investigating the kinetics of reactions between ozone molecules and a variety of chlorinated chemicals. By studying reactions that might be involved in the destruction of the ozone layer, they can identify the most important ones and so construct chemical mechanisms for ozone depletion. Such mechanisms can be used to predict future ozone levels. Studies of the reactions of ozone with chlorofluorocarbons (CFCs) identified these latter molecules as rapid ozone depleters. The production and use of these substances are now regulated internationally through the so-called Montreal Protocol.

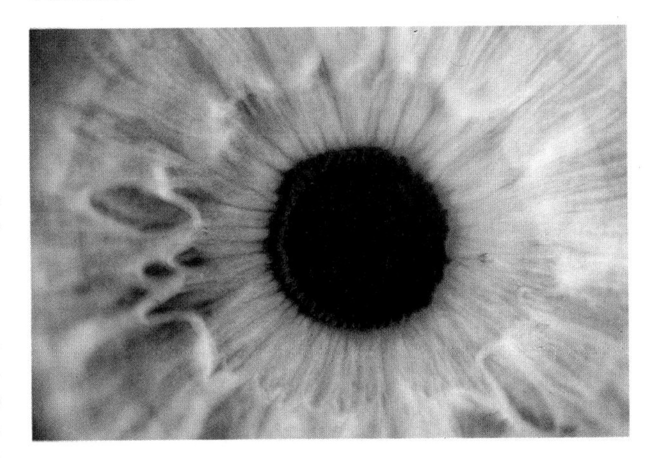

Above: The eye's iris expands in dull light and contracts in bright conditions, but most changes in sensitivity are provided by retinal reactions.

Limnology

The branch of HYDROLOGY concerned with the study of lakes, ponds, rivers, streams, swamps, and reservoirs is called limnology. It also looks at the ecology of the inland waterway system, physically, chemically, and biologically.

Limnology studies the physical effects of the weather – heating, cooling, and precipitation – on standing water, as well as the chemistry of the minerals and nutrients dissolved in the water. It examines the biological processes of the plants and animals that grow in the water and their relationships to one another.

Limnology is one of the scientific disciplines at the forefront of the ecology movement. The lakes of Canada are being studied for the effects of acid rain which has poisoned much of the water there. The polluted lakes of the republics of the former Soviet Union are also of great interest to limnologists.

Lake Baikal in southern Siberia is of particular interest. At nearly 1,800 feet, it is the deepest lake on Earth. A three-seater submersible is being used to plumb its depths. Pebbles and crystals recovered from the bottom of Lake Baikal indicate that it may be as much as 30 million years old.

Metallurgy

Pure gold, copper, silver, and iron from meteorites occur in nature, but only in small quantities. Most metal appears in chemical combinations in minerals known as ore. It is the job of metallurgy to extract the metal from the ore so that it can be used to make anything from cars and soda cans, to the tiny wires in computers.

Metallic minerals are mined, then crushed and ground, so the pure ore is separated from the rock. The ore is then smelted – it is heated until it is freed from its chemical bonds and the liquid metal runs free. Some metals can also be extracted from ore by electrical means, or by dissolving the ore in an acid or salt solution.

Metallurgy also studies how metals can be combined to make alloys or treated to develop useful properties. Metals are heated or worked to alter their crystalline structure and make them stronger, harder, or more pliable.

There is only a limited supply of metal and many of the purest sources of ore have already been worked out. In many places only extremely poor ore is left, making extraction a difficult and costly business. But low-grade ores are now being exploited with the help of bacteria.

Microorganisms have been discovered that live by oxidizing the sulfur that binds copper, zinc, lead, and uranium, releasing the metal. This process is cheaper and less polluting than smelting, which releases large amounts of sulfur. Airborne sulfur is one of the main causes of acid rain. Bacteria are now used to extract metal from the spoil heaps left over from old workings.

Morphology

Morphology is a part of biology which studies the size, shape, and structure of animals, plants, and microorganisms. It examines the similarities between the bones of the human arm, the wing of a bird, and the front leg of a frog, for example, and relates their form to their differing functions.

Originally, morphology was used as a way to classify animals and plants into species or families. But later it was used as a tool in the development of the theory of evolution. Morphologists also look at how the shape and size of leaves, for example, are related to the environment in which a plant grows and how the speed of an animal relates to its weight and musculature. This means they can look at fossils and work out how long-extinct creatures lived and how they are related to modern species.

Another important area of study for morphologists is the way plants and animals develop from a seed or an egg. This is known as developmental morphology or morphogenesis.

In the study of the evolution of modern man, dental morphology is of particular importance. It studies the shape and function of the mouth and teeth, and reveals what our distant ancestors ate, the sort of sounds they could make, and how closely they are related to ourselves.

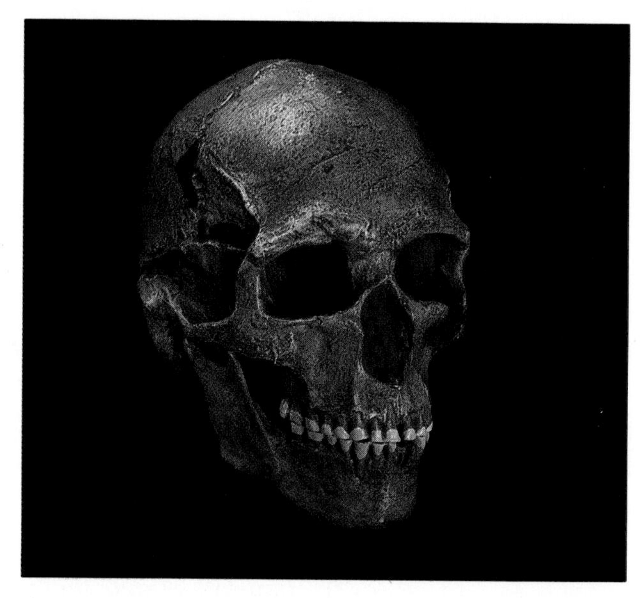

Above: This human skull, dating from 30,000 BC, is very similar to a modern one. The teeth in particular reveal much about diet and lifestyle.

Paleobotany

Paleobotany is an attempt to build up a picture of the plant life of the long distant past through the study of fossils of ancient vegetation.

The fossils of prehistoric leaves, stems, flowers, fruits, seeds, spores, pollen, and wood have been preserved in rocks, shales, and sandstones. The best are obtained from rocks originally desposited as muds at the bottom of ancient lakes and swamps, and on ancient floodplains. Some plant fossils are preserved under layers of volcanic ash and, very rarely, in ancient lava flows.

Coal seams are a rich source of plant fossils – coal itself is formed from dead vegetation that accumulated in ancient swamps. Other fossilized plants are found in the shales that make up the roofs of coal seams and the underlying clays.

The distribution of plant fossils of similar and related varieties now helps scientists to build a picture of how the continents once fitted together.

Flowering plants became dominant 65 million years ago. One of the theories of the death of the dinosaurs links their mass extinction to the appearance of flowers. Brightly colored flowers contain poisonous alkaloids. Plant-eating dinosaurs who ate them would have died, the theory says, leaving the meat-eating dinosaurs to starve.

Right Fossil of a fern plant, *Neuropteris*, which thrived some 300 million years ago at a time when the only land animals were amphibians.

Paleomagnetism

The magnetic field of the Earth has not always been the same. Its strength has varied, the magnetic poles have wandered and even reversed. Paleomagnetism is the study of these changes.

There are two main kinds of rock, igneous and sedimentary. Igneous rock is formed when molten rock cools and solidifies. While they are setting, tiny magnetic particles in the molten rock align themselves with the Earth's magnetic field.

Sedimentary rock is formed when particles are deposited at the bottom of seas and lakes. As they settle, magnetic particles also turn in the direction of Earth's magnetic field.

By measuring the magnetic field of rock samples, a picture of how the Earth's magnetic field changed throughout prehistoric times can be built up. The field reverses every 100,000 to 100 million years. This changeover takes 1-2,000 years.

Rocks in the Atlantic ocean floor show distinct magnetic stripes running north–south, marking the periodic reversing of the Earth's magnetic field. This shows that rocks are forming in the middle of the ocean and that the Atlantic is gradually widening.

The paleomagnetic record is one of the important ways that scientists have shown that the continents sit on huge plates that have drifted through prehistoric time.

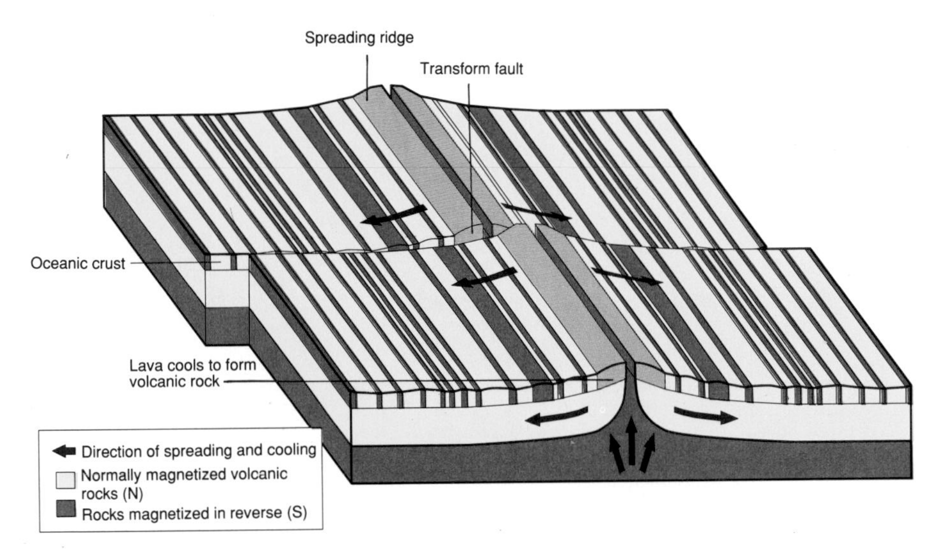

Right: The Earth's magnetic field reverses polarity from time to time. Paleomagnetic studies of seabed rocks provide evidence for this.

Paleontology

Paleontology is the study of fossils. Although the Earth was formed around 4.5 billion years ago, the earliest fossil is about 3 billion years old. It was a bacterium. The fossils of algae 2 billion years old have been found in Canada and the earliest fossilized animal dates from around 600 million years ago. The first vertebrate – a primitive fish – is about 350 million years old. Reptiles evolved soon after.

Although small mammals were alive when the dinosaurs became extinct around 65 million years ago, the fossil record shows that humankind has only existed for the last few million years. The fossil trail shows that human beings evolved in Africa and gradually spread into Europe and Asia. The distribution of more ancient fossils mark the positions of prehistoric seas and forests.

The fossil record also shows how the Earth's climate changed all over during prehistoric times. Paleoclimatology is now being used to help us understand the consequences of global warming.

Above: The fossil of a trilobite found in Coal County, Oklahoma. These arthropods dominated the seas some 500 million years ago.

Paleozoology

Paleozoology is the study of prehistoric animals through their remains preserved in the fossil record. Fossils were first studied in a systematic way in the early 1800s. Since then paleozoologists have been able to classify the different types of dinosaurs and work out much about their behavior from the fossil record.

In the 1880s, the fossil of a "feathered reptile", *Archaeopteryx*, was discovered. It made an almost perfect link between reptiles and birds, and helped confirm the theories of evolution put forward by Charles Darwin and others. But recently one top scientist caused a controversy by suggesting that the *Archaeopteryx* fossil was simply a clever fake. This claim, however, is not widely accepted.

Scientists have recently found fossilized blood cells from fish 100 million years old and they are searching the remains of ancient bones for scraps of DNA from which they can make a "genetic fingerprint".

One of the great mysteries of paleozoology is the mass extinction of dinosaurs some 65 million years ago. There are over 40 different theories of how dinosaurs died out. The current favorite is that a huge asteroid hit the Earth and the dust thrown up radically altered the climate (see GEOLOGY).

Above: *Archaeopteryx*, the primitive birdlike fossil. The impressions of its feathers in the rock have been the cause of an accusation of fakery.

Podiatry

According to a recent survey 62 per cent of Americans think it is normal for their feet to hurt. Not so, according to the nation's 12,000 podiatrists—health care professionals who treat injuries and diseases of the feet. If a person's feet hurt, they say, there is something wrong and it can be corrected. The task of deciding what is wrong is not simple, however: each foot contains 28 bones, 35 joints, 19 muscles, and between 112 and 117 ligaments, creating a flexible arched structure that cushions the shock of walking and running for the leg bones.

Over 300 foot ailments have been identified, which podiatrists treat through surgery, exercise, or the prescription of shoe inserts called orthoses (or orthotics) to correct misalignment of the bones. Their business is booming thanks to the popularity of jogging and aerobics, which can boost the load on a person's foot to four times their weight. An inherited imbalance such as unequal leg length can cause excessive stress on parts of the foot.

New medical technology has simplified many treatments. Lasers remove skin lesions and fungus infections; arthroscopic surgery allows repair of the ankle joint through a tiny incision and will soon be applied to the smaller joints of the foot; and magnetic resonance imaging supplies pictures of the soft tissues, revealing muscle and ligament problems X-rays cannot see.

Polymer chemistry

Polymer chemistry has provided many important modern materials – glass, concrete, paper, rubber, and plastics. Polymers are large molecules, some of which occur naturally. Diamond and graphite – the "lead" in pencils – are both polymers of carbon. The different arrangement of their atoms gives them different properties. New polymers of carbon – fullerenes – are being developed (see ORGANIC CHEMISTRY).

Cellulose, sugars, and proteins are also polymers, but the breakthrough in polymer chemistry came when scientists discovered how to link smaller molecules, known as monomers, together. This process is known as polymerization.

Polymers synthesized from simple hydrocarbons such as ethylene and propylene produced plastics. In polyethylene, up to 10,000 ethylene monomers are linked in a long coiled chain. The result is a transparent plastic, used in bottles and packaging. Each polypropylene molecule contains 50,000 to 200,000 propylene monomers. Polypropylene is also used to make textiles and molded objects.

Plastics have caused environmental problems, though. They do not break down easily once they have been thrown away. However, polymer chemists have now designed new plastics that can be eaten by microbes, so when they are discarded they will break down naturally – and disappear.

Radiology

Radiology is the branch of medicine which uses X-rays, radioactive materials, and other forms of radiation.

One problem with a standard X-ray photograph is that the images of each layer of the body are superimposed on top of each other. Modern computerized tomography – or CT – overcomes this. In a CT scan, the X-ray source and the detector move around the body and computer is used to build up a picture of a single slice through the body. After pictures of a number of slices have been built up, the computer creates a three-dimensional image of an internal organ.

Radioactivity is also used a diagnosic tool. Radioactive substances are injected or swallowed. Once in the blood stream they can be used to locate tumors. When the tumor takes up the radioactive material, it can be detected using a gamma-ray detector.

Radiation is also used as a therapy to destroy cancers. It disrupts the genetic material in cancer cells as they multiply. Beams of radiation from radiative materials are sometimes used, or radioactive needles or pellets are implanted in the body.

Beams of high-energy X-rays or electrons, protons, or neutrons are now being used. These are more controllable. Different types of beams penetrate the body to different depths, allowing the maximum energy to be concentrated in the cancer and the minimum in the healthy tissue.

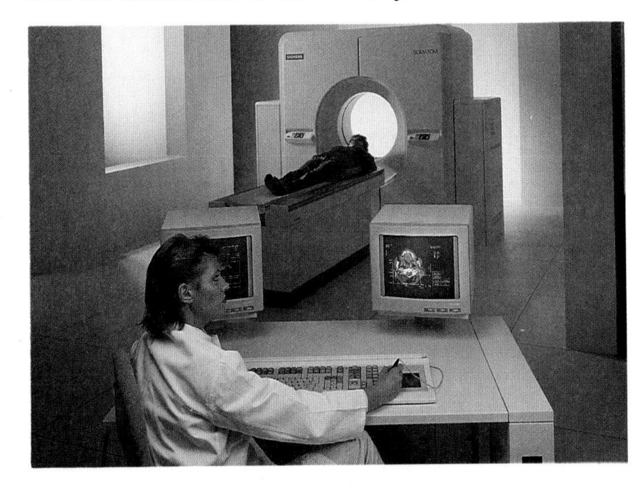

Above: CT scanners provide X-ray images of thin slices of the body to provide doctors with three-dimensional views of internal organs.

Thermodynamics

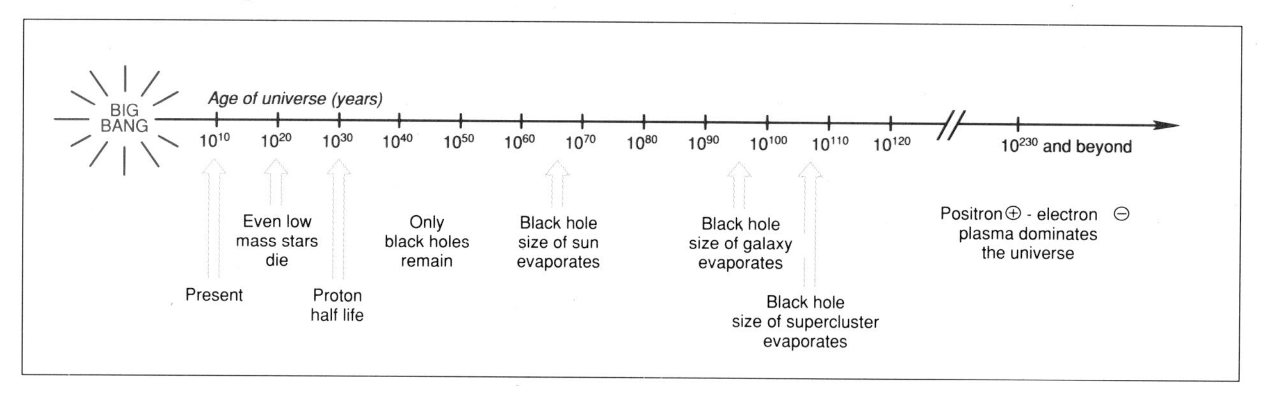

Above: Scenario for the end of the universe. Eventually only electrons and positrons will remain, separated by huge distances.

Thermodynamics refers to the study of heat transfer, and as such it appears in many differing topics, from PHYSICAL CHEMISTRY to PETROLOGY. But its basic laws are common to all disciplines.

The First Law of Thermodynamics says that the amount of energy in the universe is constant. No energy will come into the universe, none will go out, none will be created, and none will be destroyed.

The Second Law shows how this energy can move about – and leads to the conclusion that the universe is running down. Any closed system, and the universe is the biggest closed system of all, must proceed to a state of greater disorderliness or entropy.

In due course, countless billions of years hence, the universe must approach a thermal equilibrium, where nowhere is hotter or colder than anywhere else, and everything swills about in an eternal lukewarm lethargy. It was once thought that the universe would end in this state of "heat death." But during the 1980s, it became accepted that after about 10^{100} years when, according to the work of Stephen Hawking, even supermassive black holes will have evaporated, there will still be matter in the form of positronium – pairs of electrons and positrons, which are positive electrons. This matter will remain, and there will never be a heat death.

Topology

Topology is the branch of mathematics which deals with shapes and their transformations. Although topology began as an abstract type of geometry, computers have given it a new lease of life. Topology is even used today to make amazing transformations in movie special effects and computer-generated animation.

The discipline began when it was noted that in any polyhedron – a solid geometric object – the number of faces plus the number of corners minus the number of edges was two. And for a polyhedron with one hole in it, that same sum always comes to zero.

Topographically, a sphere, a cube, and a formless blob – without a hole in it – are the same. They are all of Genus 0. A doughnut is Genus 1. It can be transformed into a cup, for example, without changing its Genus. The hole appears between the handle and the body of the cup. The rest of the cup is simply a transformation of the outside of the doughnut. Objects with two holes are of Genus 2 and can be similarly transformed.

Topologists also study strings, tangles, and knots. Although much of their work is theoretical, the results often find applications in other fields – like understanding the long strings of chemicals that make up DNA or how magnetic fields deform.

Chemists have now discovered that the topology of a complex molecule predicts its chemical properties and even its taste.

Above: Movie makers use topology to calculate how computer-generated surfaces, as in *The Lawnmower Man*, will reflect their surroundings.

Index

In alphabetizing this index, each entry is placed in alphabetical order up to the first punctuation mark, disregarding spaces and hyphens. Page references give volume and page number. Bold page numbers indicate a main article. Some entries have one or more subentries, which begin one space from the left margin and are listed in alphabetical order. Where a main entry or a subentry occupies more than one line, the second and subsequent lines begin two spaces from the left margin. All articles are illustrated, so illustrations found in other articles only are indicated by page numbers in italics.

Picture Credits

The publishers extend their thanks to the many companies and individuals who have kindly provided illustrative material for this encyclopedia. The credit list works as follows: Alphabetical name of supplier (agency, or company, and photographer); page and position.

L = Left; R = Right; C = Center; B = Bottom; T = Top.

A B Dowsett/SPL: 163TR; Adam Hart-Davis/SPL: 210TL; Agricultural Genetics Co Ltd: 16CL; Alexander Tsiaras/SPL: 22BC, 52B, 86TR, 188t, 205BL, 259TR; Alfred Pasieka/SPL: 57B; Allsport/Vandystadt: 249BL; Allsport: 249BR; American Journal of Physics via Jim Baggott: 238CR; Andy Walker/Midland Fertility Services/SPL: 95TR; Argenium/SPL: 97CR; Associated Press/Topham: 109TR, 109BR, 228TL, 228TR, 228CR; Bell Helicopter Textron: 11CL; Bill Clegg/University of Newcastle upon Tyne: 83CL, 84TL; Biophoto Associates/SPL: 215BL; Biophoto Associates: 34TL, 54B, 55TL, 119TR; Biosym Technologies Inc/SPL: 224CR; Blatchford: 37BL(inset), 37BL, 37BR; BMW (GB) Ltd: 158BL; BNR Europe Ltd: 76T; Boeing Corp: 9CR, 9B; BOSE: 267TL; Brandon Harris RR: 194BL; British Aerospace: 13TR, BR; British Geological Survey: 244TL; British Petroleum: 201TR; Bruce Frisch/SPL: 153BL; Calgene Inc: 17TL, 18TL; California Institute of Technology: 223B; CDC, Atlanta: 107TR; Cellmark Diagnostics: 112TL; Center for Particle Physics/University of California: 214B; CERN Photo: 211T, 211B, 212R, 213T, 237TR; Clive Freeman, The Royal Inst/SPL: 226TL; CNN International: 255BR; CNRI/SPL: 144TR, 166TC, 169B; Columbia University: 182B; Cook UK Ltd: 240TL, 240BR; Copyright Cable and Wireless Visual Resource: 254BL; Courtesy of University of Glasgow/Galaxy Picture Library: 31TC; Crown Copyright: 182T; CSC INDEX: 50TR; CSM Associates: 132BL, 132BC; David Gifford/SPL: 260T; David Newnham; 224TL; David Parker/Seagate Microelectronics Ltd/SPL: 91BL; David Parker/SPL: 110TR, 110BR, 227BL, 234TR; Division Ltd: 73TR, 73T(inset); Dornier: 245R; Doug Allan/OSF: 24CR; DOW Separations: 59BR; Dr A Lawrence: 252BR; Dr Alexander Lawton/SPL: 141T; Dr Andrew Smith/University of Sussex: 35BR, 36T; Dr Arthur Winfree/SPL: 225TL, 225TR, 225CL, 225CR; Dr Beer-Gabel/CNRI/SPL: 164CL; Dr Brian Eyden/SPL: 216B; Dr C J Adkins/University of Cambridge: 76B, 77TL; Dr David Miller/SPL: 272TR; Dr Fred Espenar/SPL: 49TC; Dr Harry Kroto, University of Sussex: 199B, 200TL, 200TR; Dr J Fraser Stoddart, University of Birmingham: 198B; Dr J Littlechild, Exeter University: 197T; Dr J M Squire, Imperial College, London: 39B, 40TL, 40TR; Dr Jeremy Burgess/SPL: 33BL; Dr Jeremy Burgess/SPL: 96T, 188BR; Dr Jim Flegg: 139TR, 139CR, 140TL, 140TR, 207TR; Dr John Mazziotta ETAL/Neurology/SPL: 179BL; Dr R A Jarvis/University of Oxford: 27TR; Dr R D Adams: 244TR; Dr R Gibson/University of Dundee: 75TR, 75BR; Dr R L Brinster/University of Pennsylvania: 43BL; Dr Raymond Damadian/SPL: 22R(inset); Dr Robert Marshall/SPL: 180TR; Dr Robin Williams/SPL: 97CL; Dr Royle/Long Ashton Research Station: 19BL; Dr S F Holland, Dpt Earth Sciences, Cambridge: 271TL; Dr Tony Brain, Kings College, London: 144TL, 191TR; Drs R Balice-Gordon/J Lichtman/Washington University School of Medicine: 56CL, 56BL; Dynamic Imaging: 239TR; EBARA Environmental: 62TR; Eli Lilly and Co: 236TL, 236TR; English Heritage Photo Library: 25TR, 25BR; Environmental Picture Library: 60TL; Erika Hagelberg/COI/University of Cambridge: 28TL, 28BL; ESRI (UK): 124BL, 124CR; Fermilab: 212TL; Fisons Instruments: 122BR; Forrestry Commission: 269TR; Francoise Sauze/SPL: 181BL; Frank Spooner Pictures: 104TL, 105TL, 105BR, 134TL, 262TL; French Railways: 66BR; Galaxy Picture Library/RobinScagell: 30TL, 30CR, 31TL, 79T, 80T, 80BR, 82T, 241TR, 252B(inset); GE Medical Systems: 94TL; General Electric: 88TL; Geoff Tomkinson/SPL: 135B, 161T, 171T, 221TR, 222BR; George F Mobley/National Geographic Soc: 266BL; GI Bernard/OSF: 147B; Gill Harris/Vetinary Record: 261BL; Greenpeace: 125B; Gregory Sams/SPL: 57T; GSF Picture Library: 126TR, 276CL; Guy Gillet/SPL: 193CL; Hadrian Stirling: 23BR; Hank Morgan/SPL: 115B; Hank Morgan/SPL: 162L, 164BR, 168TL, 177TR, 190CR, 222TL; Hanny Paul/Gamma/Frank Spooner Pictures: 68B; Hattie Young/SPL: 217L; Hencoup/Galaxy Picture Library: 270; Historic St Mary's City: 70TL, 70TR; Honshu-Shikoku Bridge Authority: 63BL, 63CR; Hurco Europe Ltd: 160TL; Ian W Dalziel/GSA Today: 128TL; IBM: 72TL, 72TR, 73BR; Imperial Tobacco Ltd: 45B; Intel: 71CL, 71BR; J G White, W B Amos and M Fordham/SPL: 96B; James Holmes/Celltech Ltd/SPL: 44TL; James Howden: 64TR; James King-Holmes/ICRF/SPL: 117TL; Jane Burton/Bruce Coleman: 48C; Jeff Foott Productions/Bruce Coleman: 263TR; Jerry Mason/SPL: 176TR; Jervis Tuttell: 204TL, 204TR; Jet Joint Undertaking: 101TL, 102TR; John Durham/SPL: 35TR; John Mead/SPL: 241BL; John Walsh/SPL: 269CL; John Watney: 137B, 138BL; John Wilson/SPL: 171B; Keith Scholey/Planet Earth Pictures: 23BL; Ken Balcomb/Bruce Coleman: 265BR; Ken Lucas/Planet Earth Pictures: 113T; Keymed: 205TR, 205CR; Kobal Collection: 278B; Laurie Campbell/NHPA: 24TR; Lawrence Livermore Lab/SPL: 233BL; Lee Simon/Stammers/SPL: 169TR; Lockheed Corp: 12TR; Lumonics: 157TR; Marshall Cavendish Library: 38TR, 58TR, 92CR, 100TR, 101CR, 114T, 185TL; Martin Dohrn/SPL: 208/9, 273B; Massachusetts Inst. of Technology: 195B, 196TL, 196TR; Matt Samson/Environmental Picture Library: 99BL; Michael Nichols/Magnum: 265TR; Mike Lindsay/Leeds University: 250BR; Mirco De Cet: 10BL; Monsanto: 16TL; Motorola Inc: 93CR; Munro and Foster: 203BL; NASA GSFC/SPL: 69TR; NASA, Goddard Inst for Space Studies/SPL: 67; NASA/Galaxy Picture Library: 149CL, 149BR, 214T, 229BL, 230TL, 231TL, 231BL, 232TC, 232TR, 232BL, 232CR, 245BL, 246TL, 246TR, 246BL, 247T, 248T, 256CL; NASA/SPL: 123TR, 168TR, 267BR; NASA: 7BL, 8BL, 10CR, 186TL; National Center for Atmospheric Research, USA: 167BL, 167BR, 168BL; National Medical Slide Library: 133BL, 133BR; Natural History Museum: 126L, 274B, 275C, 276CR; Nigel Cattlin/Holt Studios Int: 266TL; NOAA: 103BL, 243BL; Nobelpharma: 85TR, 206TR; Nuffield Radio Astronomy Observatory: 242CL, 242c, 242CL; Oxford Magnets: 78BL; Oxford University: 39T; Oyo (UK) Ltd: 131TL, 131CL; Panos Pictures: 255BL; Paul Shambroom/SPL: 234TL; Paul Williams: 253CR; Peter Davey/Bruce Coleman: 264B; Peter Menzel/SPL: 15BL, 100CR, 105TR, 165TL, 178TL, 216T, 218T, 251BL; Peter Parks/OSF: 48B; Peter Ryan/Scripps/SPL: 172T; Peter Ryan/SPL: 190TR; Pharmaceutical Proteins: 42BL; Philippe Plailly/SPL: 104BR, 116TL, 136TL, 178BL, 178R; Philips: 92BL, 93TL, 93TR; Photo by Gregory Van Duyne/Cornell University, courtesy of Andrew Karplus and John Clardy: 41BL, 41BR; Photo Courtesy of Roy Szweda, IIIvs: 145TR, 145B, 202TL; Photo Courtesy of the Welding Institute, Cambridge, UK: 160TR; Photos Horticultural: 48T; Pont de Normandie Centre: 65CB; Popperfoto/AFP: 235TR; PRA Communications: 159CR; Prof Adam M Dziewonski/Harvard/Earth and Planetary Science: 243CR; Prof John Guest/ULO Planetary Image Centre: 220T; Prof Marcel Bessis/SPL: 136TR; Prof Peter Maitlis/University of Sheffield: 146T; Public Health Laboratory Service: 108BR; QA Photos: 65BL; Quadrant Picture Library: 10TR, 11BR; R Barrett: 154TL, 154TR, 155TL, 155CL; Rediffusion Simulation: 14B; Research Lab for Archaeology, Oxford University: 26TR; Rex Features: 92TL, 183BL, 184TR; Richard and Sally Greenhill: 141B; Rob Stepney: 192TL; Robert Hessler/Planet Earth Pictures: 151BL, 152TR; ROE/AAT Board 1987: 79B; Roger Rossmeyer, Starlight/SPL: Intro, 29BR; Royal Greenwich Observatory: 268BR; S Maddox/University of Oxford: 80CR; Sandoz/J-P Musso/Petit Format/SPL: 51T; Sanyo Energy (UK): 77TR; Science Photo Library: 119CR; Science Source/SPL: 21BL; SERC/Galaxy Picture Library: 189CR, 189BL; SERC/Galaxy Picture Library: 69TL; Ship and Ocean Foundation, Japan: 89t; Siemens: 83BR, 239BR, 277BR; Silsoe Research Inst: 20TL, 20TR; Simon Critchley: 170; Simon Fraser/Dpt of Neurology/Newcastle General Hospital/SPL: 22TR, 180TL; Simon Fraser/Royal Victoria Infirmary, Newcastle/SPL: 217R; Simon Fraser/SPL: 60BL; Sinclair Stammers/SPL: 175TR, 208TR, 209TL; SIU/SPL: 259BR; Somerset Levels Project: 68TL; SPT Geophysical Services, Swanley, Kent, England: 129BR, 130T, 130CL, 130BL; Stephen Tait: 219T, 219B; Switched Reluctance Drives Ltd: 87T, 87B; Syndication International: 14T; Takeshi Takahara/SPL: 91BR; Texas Instruments: 173BL, 174TR, 174BL; Thomas Moriarty Associates: 158TL; Thussen Industrie AG Henschel: 157BL; Tim Beddow/SPL: 191CR; Tioxide: 61TL, 61TR; Tom McHugh/SPL: 49CL; Toshiba Electronics (UK)Ltd: 74TR; Toyota (GB) Ltd: 156; Trimble Navigation Europe Ltd: 271BR; Tropix/M and V Birlev: 68TR; Tropix/P Frances: 165TR; University of Arizona: 150BR; University of Bradford: 26CR; University of Edinburgh: 46TR, 47T, 47C, 47B; University of Southampton: 19BR; University of Wisconsin, Madison: 223B (inset); US Department of Energy/SPL: 233BR; USDA/SPL: 34BR; V Rae/Reading University: 121BL, 121CR, 122TL; Volvo: 90B; W L Gore and Associates Inc: 85BL; Walter Jaffe/Leiden, Holland Ford/JHU/STScl/NASA: 32TR; WHO/TDR/J Maurice: 257BR; WHO/TDR/LSTM: 258TR; WHO/TDR: 257BL, 258TL; Will and Deni McIntyre/SPL: 162BR, 188BL; Yoshinori Kobayashi: 114R.

Contributors

Dr Robin Adams; Dr Rodger Allen; Dr Antony Anderson; Dr Jim Baggott; Dr Bob Bingham; Andrew Blake; Edward Boden; Neil Bone; Dr David Bradley; Nigel Cawthorne; Dr Bill Clegg; Storm Dunlop; Dr Mike Easterbrook; Dr Jeremy Evans; Dr Jim Flegg; David Fowler; Dr Desmond Gilmore; Dr Jeremy Gray; Wendy Grossman; Bill Gunston; Prof. Norman Hammond; Dr Richard Harding; Dr Marc Helman; Clare Hill; Dr Peter Hobson; Prof. Cyril Hogarth; Dr Tony Jones; Sharon Kingman; Dr Adrian Linacre; Dr John Mason; Prof. Clive McCann; Dr Miranda McQuitty; Dr Sean McWhinnie; Dr Michael Millar; Dennis Morallee; Dr Adrienne Morgan; Dr Steve Mullins; Dr John Phillips; Dr Joy Rae; Peter Rees; Caroline Richmond; Ian Ridpath; Robin Scagell; Dr Barbara Shollock; Mike Sibley; Paul Simons; Dr Andrew Smith; Dr Walter Sneader; Martin Spring; Dr John Squires; William Steele; Dr Rob Stepney; Dr Hadrian Stirling; Prof. Mervyn Stone; Dr Christine Sutton; Dr Stephen Tait; Jane Vigus; Graham Warwick; Dr Kevin White; Prof. Heinz Wolff; Dr Robert Youngson.

For the Publishers: Robin Scagell (Editor); Ellen Wasserman (Executive Editor); Terry Jennings B.Sc., Ph.D. (Consultant Editor).